Richard B. Fisher wa
a British citizen. He h
Yale University and t
After 15 years as a pa .
and Britain, he began
*Manual of Brain Game*

Also by Richard B. Fisher

*The Chemistry of Consciousness*
*Joseph Lister 1827–1912*
*Syrie Maugham*

with George A. Christie
*A Dictionary of Drugs*
*How Drugs Work*

*Richard B. Fisher*

# The Dictionary of Mental Health

A PALADIN BOOK

**GRANADA**
London Toronto Sydney New York

Published by Granada Publishing Limited in 1980

ISBN 0 586 08339 1

A Granada Paperback UK Original


Granada Publishing Limited
Frogmore, St Albans, Herts AL2 2NF
and
3 Upper James Street, London W1R 4BP
866 United Nations Plaza, New York, NY 10017, USA
117 York Street, Sydney, NSW 2000, Australia
100 Skyway Avenue, Rexdale, Ontario, M9W 3A6, Canada
PO Box 84165, Greenside, 2034 Johannesburg, South Africa
61 Beach Road, Auckland, New Zealand

Set, printed and bound in Great Britain by
Cox & Wyman Ltd, Reading
Set in Monotype Plantin

# Foreword

PSYCHOLOGY* and PSYCHOTHERAPY are both defined in this *Dictionary*. Both are fields riven by controversy. Accordingly, these entries describe the various theories and schools impartially.

Inasmuch as I am not myself a physician, the *Dictionary* contains no inbuilt partisanship. It would not be possible, however, to write about mental health, a subject on which every one of us has intimate knowledge, without some bias. Mine is perhaps most clearly set out and explained in the entry called HEALTH, MENTAL. Although mental disease may always be triggered by some environmental circumstance, it is *caused* by a physical malfunction, probably in the BRAIN. Without the physical malfunction, a socially-based disturbance may nevertheless exist, but its treatment, if any is really required, will be in the nature of social change or priestly reassurance rather than scientific medicine. This hypothesis explains the importance I have given to entries describing the physical aspects of MIND, such as ENZYME, HORMONE, NEURON, TRANSMITTER, and to the new field of psychobiology

Traditional psychotherapy has failed to cope with mental disorders let alone stem their rising incidence. Indeed, this very failure is in part the reason for the explosion of new techniques – bioenergetics, Encounter groups, psychodrama, and so on – since the Second World War. Many of them are semi-mystical and, without exception, they are quasi-scientific. The theories on which they are based are often untestable and occasionally, errant nonsense. They are like the violent thrashings of a drowning man to whom any expedient offers a little hope. Many psychiatrists are fully alive to the flaws in

* With a few obvious exceptions, words in small capitals are the headings of entries in the *Dictionary*.

their therapeutic tools and use them – if at all – because, to adapt an admirable aphorism, in the land of the blind, the one-eyed man might become king.

*The Dictionary of Mental Health* takes the position that although many mentally-ill people need a doctor's help, many more do not. This latter group may be lonely or worried, but these people are not sick. A great many so-called therapists who are not doctors have found that lonely, worried people become willing victims of exploitation for political as well as financial gain. Yet these pseudo-patients would often get the relief they need by talking to a friend or a member of the family, if there is someone, or from self-examination if there is not. I hope that the *Dictionary* eliminates some of the mystery surrounding the mind and its disorders, and that the reader will discover in it clues indicating whether he is normally anxious, depressed and unhappy or really ill. If he is unhappy, perhaps the appropriate definition will help, but if he feels that he is sick, he should consult his general practitioner without delay. The GP will usually be able to advise on what ought to be done next. Like any other disease, an illness of the mind often responds best to early treatment. Certainly, no one should take any of the specialized drugs named in the various entries without a doctor's recommendation.

I wish to acknowledge gratefully the advice of Dr Sydney Gottlieb who read and criticized the manuscript of this book. It has been improved because of his professional experience. I am also grateful to Dr Peter Evans, whose excellent report for the publisher was immensely helpful. Of course any errors that the book still contains are entirely my responsibility.

RBF

*London, June 1979*

# A

**ABREACTION** See PSYCHOANALYSIS

**ACALCULIA**
(Latin: *a*=negative+*calculare*=to reckon) 1. inability to do simple arithmetic. 2. loss of the ability to read or use mathematical symbols. Symptom of BRAIN DAMAGE or Gerstmann's SYNDROME. See also -LEXIA, -PHASIA.

**ADDICTION**
(Latin: *addictus*=assigned by degree, made over, bound, elevated; *ad*=to+*dicere*=to say, pronounce) 1. the state of being physically dependent on a drug. 2. the state of being dominated by a habit, sometimes called psychological addiction or habituation.

The World Health Organization defines addiction as 'a state of periodic or chronic intoxication produced by the repeated consumption of a drug'. There is a tendency to increase the dose of the drug in order to perpetuate the physical and psychological effect. Conversely, discontinuation of the drug leads to acute reactions collectively called withdrawal symptoms.

Addiction is commonly associated with a specific drug; e.g. ALCOHOL addiction, AMPHETAMINE addiction, heroin addiction (see OPIATE), nicotine addiction. Each of these substances alters the behaviour of NEURONS in the BRAIN as well as elsewhere in the body. It seems probable that the state of dependence arises because of the physical changes induced by the drug. The tendency to increase the dose probably reflects an increasing tolerance; that is, the induced change in cellular chemistry requires more of the drug to maintain cell function. Withdrawal symptoms are due to the sudden STRESS caused when altered cell chemistry is forced by the absence of the drug to readjust suddenly towards pre-drug dynamics. For example, delirium tremens are hallucinations caused by the sudden withdrawal of alcohol which causes neurons in the brain that were previously depressed by the drug to display HYPERACTIVITY.

Only parts of these complex chemical processes have been described. True addiction involves a psychological element, but to say this may mean that physical effects in the brain are always accompanied by psychic effects. Thus, it is not true that anyone who uses an addictive drug automatically becomes an addict. The great majority of occasional drinkers never suffer. Many psychiatrists believe that there is an addictive PERSONALITY, a person who becomes addicted after one or a very few exposures. Presumably, this phenomenon would not be purely physiological; in part, it is the individual's response to experience or to some inherited trait.

By far the most common drugs of addiction are nicotine and alcohol. Users of either of these socially-acceptable drugs many times outnumber the users of all the illegal addictive drugs put together. Nicotine is a stimulant, and it is probably not the drug itself which causes the most serious side-effects of smoking: bronchitis and lung cancer.

Alcohol, on the other hand, causes immense suffering, both personal and social. In the United States, there are thought to be over five million alcoholics, roughly one person in forty. In England and Wales, the figure may be about half a million, or roughly one in a hundred. Much alcoholism is hidden not only from medical and legal authorities, but from the addict's family. Nevertheless, reported cases continue to rise in both countries. The death rate from cirrhosis of the liver, the most common complication of excessive drinking, has risen in England and Wales by 233 per cent since 1971. In New York state, cirrhosis is now the third most common cause of death, immediately after cardiovascular disease and cancer. There is every indication that the alcoholism toll is growing.

Family histories of alcoholics suggest that some addicts inherit their predilection for the drug, yet such studies cannot exclude the influence of parental example or the effect of family disruption caused by a parent or sibling who is an alcoholic. That is, environment is probably at least as important as GENETICS in the development of alcoholism.

Certainly the incidence of alcohol addiction is decisively influenced by cultural factors. Thus, there are few alcoholics amongst Moslems, whose religion forbids the drug. One of the highest rates of alcohol addiction is found in Sweden. Our own culture makes drinking a symbol of masculinity. Yet perhaps the most disturbing trend in Great Britain and the United

States has been the rapid rise in the number of women alcoholics. Some of these women become pregnant, of course, leading to a steady increase in the numbers of infants born with symptoms of alcohol addiction, including DTs. Many psychologists believe that the reason for the growth in female alcohollism is the increasing isolation of the English-speaking housewife.

Some alcoholics can be helped by a drug, disulfiram (Antabuse). Even a minute amount of alcohol reacts with it to produce headache, vomiting and other symptoms of a severe hangover. Indeed, the reactions can be so violent that disulfiram should be used in hospital under medical supervision. It may stop the drinking by putting the patient through a form of aversive therapy (see PSYCHOTHERAPY).

Other forms of psychotherapy are of doubtful value, but the support and faith offered by Alcoholics Anonymous have unquestionably helped thousands. Even so, few alcoholics are cured; they are never released from the compulsion induced by even a social half-pint of beer.

Addiction to the so-called 'heavy' drugs, AMPHETAMINE, BARBITURATES, cocaine and the opiates, all of which are illegal without a prescription, occurs far less often than alcohol addiction. For example, there are probably not more than 5,000 opiate addicts in Great Britain. The suffering they cause is statistically insignificant, whatever the cost to the addict, and it would be hard to prove that death from alcohol poisoning is any less horrific than death caused by an overdose of heroin. Hard drugs have attracted so much attention precisely because they are exotic. They are far harder to obtain than alcohol, and even under the humane British laws, obtaining them may be dangerous. In London, there are heroin addicts who claim that they get no lift at all from their prescription dose – an example of the psychological element in addiction, if ever there was one.

There is no drug like disulfiram to give the heavy-drug addict a quick course of aversive therapy. A synthetic opiate, methadone, has been used to wean addicts on the theory that it is less addictive than heroin, but the claim is unsupported by evidence. TRANQUILLIZERS may ease the withdrawal process, but they do not help most addicts. Clonidine, a drug which inhibits the activity of some neurons in the brain, has been reported to suppress withdrawal symptoms. At present, however, the most effective technique is withdrawal during drug-induced sleep or heavy sedation, though acupuncture and even superficial electrical stimulation of the skin behind the ears are reported to reduce craving and withdrawal symptons. All withdrawal should be supervised by a doctor. As in the case of alcohol, it may be easier with the support of former addicts who can talk the patient through bad patches. There is no certainty of cure. By its very nature, addiction is a self-imposed hell without which the addict suffers even more. See also HALLUCINOGEN.

## ADLER, ALFRED

Psychoanalyst; introduced the concept of the inferiority feeling (inaccurately: inferiority COMPLEX). Adlerian PSYCHOANALYSIS is humanistic and holistic, displaying awareness of social problems experienced by the patient. b. Penzing, Austria, 1870. d. Aberdeen, 1937. University of Vienna Medical School, MD, 1895. Association with FREUD began, 1902. Published view that aggressive drive is primary instinct, and that feeling of inferiority rather than sexual repression in childhood causes mental illness, 1908. Public break with Freud, 1911. Established first child guidance clinic, Vienna, 1921, followed by about thirty more, all of which were closed by the Austrian government, 1934. Visiting professor, Columbia University, 1927. Visiting professor, Long Island College of Medicine, 1932. *Study of Organ Inferiority and Its Psychological Compensations*, 1907. *The Neurotic Constitution*, 1912. *Understanding Human Nature*, 1918. *What Life Means to You*, 1931.

## AFFECT

1. Of or pertaining to the EMOTIONS. 2. feelings aroused by an emotion. Although the word appeared in psychological literature before FREUD, he confined its meaning to pleasant or unpleasant feelings induced by a stimulus. For some writers, affect includes the sense of one's will or one's conative power, but the word, affective, is now usually used with the word, conative to identify the two non-intellectual aspects of PERSONALITY. Affective diseases or disorders are those which disturb emotional responses (see ANXIETY, DEPRESSION, SCHIZOPHRENIA).

## AGE

The state of consolidation, decline and degeneration leading eventually to death, delineated by social as well as biological factors. Ageing, or senescence, in any population can be described graphically by either one of two curves:

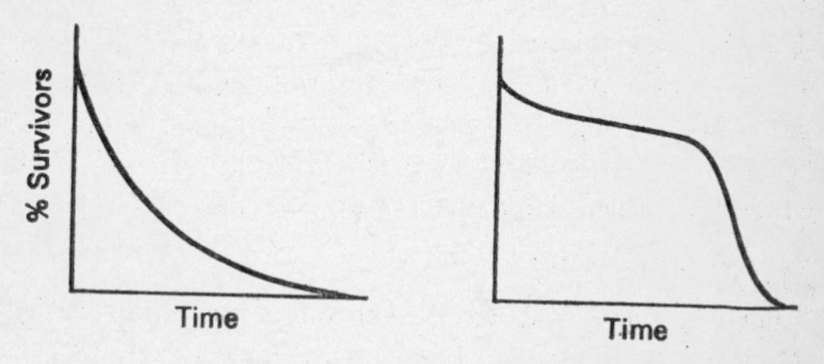


The curve on the left (a logarithmic curve) represents survival of individuals in which the causes of death are mainly accidents. They do not vary greatly with chronological age because, within limits, the chance of being eaten by a tiger or of falling victim to pneumonia are roughly the same at any age. This curve applies to animal societies as well as to humans.

The curve on the right describes what has happened to ageing in advanced industrial societies where accidental death by violence or disease has been restricted by effective law, better diet, improved conditions of work and scientific medicine. The 'squareness' of the right-hand curve increases as we learn to protect ourselves against gross natural disasters. Life expectancy at birth increases because, with improved diet the individual is better able to resist infection, exceptionally cold or hot weather and the threat from animal predators. Medical science further postpones death. If circulatory disease and cancer could be controlled or prevented, the curve describing age at death in advanced societies such as our own would become 'square'.

Note, however, that the time axis is very little changed between the first curve and the second. There is no reason to believe that the control of circulatory disease and cancer would significantly stretch it. More people would live to be 75 or 80, but the number who live longer would not greatly increase. At present, there is little hope for a lengthened life span. The number of centenarians has not grown significantly during the last two hundred years despite the doubling of life expectancy.

Unless there is some quite unforeseen breakthrough in the understanding of life processes, three score years and ten will mark the upper limit for most of us.

Senescence seems to be built into the genes (see GENETICS). How or why we age is not known, nor do we know how we develop from a single fertilized egg to a multicellular organism of fascinating complexity. One theory of ageing holds that mutational errors in the genes accumulate during a lifetime causing new cells formed from existing cells in the body to lose their viability. Although there is some evidence for the theory, it cannot explain why NEURONS die at the rate of roughly 10,000 a day from the age of about 20. Neurons cease to divide and reproduce sometime after birth and long before adolescence.

An alternative theory argues that accidental errors occur in the biochemical functioning of cells, and in time, the number of these accidents increases until the cell can no longer operate. The theory fits the known facts better than the mutational theory, but the two are not mutually exclusive. Whatever the reasons, in common with all other creatures, we shall continue to age and die – for the present, at least.

Advances in medical science have done two things for us. As the right-hand curve shows, they have greatly increased the number of people who live into 'old age'. Of much greater importance, better medicine has improved the quality of life for millions of elderly people. The improvement in general health which assures longer life (as well as greater average height and better teeth) means that the old person is stronger and healthier, by and large, than were old people in the past. Better socio-medical facilities reduce the impact of such debilitating factors as retirement, poverty, isolation and BEREAVEMENT. This is not to say that the social problems of ageing have ceased to exist, but only that they are recognized and attempts are made to deal with them.

However, there are great differences between the provision of socio-medical facilities for the aged in the United Kingdom and the United States. The British National Health Service effectively screens the elderly, and their relatives, from the financial burdens of ageing. In the United States, where medical facilities remain largely private, neither Medicare nor the private health insurance schemes can do more than cushion the costs of hospitalization and medical treatment. Home care and the provision of facilities for normal intercourse amongst healthy old people remain largely an expensive luxury in the United States which even the higher standard of living in America cannot always cope with successfully. It remains to be seen whether the growing number of elderly Americans, many of whom are organized into pressure groups such as the Grey Panthers, will not force significant changes in care for the elderly along paths explored by the British National Health Service. In both countries, pensioners' lobbies have growing political muscle.

There are now about 8 million people over the age of 65 in Great Britain and about 30 million in the United States. They represent 15 per cent of the population, a percentage which is growing, though more slowly as the survival curve approximates squareness.

If the word, 'health', means anything (see HEALTH, MENTAL), the great majority of old people are healthy. Age is not a synonym for disease, and it should not be a synonym for incompetence. There is no evidence that INTELLIGENCE declines with age. Indeed, for most people a declining intellect is a symptom of rapidly approaching death. No doubt the ability to remember recent events declines with age, but even this familiar phenomenon is not consistent.

Some people in their eighties are able to learn and retain new information if the information interests them and fits into their intellectual framework. If the creative genius of Picasso or Casals at 80 is rare, so it is at any age. Special LEARNING experiments and tests with drugs thought to improve MEMORY have been carried out on old people with positive results, but all such research stumbles over an unanswered question: to what extent are the improvements due to the additional attention given to experimental subjects who may be lonely and isolated? In any case, neither legal nor moral judgment can be shown to deteriorate with age.

Yet there is no denying that the old slow down and begin to deteriorate. Bones become brittle. Connective tissue thins and loses its elasticity. The substance of the brain shrinks from a dry weight of about 1,300 grams to roughly 1,000 grams.

Inevitably, these physical changes reveal themselves in posture, skin, features and behaviour. Yet it is the social role assigned to age which ultimately determines the meaning of physical changes. If the entire object of life is happiness, and happiness can exist only with a toothy smile, smooth skin and a full head of well-controlled hair – two extremely dubious propositions – then age is indeed a sad and hopeless state. But if the ability to understand, reflect and adapt are at least as relevant to living, then the significance of physical senescence declines.

Nevertheless, the healthy old person eventually becomes the exception. Circulatory disease, cancer and infectious illnesses occur more often. Perhaps even more depressing is the effect of the ageing brain on behaviour and emotions. Intelligence also suffers if the old person develops senile DEMENTIA, now thought to be the fourth or fifth most common cause of death in the United States. About 40 per cent of patients in British geriatric hospitals show psychiatric symptoms as serious as those displayed by the aged housed in mental hospitals. Well over a third of all mental hospital patients in England and Wales are over 65, as compared with 15 per cent of the general population. But there may be three times as many old people suffering from psychiatric disorders in the general population as there are in hospitals.

The most common mental disturbance of old age is DEPRESSION. Often the disease is affective, resulting from bereavement, isolation or declining health and vitality. Thus, male suicides have declined in the general population over the past fifty years in most countries. Amongst elderly men, however, the suicide rate remains roughly unchanged, and it has risen amongst women, especially the elderly. Unless the patient is chronically ill or psychotic, depression amongst the elderly is best managed at home.

On the other hand, SCHIZOPHRENIA or late paraphrenia, and dementia often require hospitalization. These conditions are less frequently encountered amongst non-institutionalized elderly. In all age groups over 65, depressive illnesses cause hospitalization in England and Wales less often than dementia, but more often than schizophrenia. The prognosis in senile dementia is poor in almost every case. The outcome of depression and schizophrenia depends on the severity of the symptoms and the patient's medical history, as it does in younger people too. The worse the illness and the longer the patient has suffered from it, or from other psychiatric problems, the less he will respond to any treatment. PSYCHOTHERAPY may help reactive depression, but psychotic depression and schizophrenia can be controlled only with drugs, SHOCK THERAPY and possibly, PSYCHOSURGERY.

## AGEUSIA

(Greek: *a*=a negative+*geusis*=taste) absence or impairment of the sense of taste. Ageusia results from damage following injury to or disease in nerves connecting the taste organs (see SENSATION) in the mouth to the BRAIN. It may occur after BRAIN DAMAGE, but then it is usually associated with ANOSMIA.

## AGGRESSION

(Latin: *agressus*, from *ad*=to+*gradi*=to step, march) 1. a first attack or assault, whether provoked or unprovoked. 2. hostile or destructive EMOTIONS or behaviour. The two definitions reflect the two interpretations of aggression in humans, the instinctual (or ethological) and the psychoanalytic (see PSYCHOANALYSIS).

Perhaps the foremost exponent of the instinctual hypothesis has been the Austrian ethologist, Konrad Lorenz. Lorenz distinguishes four categories of aggression. The first three – eater against eaten, victim against predator, and the 'cornered rat' – are forms of interspecies aggression in all but the most exceptional cases. Though they can each be shown to play a role in the process of natural selection, they are not directly relevant to the understanding of aggression in humans. However, the fourth category, intraspecies aggression, is said to explain human behaviour as well as much animal aggression. By assuring the success of the species at the expense of those individuals which are less strong and adaptable, Lorenz argues, the gene pool for the whole species is strengthened. Thus, intraspecies aggression is a positive evolutionary force in the same way as interspecies aggression.

The purest psychoanalytic interpretation absolutely contradicts the ethological argument. Those who consider that aggression is instinctual hold that it is positive if not actually morally good, but FREUD believed that aggression reflects the evil in man. He sought an explanation for irrational, self-destructive behaviour and hit upon a fundamentally negative MOTIVATION which he called the death wish. The death wish is the dark counterweight to man's fundamental positive motivation, the pleasure principle. Thus, aggression may arise from repression, frustration or guilt, and far from being a positive force, it is totally negative. In psychoanalytic opinion, there is no difference between the aggressive play of children and the explosion at Hiroshima.

Some of Freud's followers were so distressed by the social evil of aggression that they proposed to root out aggression, if not the death wish, by removing all sources of guilt and frustration from the paths of growing children. The young were never to be opposed. They were to be encouraged to do as they pleased. Whether at table, at bedtime or at school, the child's wishes and interests were to be given free expression. The results of this astonishing dogma were disastrous for a generation of the children of a large number of intellectuals, and the shock waves are still with us, for example, in the educational philosophy which stresses choice to the virtual exclusion of content. What the doctrine of free expression did establish, however, is that if there is anything more frustrating than 'no', it is a mindless, structureless 'yes'. Each of us acquires a picture of ourselves in part at least from the way others react to our excesses.

Freud himself was never satisfied with his dualistic formulation of motivation. Though he was unable to resolve his difficulty, he characteristically admitted it. Most psychiatrists now also recognize that aggressive behaviour need not always be self-destructive or, indeed, irrational. Instead, psychologists tend to look for a rational explanation behind individual acts of aggression. The child who pinches his younger brother is said to be jealous and to need more love and firmness. The husband who beats his wife is said to be frustrated by a boring job. The mother who batters her child is lonely, bored and exhausted by the child's demands. Thus, aggression is still seen as an evil which can be explained and eliminated. Yet the behaviour labelled 'aggression' blends into acceptable activities, such as competition or the definition of the self (see MIND, PERSON-

ALITY). Although baby-battering is life-threatening and wrong, a good spanking is neither. Nor is the 'good' child one who never fights with his fists, teeth and feet. Aggression is not evil *per se*.

Does that make it an instinct as the ethologists argue? In the sense that living may demand physical struggle, it is no doubt essential on occasion to strike first. It is far more self-destructive, for example, to give a black man your wallet under threat because your white conscience feels guilt about black slavery than to hit him first, even at the risk of a fight you could lose. But can it, therefore, be said that human aggression is based on instinct, in the same way as defence of territory by a lion? An affirmative answer over-simplifies in the opposite direction. Not all aggression is evil, but surely some is. Lorenz and others reply that war and other forms of self-destructive human aggression arise when humans lose sight of their real interests; in short, when we act irrationally. Thus, psychoanalytic evil seems to have crept in to challenge the instinctual good.

With the emergence of modern biology based on an understanding of organic chemicals such as DNA (see GENETICS), research has been directed towards the molecular basis of behaviour. In the early 1960s, it was found that by sending small electrical currents through microelectrodes implanted in a region of the hypothalamus (see BRAIN) of experimental animals, it was possible to elicit bared teeth, erected hackles and readiness to attack. Long before the introduction of frontal lobotomy (see PSYCHOSURGERY), moreover, it was known that accidental division of the frontal lobe from the rest of the brain could produce aggressive behaviour. In animals, experiment associates aggression with the presence or absence of TRANSMITTERS in the brain. The transmitters seem to be particularly significant in the amygdala which, like the hypothalamus, plays a role in regulation of emotional life. Also of interest is the role of HORMONES in aggressive behaviour. Adrenaline (epinephrine), for example, is always present in the blood of animals confronted with the need to fight or flee. Higher levels of the principle male hormone, testosterone, have been tentatively associated with aggression, even in women. The highest blood level of testosterone ever recorded was found in alcoholic rapists.

Though it is early days, this biochemical and neurophysiological research has already shown that there are physical correlates of aggressive behaviour. Perhaps eventually, the physiology of aggression will discover a boundary between useful, 'instinctual' aggression and evil, irrational aggression, if one exists.

## AGNOSIA

(Greek: *a*=a negative+*gnosis*=perception) loss or impairment of SENSATION, usually specified as auditory, gustatory, olfactory, tactile, or visual agnosia. Agnosia may reflect either physical damage to the nervous mechanisms subserving the sensation, or impairment of the ability to perceive the sensation despite intact nervous machinery. The latter form of agnosia may be due to a NEUROSIS such as HYSTERIA, e.g. hysterical blindness.

## AGRAPHIA

(Greek: *a*=a negative+*graphein*=to write) loss or impairment of the ability to write. Agraphia is caused by damage to the language centre in the parieto-temporal region of the BRAIN cortex. Depending on the exact area damaged, agraphia may be absolute, atactic (in which the patient cannot write at all), acoustic (loss of the ability to write from dictation), anemonic, jargon or verbal (loss of the ability to write sensibly though the patient may be able to form letters or words), literal (the inability to form letters), mental (thoughts cannot be put into phrases; see -PHASIA), motor (loss of motor control necessary for writing; see PSYCHOMOTOR DISEASE), musical (loss of the ability to write musical notation), or optic (inability to copy although the patient can still take dictation). See also -LEXIA.

**AKINESIA** See -KINESIS

## ALCOHOL

(Arabic: *al-koh'l*=something subtle) 1. a drug, $C_2H_5OH$, ethyl alcohol or ethanol. 2. a class of organic chemicals formed from hydrocarbons by substituting one or more hydroxyl (OH) groups for an equal number of hydrogen atoms. Methanol or methyl alcohol, $CH_3OH$, is a poison because it is converted in the liver to formic acid and formaldehyde. Rubbing alcohol consists of acetone, an alcohol-like chemical (methyl isobutyl ketone) and ethyl alcohol.

To the vast majority of mankind, it is the effect of alcohol on the BRAIN which makes this most ancient of drugs both interesting and useful. It often improves appetite and digestion and reduces colic and flatulence, particularly in elderly patients. It helps sleep and improves the sense of well-being, a benefit of great importance to the chronically ill. All of these advantages derive from the action of alcohol as a depressant and narcotic (see HYPNOTIC). It has other uses as well. By injecting it locally, the acute pain of angina pectoris, certain forms of neuralgia and some cancers can be relieved. By inhaling alcohol as a gas, it is sometimes possible to control the collection of fluid in the lungs resulting from incipient heart failure. As a solvent, alcohol washes away noxious oils such as those of poison ivy and poison oak, and makes cooling ointments. As a skin disinfectant, it is cheap, strong and safe. Alcohol has been used as an anaesthetic, but it is slow and the effective dose for anaesthesia is dangerously close to a fatal dose.

An alcohol overdose causes death from increased cranial pressure which leads to paralysis of the hind-brain centres regulating breathing and heart rate. The most common side effects, however, are drunkenness and alcoholism (see ADDICTION). Excessive use causes serious debilitation because of dietary imbalance and lack of vitamins. The warmth which follows a drink reflects the immediate increase in blood flow through the skin and gut, an effect mediated in part by the control of the CENTRAL NERVOUS SYSTEM over the diameter of large blood vessels. It is not a sign that alcohol has supplied new energy even though the drug does provide the body with calories.

The depressant effect of alcohol begins in the reticular activating system which regulates SLEEP and wakefulness. The cortex is at first freed from the regulation of the reticular centre, creating the familiar EUPHORIA. But impairment of movement control begins at the same time, and it spreads as other parts of the mid- and hind-brain are affected. Judgment is soon affected too. How the drug acts at the molecular level is not known, but it may alter the behaviour of the membrane which surrounds NEURONS, thus changing the function of the cells.

**ALEXANDER, FRANZ GABRIEL**

Psychoanalyst, known as the 'father of PSYCHOSOMATIC medicine'. b. Budapest, 1891. d. Palm Springs, Calif. 1964. Already a physician when he became a student at Berlin Psychoanalytic Institute, 1919. Lecturer at the Institute, 1924–5. His application of psychoanalytic theory to criminality brought invitation to teach in the United States. Professor of psychoanalysis, University of Chicago, 1930. Established Chicago Institute for Psychoanalysis, 1932; Director, 1932–56. Faculty of department of psychiatry, University of Illinois Medical School, Chicago, 1938–56. Research on PSYCHOTHERAPY and psychosomatic medicine, Mt Sinai Hospital, Los Angeles, 1956. *The Psychoanalysis of the Total Personality*, 1927. *Roots of Crime*, 1935 (with William Healy). *Fundamentals of Psychoanalysis*, 1948. *Western Mind in Transition: An Eyewitness Story*, 1960.

**ALEXIA** See -LEXIS

**ALZHEIMER'S DISEASE** See DEMENTIA

**AMBIVALENCE**

(Latin: *ambi*=both sides+*valentia*=strength, power) 1. simultaneous presence of opposite attitudes, for example, love and hate, towards the same object or event. 2. as 1, the symptom of a PSYCHOSIS, especially SCHIZOPHRENIA. The word was originally a psychoanalytic concept (see PSYCHOANALYSIS). Ambivalence is a cause of conflict within the PERSONALITY, though FREUD believed that the two opposing attitudes might exist compatibly in children; for example, the love-hate aroused by the father during the Oedipal period. In its second meaning, ambivalence was first used by BLEULER.

**AMNESIA**

(Greek: forgetfulness) loss of MEMORY.

Broadly speaking, there are two kinds of amnesia according to the time of the memory loss with relation to the TRAUMA or disease which caused it. Post-traumatic or anterograde amnesia is loss of memory of the period after the causative event. In retrograde or retroactive amnesia, memory of the period before the event is lost. Retrograde amnesia never occurs without post-traumatic amnesia, but post-traumatic amnesia can occur without retrograde amnesia.

Post-traumatic amnesia incorporates any period of unconsciousness following an injury, and it may extend into the period of apparent functional recovery. When the patient regains consciousness and any remaining confusion clears, however, he usually retains his memory for the events after awakening. He may also recall sporadic 'islands' of events within the time that he had seemed to be unconscious. Indeed, if the amnesia was caused by intracranial pressure from cerebrospinal fluid or from haemorrhage rather than by the blow itself, the patient can regain memory of the events immediately following the accident, but amnesia will persist for the period from the build-up of pressure to its release. Conversely, some patients may perform a job satisfactorily for some time after being injured but retain no memory of doing so. For example, after a blow to the head, a football player can continue to play and may even score a goal but remember nothing. It is also possible for him to run, tackle and play the ball, and to reveal his injury by heading for the wrong goal.

Retrograde amnesia is the characteristic memory loss beloved of thriller writers. During the period soon after the injury, amnesia may wipe out the memory of many years. The patient can indeed lose his name and identity, but recovery begins very soon after he regains consciousness. The earliest events are recalled first so that the possibility of long-term total amnesia is remote, though it has occurred. Slowly, the events leading up to the trauma return in chronological order from the earliest to the most recent. In most cases, a brief period – usually less than thirty minutes, often no more than a few seconds – remains permanently lost. Inasmuch as the lost memory includes the actual traumatic event, however, even so brief a loss is striking. The longer the post-traumatic amnesia, moreover, the longer the period of permanent retrograde amnesia is likely to be.

Amongst younger people, the most frequent cause of amnesia is a blow to the head. Physical disorders which damage brain tissue, such as carbon monoxide poisoning and oxygen starvation (anoxia), and epileptic attacks may also be accompanied by amnesia (see PSYCHOMOTOR DISEASE). SHOCK THERAPY can produce amnesia, and there is evidence that older people and patients who have undergone a number of courses of treatment experience longer periods of retrograde amnesia. In old people, the ability to retain new memories declines while past memories are retained, but in about 20 per cent of those over 80, senile DEMENTIA causes general amnesia affecting old memories as well as new ones.

Chronic alcoholism (see ADDICTION) can produce a severe form of amnesia called Korsakov's SYNDROME. It is post-traumatic, inasmuch as the patient is unable to recall recent events. An alcoholic with Korsakov's may forget a visit from a friend within minutes of the guest's departure. Korsakov amnesia can also be patchy.

Hysterical amnesia has no known physical cause (see HYSTERIA). It includes an apparent post-traumatic amnesia as well as the retrograde amnesia which hides the putative socio-psychological origin of hysteria. For example, a man with serious business difficulties loses all memory of them, and he also wanders the streets lost in a post-traumatic amnesia which reinforces his escape from the business pressure. HYPNOTISM may be the most efficient treatment. If it is successful, the retrograde amnesia disappears, but the post-traumatic period may remain permanently confused and patchy.

The nature of the biophysical changes in the brain that underlie amnesia is hidden in the unknown events of memory. Permanent brief periods of retrograde amnesia may be explained by the fact that the brain has not had time to consolidate as long-term memory the sensations immediately preceding the trauma before the patient lost consciousness. The process of consolidation involves the temporal lobe of the cortex and the hippocampus. Thus, Korsakov's syndrome is associated with degeneration of a segment of the temporal lobe which plays a role in sensible and coherent language use (see -PHASIA). Damage to the hippocampus can also lead to a defect in immediate memory analogous to the disorder experienced by Korsakov patients. In both Korsakov's and dementia, moreover, there is an abnormality in the ENZYME required for biosynthesis of the TRANSMITTER, acetylcholine, which carries nervous signals between some NEURONS in both the temporal lobe and the hippocampus. Possibly such a biochemical disorder is associated with other amnesias. Whatever the effect of trauma on the consolidation of long-term memory of events close to it in time, the recovery from most amnesic states may be evidence that it is recall which is somehow damaged and not memory storage as such. In other words, the memory of the event is there, but for some reason, it is unobtainable.

## AMPHETAMINE

A drug which excites nervous activity, especially in the CENTRAL NERVOUS SYSTEM. Amphetamine is one of the earliest psychoactive drugs, synthesized in 1887 by Ebelnau, a German chemist. Its trade name is Benzedrine.

Doctors have restricted the prescription of amphetamine because substitutes have fewer undesirable side effects. The most serious are ADDICTION and poisoning.

Amphetamine was first used to treat narcolepsy, a tendency to fall asleep involuntarily. It may be used as an anti-depressant and is particularly effective as an antidote to the depression coincident upon barbiturate poisoning. Amphetamine was one of the first drugs that could control appetite, but it is now rarely used for this purpose. Students, athletes and politicians who must stay alert over long periods may still find it helpful, but it is seldom legally available and always potentially dangerous, especially in athletics.

The immediate problem caused by the drug is fatigue and the nightmares that follow its use. Amphetamine addicts, on the other hand, are sometimes depressed and narcotized by the drug. Poisoning usually follows chronic use, but it can happen to naive subjects, and it is always dangerous. Doses as low as two milligrams have been fatal to sensitive individuals. The most common symptom is a PSYCHOSIS which looks remarkably like acute SCHIZOPHRENIA. The antidote is a barbiturate, but if the patient has high blood pressure, phentolamine or a related drug may also be necessary. Amphetamine poisoning should always be treated by a doctor, if possible in hospital.

Amphetamine is chemically similar to the HORMONE, adrenaline (epinephrine), and to the TRANSMITTER, noradrenaline. It causes the kind of circulatory speed-up, based on more rapid heart action, which is also produced by adrenaline. Its effect on the brain and elsewhere in the nervous system is due in part to its noradrenaline-like action, but the drug may also mimic the effect of another transmitter, serotonin. Tolerance and addiction may develop because RECEPTORS for the transmitters are pre-empted by amphetamine, causing changes in the electrical properties and the functions of the NEURONS. More precise description of the action of amphetamine at the molecular level is not possible.

**AMYGDALA** See BRAIN

## ANAESTHETIC

(Greek: *an*=a negative+*aisthesis*=sensation) a drug which induces anaesthesia, the loss of SENSATION, especially the sensation of pain. A general anaesthetic also causes loss of CONSCIOUSNESS. A local anaesthetic such as cocaine, novocain or an epidural block reduces or eliminates sensation from a body region, but used as local anaesthetics, these drugs do not act in the BRAIN.

Apart from its pain-killing property, the most important quality of an anaesthetic is reversibility. Loss of sensation and consciousness must cease within a well-defined time limit. One of the most serious drawbacks of ALCOHOL as an anaesthetic is that the anaesthetic dose is very close to the fatal dose.

Ether (ethyl ether) was the first general anaesthetic to be used safely and consistently in surgery. It was introduced in Boston, Massachusetts, on 16 October 1846 by the senior surgeon, John Collins Warren, using an apparatus designed and operated by the discoverer of ether anaesthesia, William Thomas Green Morton, a Connecticut dentist. Chloroform was first used in childbirth by James Y. Simpson, professor of midwifery at Edinburgh University, in January 1847, and in surgery by Simpson working with James Miller, an Edinburgh surgeon, in November. It is still used in midwifery, often with minimal apparatus for self-administration. The third early anaesthetic, nitrous oxide or laughing gas, is seldom used in general surgery because it is hard to produce deep, prolonged anaesthesia with the drug.

Nitrous oxide can ignite when it is mixed with oxygen. Both ether and chloroform are extremely volatile and will explode in the presence of an accidental spark. After the Second World War, the Medical Research Council of Great Britain supported the search for a non-explosive general anaesthetic which could be administered as a gas. Halothane (Fluothane) was produced in 1956 and is now the most frequently used general anaesthetic. Chemically-related substances and some new gases based on a cholesterol-like molecule have also found places in surgical practice.

Because the induction of anaesthesia with halothane is slow and recovery is prolonged, the patient is customarily pre-medicated before he reaches the operating theatre. An OPIATE may be given to reduce any existing pain followed by a muscle-relaxing drug (see ANALEPTIC) and a fast-acting BARBITURATE to induce rapid loss of consciousness. A TRANQUILLIZER may be used in place of one of these drugs. The type of pre-medication depends on the nature and length of the operation.

The most serious side-effect from anaesthesia is impairment of breathing, which may be followed by circulatory collapse. The gas affects the whole brain including the hind-brain centres where breathing and heart rate are regulated. The anaesthetist can all but eliminate this danger, however, by regulating the amount of oxygen mixed with the anaesthetic gas. If more oxygen is mixed in, the anaesthetic is slower and may be less profound, but if too little oxygen is used, the risk of breathing difficulties increases.

Nausea and vomiting are usually less serious side effects. Proper pre-medication reduces the risk, and unlike ether and chloroform, halothane is pleasant smelling. Halothane has been associated with birth defects, however, and should not be used during pregnancy.

The mechanism of action of the anaesthetics at the molecular level is a mystery. It has been thought that the gas molecules alter properties of the membranes surrounding NEURONS, changing their electrical properties, but the evidence is contradictory. The gases may attach to membrane RECEPTORS and change the behaviour of protein molecules inside the neuron as well as those in the membrane. The biophysical effect on each neuron is probably very slight, and the gross physical effect is the result of a spreading action affecting millions of neurons.

## ANALEPTIC

(Greek: *analepsis*=repairing) 1. a drug which stimulates the CENTRAL NERVOUS SYSTEM. 2. a restorative tonic.

By far the commonest analeptics are contained in coffee, tea, cocoa made from the seeds of *theobroma cacao*, and those cola drinks based on nuts of the tree, *cola acuminata*. All of these popular drinks contain caffeine. A second analeptic, theophylline, occurs in tea, and cocoa contains theobromine. The three drugs are chemically similar and are called xanthines.

Of the three, caffeine is the most powerful brain stimulant and theobromine the weakest. Caffeine may be an effective antidote against poisoning by sleeping-pills such as BARBITURATES.

An attempted suicide is usually given hot coffee or tea after the poison has been pumped out of his stomach. If the HYPNOTIC drug has left the gut and entered the blood, caffeine may be used as a pure drug. In this form, it may also be used to counteract acute asthmatic attacks. Theophylline, however, is preferred as a heart stimulant. It is a stronger diuretic than caffeine (a diuretic increases urination). All of the xanthines work directly on the heart and kidneys. In the BRAIN, the xanthines stimulate nervous activity, first in the cortex and then in the medulla. They alter the chemical behaviour of cells in muscle as well as in nervous tissue, but the precise events are unclear. Their actions in the cortex contribute to the sense of alertness and well-being derived from tea and coffee, but they stimulate breathing and heart rate by acting in the medulla.

Analeptics can cause poisoning, but it is almost impossible to obtain a lethal dose from tea, coffee, cocoa or cola drinks. Children may be sensitive to their stimulant effects, however, and should be given them with caution. Patients with peptic ulcers or high blood pressure would also do well to avoid these drinks. The question whether tea, coffee or indeed cocoa keep you awake can be answered only by the individual. For reasons that are not clear, some people SLEEP soundly after a cup of black coffee while others are insomniac. A few people are so sensitive to the xanthines that a small amount makes them sick.

AMPHETAMINE, leptazol (US: pentylenetetrazol; Cardiazol, Metrazol, Pentrazol) and several less common drugs are also analeptics. They may be used as antidotes for ALCOHOL, BARBITURATE or OPIATE poisoning. Leptazol also counteracts the depressant effect of ANAESTHETICS on breathing and heart rate.

**ANALGESIC**

(Greek: *an*=a negative+*algesis*=pain) 1. a drug which induces analgesia, the relief of pain, without loss of CONSCIOUSNESS. 2. pain relieving (see SENSATION).

The oldest analgesics, ALCOHOL, cannabis sativa (see HALLUCINOGEN) and the opiates, act by altering the functions of NEURONS in the BRAIN. Modern analgesics beginning with aspirin (synthesized by a German chemist named Dreser in 1899) act at or near the site of pain. They are not effective against severe pain involving brain centres that regulate awareness of pain. In so far as migraine HEADACHES reflect a disturbance in the brain – and the theory that they do is controversial – ordinary analgesics cannot be expected to help. Similarly, the intradural or caudal block used to relieve the pain of childbirth is an ANAESTHETIC solution, made up of a local anaesthetic such as metycaine, injected into the lower part of the spinal cord where the main nerve trunks to the abdomen and legs originate. Analgesia is obtained, in these cases, without reference to the brain.

Continuous sound is now used to achieve audio analgesia, especially in dentistry. The second definition, above, is more appropriate to audio analgesia, and there can be no doubt that brain centres are involved. However, the mechanism by which sound reduces pain is not understood.

**ANANKASTIC** See OBSESSION

**ANEURISM** See BRAIN DAMAGE

**ANOSMIA**

(Greek: *an*=a negative+*osme*=smell) loss of the sense of smell. The loss can be selective so that some odours are still sensed (see SENSATION).

Anosmia may be congenital, and occasionally it is hereditary (see GENETICS). After head injury and during DEPRESSION, strong scents may smell unpleasant. Hallucinations of smell, called parosmia, can occur apart from other symptoms.

The sense of smell tends to become less efficient with age, but it is also thought that a large number of people are partially or wholly anosmic. People seldom complain of the deficiency, probably because the sense of smell is relatively unimportant for humans.

## ANOREXIA

(Greek: absence of appetite) loss of desire for food.

Anorexia may be a symptom of DEPRESSION, especially in old people. It may accompany OPIATE withdrawal (see ADDICTION) and chorea (see DEMENTIA, PSYCHOMOTOR DISEASE). The diagnosis of anorexia in children is less common now because parents tend not to insist that all food must be eaten at regular mealtimes. In part, anorexia may be a symptom of ANXIETY.

It is possible to cause anorexia in unfed animals by electrical stimulation through microelectrodes implanted in a region of the hypothalamus (see BRAIN, SENSATION). If the stimulation is continued, the animal may actually die of starvation. See also ANOREXIA NERVOSA.

## ANOREXIA NERVOSA

A nervous disorder the most important symptom of which is loss of appetite combined with refusal to eat. It is sometimes called hysterical anorexia, but the name implies that there is an identifiable psychic cause (see HYSTERIA), an implication which is wholly unjustified. According to some doctors, the disease may also be characterized by a prodigious appetite accompanied by an astonishing variety of devices like vomiting to expel the food or use it up. Anorexia nervosa is a very serious disorder. In roughly one out of ten cases, it ends fatally. It is almost entirely confined to women between the ages of 18 and 25, but it may occur as early as 14 and as late as 30. Rarely, the condition appears in young men.

The patient often begins by rigorous dieting. The fad is so popular that no one notices anything wrong until the weight loss becomes excessive, often as much as 50 pounds. She has already stopped menstruating by this time. Her breasts have shrunk, and other sexual characteristics, such as the distribution of body hair have been obscured. Blood levels of the male hormone, testosterone, are much elevated, but so is the level of the female hormone, oestriol. On the other hand, the main female hormones, oestrone and oestradiol, are much reduced. As the patient regains her body weight, these values return to normal. Any attempt at force feeding will almost certainly be followed by vomiting, however. The patient finds fats and carbohydrates especially nauseating. Hospitalized patients may have to be physically restrained from taking long walks or other exercise which they think will burn up calories. SLEEP is often very disturbed, but the patient welcomes insomnia. (Note that in DEPRESSION, sleep disturbance is common, but it is never welcome.) As her body weight falls to that of a five year old, the danger from pneumonia and tuberculosis mounts. If the decline cannot be checked, the patient dies from infection if not starvation.

Anorexia nervosa is almost certainly a psychological or FUNCTIONAL disorder. The patient may have shown earlier hysterical or obsessional symptoms, and there may be a family history of NEUROSIS. However, ORGANIC causes implicating the appetitive centres in the hypothalamus (see ANOREXIA, BRAIN) cannot be ruled out. The trigger is often an extreme family situation such as the death of a parent or an engagement to marry about which the patient is ambivalent (see AMBIVALENCE). Yet with the possible exception of aversion therapy (see below), PSYCHOTHERAPY seldom helps. The patient usually lacks insight and often disdains reason.

If the weight loss is severe, the patient may have to be hospitalized, and every nursing skill devoted to inducing her to eat. Psychological exploration may be conducted simultaneously to obtain background information. A TRANQUILLIZER may be prescribed to reduce the patient's resistance to food and to keep her quiet. An antihistamine, cyproheptidine (Periactin), has also been useful for some patients. In extremis, it may be necessary to employ insulin, not as shock treatment, but as aversion therapy. Insulin drives sugar out of the blood, and a dose can be fatal. The patient is told that she is to be given insulin, and that it will kill her if she doesn't take food, especially sugar, within a short time. If the patient still refuses to eat, the doctor can intervene with a glucose injection which will counteract the insulin. Such a technique is obviously too dangerous to be employed casually.

Most patients eventually recover their proper body weight and sexual characteristics. The effects of anorexia nervosa may persist, however, as neurosis and sexual frigidity (see DEVIATION, SEXUAL).

**ANOXIA** See BRAIN DAMAGE

**ANTICONVULSANT DRUGS** See PSYCHOMOTOR DISEASE

**ANTIDEPRESSANTS** See DEPRESSION

**ANXIETY**

(Latin: *anxietas*=nervous restlessness) 1. the state of uneasiness or concern about some uncertainty. 2. the state of unjustified and excessive uneasiness verging on fear of either a particular thing or situation, or some generalized uncertainty.

The two definitions indicate that the morbid state of anxiety is often hard to distinguish from a natural condition. Indeed, if your child is ill, if your business has lost money and the indicators show little reason to expect improvement, if you have an important examination approaching for which you think you are ill-prepared, if you have heard an unidentified noise outside your tent – if in hundreds of analogous circumstances, you did not feel anxiety, your MENTAL HEALTH might well be questioned. Anxiety is part of the normal continuum of responses to life. Concern about the uncertain alerts the body, focuses the ATTENTION and brings the MEMORY and intellect fully into play. Adrenaline (epinephrine) and other HORMONES enter the blood stream increasing heart rate and breathing and mobilizing sugar and fat from body stores to provide fuel for muscular activity and alertness. The skin conducts electricity slightly more easily, and blood flow to the muscles increases. Anxiety has survival value.

The physiological symptoms of normal anxiety also accompany the distressful and irrational symptoms of excessive anxiety. Diarrhoea and an increased desire to urinate are common. Tension, agitation and restlessness become oppressive. Appetite for food declines. Women become frigid and men impotent (see DEVIATION, SEXUAL). SLEEP is disturbed, especially in the second half of the night, and inordinately troubled by nightmares. The patient may become depressed and attempt SUICIDE.

Morbid anxiety is the commonest form of neurotic illness (see NEUROSIS). It is possible that patients have a GENETIC predisposition to anxiety, and there is evidence that the disorder runs in families. Yet the family connection could reflect environmental circumstances because anxious families may breed anxiety. Children and adolescents of both sexes who have difficulty in adjusting socially to pubertal changes often become anxious. Young housewives separated for the first time from their parents and left alone for days on end, often with a small child, develop neurotic anxiety. The middle aged tend to escape the disorder, but it recurs with increased severity in women after the climacteric and somewhat less often in men of the same age.

Anxiety patients tend to fall into one of two groups: those who suffer from simple anxiety and those with phobic anxiety. Simple anxiety states are those in which the patient feels a generalized uneasiness, more or less unstructured and apparently unrelated to an environmental circumstance. Simple anxiety is often chronic, and it is the hardest to meliorate.

Phobia is derived from a Greek suffix meaning fear, horror or aversion. Perhaps the least disabling phobic anxieties are those which are focused on an animal, thing or situation. The patient who is terrified of mice, spiders, heights or of being alone often learns to cope. He will not visit a doctor unless his circumstances change. For example, a secretary, afraid of heights whose boss moves to the thirtieth floor, finds herself facing a crisis. Simple anxiety frequently intervenes, but the phobia must be identified and treated if the condition is to be relieved. These anxious patients may be dependent on a relative or some other person – like the secretary's boss – who more or less knowingly protects them against the phobic object. The origin of the neurosis may lie in infancy or childhood. For example, a patient who fears cats has had an early scare from a nearby explosion when he was holding a cat. Even though the cause is forgotten, however, phobic patients may respond to behaviour therapy (see PSYCHOTHERAPY).

More complex phobias are harder to treat. Agoraphobia literally means fear of open spaces. Claustrophobia is applied to the fears of patients who are anxious in social gatherings and enclosed public spaces such as shops or tubes, and even on occasion, in their own homes. These seriously disabled people may find it possible to move about in the company of someone whom they trust, but their fear of going out can anticipate the actual event and make it impossible. Agoraphobic and claustrophobic patients often complain of DEPERSONALIZATION and DEREALIZATION, symptoms which can also occur in other anxiety states. Their phobia may appear suddenly and without warning in later life, and an environmental explanation is hard to identify. However, the attack may be triggered by a death or a job crisis, as in simple anxiety. The more acute the onset of agoraphobia, and the fewer episodes of neurosis in the patient's history, the better are his chances of complete recovery.

Depression is a symptom of all forms of anxiety. Conversely, anxiety is a common feature of DEPRESSION, though it is less often a symptom of HYSTERIA or OBSESSION, disorders which have much in common with phobic anxiety. Careful questioning and testing (see TESTS) can usually make the diagnosis clear. It is important not to confuse the symptoms of anxiety with depressive illness as such. The tricyclic antidepressants make anxiety worse. Similarly, electroconvulsive therapy (see SHOCK THERAPY) may relieve depression, but it can exacerbate anxiety. Thus, it seems that the disorder is marked off from other neurotic disturbances by subtle physiological differences.

In a minority of cases, anxiety is a symptom of an ORGANIC illness. Dyspepsia, for example, can be caused by some physical problem in the stomach or intestine, although there is also often a psychological element in the complaint (see PSYCHOSOMATIC). One symptom of dyspepsia is anxiety. Thyrotoxicosis, a systemic poisoning due to overproduction of thyroid HORMONE by the thyroid gland, also produces anxiety symptoms. Usually they are accompanied by physical signs such as the staring eyes and the swollen lower neck of goitre. (Thyroid hormone overproduction is hyperthyroidism. The opposite condition, hypothyroidism, may also produce enlargement of the thyroid gland and anxiety.) Thyrotoxicosis can be cured by a drug reducing the output of the hormone, or even by surgery to remove part of the gland, and the anxiety will disappear with the disease. Anxiety can also indicate high blood pressure, concussion, or a rare tumour of the adrenal gland. Control or removal of the physical disorder will control or cure the anxiety.

Treatment of the more common FUNCTIONAL anxiety is far less certain. Behavioural and group therapy can be helpful, but PSYCHOANALYSIS is seldom of any use. Chronic simple anxiety or agoraphobia in a patient with a history of mental disorders, may never respond to psychotherapy. It is often necessary for such patients to control their anxiety by using a minor TRANQUILLIZER. Some patients also respond to phenelzine, one of a class of antidepressant drugs called monoamine oxidase inhibitors. PSYCHOSURGERY has been recommended in intractable anxiety.

**APHASIA** See -PHASIS

**APOPLEXY (STROKE)** See BRAIN DAMAGE

**ARTERIOSCLEROSIS, CEREBRAL** See BRAIN DAMAGE

**ATAXIA**

(Greek: lack of order) disorder of movement due to failure of nervous, and hence of muscular, coordination.

In view of the complexity of movements we perform, it is not surprising that many BRAIN centres and nerve tracts and millions of individual NEURONS are needed to assure smoothness and adaptability. The cerebral cortex, thalamus, hind brain, cerebellum and spinal cord are the most important centres regulating movement. Disease or damage in these centres or in the tracts linking them to muscles or providing them with necessary sensory information invariably causes ataxia. Parkinsonism and multiple sclerosis are only two of the more familiar diseases with marked ataxic symptoms (see PSYCHOMOTOR DISEASE).

**ATTENTION**

Direction of the MIND, consideration or regard.

Attention is one of the most prominent attributes of CONSCIOUSNESS. It can be directly related to three BRAIN regions: the colliculi where SENSATIONS of sight, sound and feeling are brought together physically; the reticular activating system which regulates wakefulness and SLEEP; and the cerebral cortex which coordinates EMOTION and MEMORY with new sensory information. DEMENTIA, epilepsy (see PSYCHOMOTOR DISEASE) and tumours (see BRAIN DAMAGE) can cause significant disturbances of attention reflecting damage to relevant brain centres. In FUNCTIONAL disorders, such as SCHIZOPHRENIA, attentional disturbances are associated with errors of PERCEPTION.

## AUTISM

(Greek: *autos*=self) abnormal self-absorption to the partial or complete exclusion of reality.

Autism may be a symptom of DEMENTIA and SCHIZOPHRENIA, and it is one of the signs of lead poisoning (see BRAIN DAMAGE). The word is also applied to a developmental disorder in children, early infantile or early childhood autism. Early infantile autism is thought to be congenital. The early childhood form appears between the first and fourth years. By and large, the conditions are indistinguishable, and are referred to collectively as autism. They affect about 4.5 out of 10,000 children up to the age of 4 in Middlesex county; based on this figure, it has been estimated that there are about 3,000 autistic children of school age in England and Wales compared with 1,422 blind children and 3,356 deaf children.

An autistic child may resist the establishment of eating, sleeping and toilet routines. He may scream without apparent reason, but more often he is unusually quiet. At about the fourth month, the infant fails to hold out his arms to be picked up. When he is held, he may not mould himself to his mother's figure. Speech may never develop normally. It can be characterized by the reversal of pronouns (for example, 'you' for 'I'), ECHOLALIA, repetition and excessive literalness. Despite early resistance to their formation, the child's later insistence on rigid patterns demands unchanging routines, any deviation from which may be met with rage and AGGRESSION, or panic.

Autistic children learn well and have unusually good memories, especially for material learned by rote. Many show exceptional musical or mathematical ability. They look intelligent and may be remarkably beautiful with graceful and efficient movements. Nothing in their appearance or superficial manner resembles the dull, vacant behaviour of retarded children (see RETARDATION). In many respects, they are remarkably bright, but lacking in adaptability, an apparent paradox.

The outlook for autistic children is poor. Out of 63 cases followed up by Louis Kanner, the American psychiatrist who identified the disorder, 3 grew up to be reasonably normal, 14 (at the age of 15) attained school levels commensurate with their ages, but continued to display severe PERSONALITY disorders, and the remaining 46 were invalids at home or in hospital. Phenothiazine TRANQUILLIZERS are used to restrain fits of rage or fear. Conventional PSYCHOTHERAPY is useless. The children often respond to a well-planned routine and to a careful teaching regimen based on the principle of operant conditioning (see PSYCHOLOGY). With care, most autistic children should be able to enter state schools by the time they are 10, but they seldom achieve a normal adjustment.

There is no evidence connecting autism with any psychological or environmental cause. A disproportionate number of autistic children are born to parents who are university graduates and have above average IQs (see TESTS), but these facts could be relevant to some GENETIC element in the disorder. The sex ratio – four boys are autistic to one girl – suggests the possibility of a sex-linked inherited trait. Where the disorder affects identical twins, without exception both twins are autistic, as might be expected if the condition is inherited as a dominant trait. On the other hand, autism is rarely seen in the parents of autistic children or in their siblings, other than identical twins. The persistence of notable abilities amongst the disabilities is reminiscent of children who have suffered brain damage. Nor do the symptoms of autism grade slowly into normality as is the case with FUNCTIONAL disorders such a ANXIETY and DEPRESSION. For these reasons, most authorities believe that the disease is organically based.

Children who suffer from a form of congenital nerve blindness, retrolental fibroplasia, often display autistic symptoms. This does not happen with children who are congenitally blind because of an error in the development of the eye rather than its nervous connections. Retrolental fibroplasia occurs primarily in premature infants who have spent the early days of their lives in breathing apparatus, and it is thought they may be abnormally sensitive to oxygen. Thus, according to one theory, autistic children have been poisoned in utero or at birth by oxygen at normal pressure!

Infantile and childhood autism have also been called childhood SCHIZOPHRENIA, but there is no relationship between the diseases. Indeed, there is little evidence that children are ever schizophrenic. It is more likely that children who have been diagnosed as schizophrenic suffer from some form of brain damage or have developed an ORGANIC disorder.

**AUTOMATISM**

(Greek: *automatismos*=self-action) 1. the sense that conscious, voluntary acts are performed without will, as though involuntarily. 2. the doctrine that all mental activity is caused by or manufactured in the BRAIN (see CONSCIOUSNESS, MIND).

Automatism is a characteristic of DEPERSONALIZATION. It may be felt by epileptics before or after a seizure, and in milder cases, during the fit (see PSYCHOMOTOR DISEASE).

**AVERSION THERAPY** See PSYCHOTHERAPY

**AWARENESS** See ATTENTION

# B

**BARBITURATE**

One of a large class of drugs which depress nervous activity, especially in the CENTRAL NERVOUS SYSTEM. The oldest barbiturate, barbitone (1902), is no longer used, but phenobarbitone (1912) is still prescribed as a sedative and sleeping pill (see HYPNOTIC) for patients with insomnia of nervous origin. All barbiturates have the ending, '-one', in the United Kingdom and '-al', or '-ol', in the United States; thus, phenobarbital.

Barbiturates have different uses depending on the speed and duration of their action. They are often classified accordingly as long-acting (for example, phenobarbitone takes effect after an hour and acts for six to ten hours), intermediate (thirty minutes to five or six hours), short-acting (pentobarbitone: fifteen minutes to two to three hours), and very short-acting (thiopentone: under five minutes to less than one hour). Thiopentone and other very short-acting barbiturates may be used as ANAESTHETICS. The intermediate and short-acting barbiturates may be prescribed as sleeping pills, but it is now more common to use TRANQUILLIZERS. Phenobarbitone may also relieve migraine (see HEADACHE), and it can control or even prevent grand mal epilepsy seizures (see PSYCHOMOTOR DISEASE). Some authorities hold that the difference in duration of action depends in part at least on the patient's response to the drug. They accept the different uses of the barbiturates, but deny the value of this classification.

Although the barbiturates are safe when taken according to a doctor's instruction, they can have two serious undesirable side effects which have restricted their use. They can cause fatal poisoning, and they can be addictive (see ADDICTION).

The danger of poisoning varies with the type of barbiturate. More of the long-acting drugs are required, but they persist in the body, in part because they are slowly broken down and excreted. Therefore, relatively low doses can build up dangerous levels in the blood. Most barbiturate sleeping pills are intermediate or short-acting. Compared with the long-acting drugs, smaller doses may cause poisoning, but these drugs are more rapidly excreted, so that there is less danger from a build up.

At first, the symptoms of poisoning look like ordinary drunkenness. The pupils constrict and then dilate. Breathing becomes progressively more disturbed. Blood pressure falls until the patient enters shock, which is followed by coma. The best treatments are physical measures, such as washing out the stomach, artificial respiration, blood transfusion and even the use of an artificial kidney to clear the body of breakdown products from the drug. The risk of poisoning increases if the drug has been injected, or if the patient has also been drinking, because, like the barbiturates, ALCOHOL depresses nervous activity.

Addiction to barbiturates is, in part, psychological, but the drugs alter the behaviour of NEURONS in the BRAIN and throughout the nervous system. They change the electrical characteristics of membranes surrounding the cells, thus reducing the efficiency of RECEPTORS for nervous TRANSMITTERS. They also act in a similar way on muscle cells. The exact molecular course of events is not understood, but the physical effects underlie addiction as well as the desirable drug actions.

Addicts often display ugly skin sores which are made worse by poor hygiene and improper diet. If withdrawal is too sudden, it can produce convulsions and may be fatal. No drug can reduce the withdrawal TRAUMA, but a tranquillizer may help by keeping the patient quiet.

**BASAL GANGLIA** See BRAIN

**BATESON, G.** See SCHIZOPHRENIA

**BEHAVIOUR THERAPY** See PSYCHOTHERAPY

**BEHAVIOURISM** See PSYCHOLOGY

**BEREAVEMENT**

The sense of deprivation and sadness brought on by the death of someone connected by close ties. The word derives from an old English word meaning to plunder, spoil, rob, and this implication of violent deprivation is important to its meaning.

Bereavement is of course a natural, normal EMOTION. Indeed, its absence can be as much a symptom of mental abnormality as excessive display. For example, a man who cannot feel grief at the death of his mother or father may suffer distorted emotions; he may even be repressing emotion in a manner that could cause him to experience physical discomfort (see PSYCHOSOMATIC). On the other hand, excessive bereavement can trigger ANXIETY, DEPRESSION or SCHIZOPHRENIA in those who are subject to these conditions. The connection between bereavement and onset of mental illness is much clearer in young people than it is in the aged, perhaps because the loss of an elderly partner is inseparable from loneliness.

There is no standard against which to measure the sense of deprivation. Words like 'excessive' are judgments made by those who think there is something wrong. Yet there are times when ordinary words of sympathy are inadequate, especially if the bereaved is fearful of death. Again, fear of death is normal enough, but it too may become morbid. In extreme cases, PSYCHOTHERAPY may be necessary if only to discover whether bereavement is masking some hidden emotional disorder.

The great majority of bereaved people respond in time to companionship and a normal routine of work, and play. For most people, the therapeutic power of the wake derives far more from the superficial socializing, jollity and drinking, which the custom permits, than from its spiritual content. It is only in today's urban isolation, where such outlets have been lost, that bereavement becomes a problem for MENTAL HEALTH.

**BERIBERI** See BRAIN DAMAGE

**BERNE, E.** See PSYCHOTHERAPY

**BESTIALITY** See DEVIATION, SEXUAL

**BINSWANGER, LUDWIG**

Psychotherapist; applied precepts of existential phenomenology to psychotherapy; that is, errors in the patient's self-image cause inadequate or incorrect relationships to develop and lead to mental illness (see PSYCHOTHERAPY). b. Switzerland, 1881. d. 1966. *Sigmund Freud: Reminiscences of a Friendship*, 1957. *Being-in-the-World*, 1963.

**BIOENERGETIC THERAPY** See PSYCHOTHERAPY

**BIOFEEDBACK**

A technique for obtaining conscious control over reflex and involuntary body processes. The word combines Greek: *bios*= life, with the cybernetic concept, feedback – a technique for automatically controlling a process by means of a machine which measures the process and uses the information to turn itself on and off. The word, biofeedback, appears to have been introduced by an American psychologist, Robert Ornstein.

Involuntary biological feedback is a common phenomenon, exemplified by the regulation of HORMONE secretion. Thus, the release of adrenaline (epinephrine) by the adrenal gland is regulated in part by the amount of adrenaline in the blood. Adrenaline release is the process measured, and the adrenal gland is the measuring instrument. Control of body temperature, urine production, heart rate and breathing are also regulated by feedback between various chemicals carried by the blood and NEURONS in the BRAIN acting in concert with neurons and other cells in the skin, kidneys, heart and arteries, respectively. All such processes are normally automatic and unconscious.

Biofeedback is a kind of LEARNING, whereby the conscious MIND appears to acquire control over such processes. This is learning in the limited sense implied by the phrase 'learning to relax'. One of the American advocates of biofeedback for therapy uses the expression 'art of biofeedback', implying that it is not a measurable phenomenon subject to testing but a generalized behaviour, like relaxation. Some people may be better at it than others.

Yoga is an example of biofeedback in action. Its practitioners can reduce their heart and breathing rates well below normal; the oxygen and nutrient requirements of their tissues must also be reduced. Perhaps the first publicized attempt by western medicine to make use of analogous techniques was an experiment by an American doctor, N. E. Miller, who taught patients to reduce their high blood pressure without drugs. A sphygmomanometer is a long, narrow box with a column of mercury in its top and a cuff, which the doctor wraps around the patient's upper arm and inflates in order to test his blood pressure. With cuffs wrapped around their upper arms, some of Dr Miller's patients learned to bring down the columns of mercury and to keep them down. Not all of them were equally successful, but a majority benefited from biofeedback (a word that Dr Miller did not use when he described his work).

By listening to a tone which changes with the ELECTROENCEPHALOGRAM, a subject can learn to control his own brain waves. He can increase or decrease the amount of alpha activity, the rhythm of wakeful relaxation, in relation to other rhythms. Skin conductance and body temperature have also been made responsive to biofeedback. The learner seems to use the information he obtains – from the sphygmomanometer or the EEG, for example – to teach himself by operant conditioning (see

PSYCHOLOGY) that is, the instrument causes him to react so as to obtain a reward: lowered blood pressure or increased alpha rhythm.

All of the effects of biofeedback demonstrated in these experiments are consistent with a generalized capacity to relax. It is possible, however, that some more specific technique is being learned. One would like to know, for example, whether it is possible to use biofeedback to reduce the amount of tooth decay, or the wax collected in the ear, or to change the adaptability of the eye – processes which seem to be both unaffected by the ability to relax and outside conscious control. Unfortunately, the tendency to treat biofeedback as a trendy alternative medicine can deny it the benefit of scientific discussion and testing. What could be an important addition to the therapeutic armoury has been relegated to the dubious if profitable domain of ESP (see HYPNOTISM, MEDITATION, SENSATION).

**BIRTH DEFECT** See BRAIN DAMAGE

**BIRTHING (BIRTH TRAUMA)** See TRAUMA

**BLEULER, EUGEN**

Psychiatrist. b. Zollikon, Switzerland, 1857. d. Zollikon, 1939. Described and distinguished between kinds of SCHIZOPHRENIA, a word which he introduced, 1908. Humanistic and individual approach to therapy. Professor of psychiatry, University of Zurich, and director, Burghölzi Psychiatric Hospital, 1898–1927. *Dementia Praecox or the Group of Schizophrenias*, 1911. *Textbook of Psychiatry*, 1916.

**BLOOD-BRAIN BARRIER**

A semi-permeable tissue separation between blood and brain, consisting of the cells lining capillaries, the membrane surrounding these cells and the thin processes of astrocytes, a kind of glial cell (see BRAIN), between capillaries and NEURONS. It is not a barrier in an absolute sense. Under normal conditions, oxygen and other gases, nutrients and other chemicals, and water, diffuse freely between blood, neurons and glial cells. Larger molecules, such as those of some drugs, however, will not pass through it. The permeability of the barrier changes under different conditions. For example, a brain injury can increase permeability. The barrier does not exist in the pineal body, the pituitary and at a portion of the hind-brain.

**BRADYKINESIA** See -KINESIS

**BRAIN**

The mass of nervous and glial tissue inside the cranium which receives, coordinates and analyzes sensory data, plans and regulates action, governs the functions of heart, lungs and viscera, determines the state of wakefulness and is the physical substrate of CONSCIOUSNESS and MIND.

The adult human brain weighs on average about 1,300 gm or 3 lb. The male brain is slightly larger than the female. Both contain about 10,000 million NEURONS at age 20, but lose about 10,000 neurons a day thereafter, so that average brain weight at death may be only about 1,000 grams. In a few exceptional cases, one neuron connects with 250,000 others, but the mean number of connections is closer to 60,000. The neurons are surrounded by, and may receive nutrients and other chemicals from, about five times as many glial cells. The brain also contains a complex network of blood vessels, and four linked ventricles or reservoirs which are connected to open areas surrounding the brain and spinal cord. They contain cerebrospinal fluid (CSF), formed by cells lining the ventricles. The fluid helps to cushion the brain against external shock, and like the blood, carries nutrients and other chemicals. The tough, three-layered membrane surrounding the brain gives additional protection, but it is not attached to the skull, and there are no connective tissues or internal membranes. The brain contains no neurons responsive directly to touch, temperature, pressure or pain. Except for major nerve trunks, the largest being the spinal cord, and large blood vessels which connect it to the rest of the body, the brain floats freely within the bony cavity of the skull.

When the skull is opened surgically, the ridged and folded tissue is most remarkable for its stillness. If a large surface artery should be exposed, it will pulse, but neither the myriad electrical impulses nor the chemical transactions going on in the pinkish-grey mass indicate their presence. Yet there is little doubt that this is the most powerful machine in the known universe.

In section, brain tissue is of two kinds: grey matter and white matter. The grey consists of neurons and their axonal and dendritic processes plus glial cells, the prevailing colour of all cells being grey. White matter consists of the long axons of neurons wrapped by concentric rings of a white, fat-like substance, myelin, synthesized by one variety of glial cell, oligodendroglia. Myelinated axons are often collected together into great tracts linking different parts of the brain. Myelin also coats the long axons of many peripheral neurons, groups of which form the white nerves visible to the naked eye. It is an electrical insulation and speeds up the signal moving along the axon.

Except for the nearly separate cerebellum and the two obvious halves of the brain, the cerebral hemispheres, formed by the deep division running from front to back, the different parts are often hard to distinguish. In some instances, the white nerve tracts form boundaries, but often the identification of areas depends upon interpretations of shadings of grey which can be altered by the sharpness and the angle of the dissecting knife. Over the centuries, furthermore, parts have been named in various languages by anatomists whose observations varied with the direction they cut through the three-dimensional brain substance. Only within the last seventy-five years, moreover, has it been possible to associate parts with their functions. At first, electrical stimulation of the living brain surface provided functional information, but more recently, microelectrodes have been used in human as well as animal brains to obtain responses to stimulation from small groups of neurons. Exploration of function has shown that apparent anatomical structures may be functionally meaningless. Nevertheless, it is impossible to describe the brain as a unit, and brain scientists, therefore, relate physiological and biochemical function to centres identified by the traditional anatomists.

The most noteworthy feature of the human brain is the cortex or outer layer which contains almost two-thirds of the brain volume and enwraps the other regions on the top and three sides. The cerebellum can be easily distinguished at the back of the brain, beneath the cortex, and the brain stem is also clearly visible beneath the cerebellum. The brain stem connects the mid-brain, well hidden within the cortex, to the spinal cord and is also called the hind-brain. Main nerve trunks to and from the face, heart and lungs reach the brain at the hind-brain. The brain stem is the oldest part of the structure from the standpoint of evolution.

The cortical surface consists of deep folds, sulci (singular: sulcus), between ridges or gyri (singular: gyrus). Ironed out flat, the human cortical surface covers about 2,000 sq cm, roughly the area of a large pillow case. The degree of cortical convolution increases with the recency of the animal's appearance on the evolutionary stage. Rat cortex is almost smooth, but the brains of chimpanzees show intensive convolutions. The deepest sulci divide the human cortex into four lobes on each side: the occipital at the back, the temporal at the bottom rear inside the ears, the parietal at the top rear, and the huge frontal lobe. The lobes are further subdivided by lesser sulci, and the entire surface has been mapped into areas which may cross the divisions into lobes, by a German neurologist named Brodmann. The cortex varies in thickness from about 1.5 to 3 millimetres, the thickest parts being in the frontal lobe, and consists of layers of neurons distinguished by their differently-shaped bodies and processes.

The occipital cortex is about coextensive with the visual cortex which receives and processes signals from the eyes. The temporal cortex deals with auditory signals and plays a significant, though poorly-understood role in MEMORY. In this region, the two hemispheres display the phenomenon known as functional lateralization. In right-handed people and a majority of those who are left-handed, the left temporal cortex controls and regulates speech, writing and reading. The right temporal zone is concerned with perception of colour and non-symbolic sound, such as music. This lateralization is apparently unique, because in all other respects, the two halves of the brain not only look alike, but also act like mirror images of each other.

Although it was discovered as a result of accidental injuries, lateralization has been tested by experiments with so-called split brains. Surgeons have divided the two cortical hemispheres by cutting a huge tract of white matter, the corpus callosum, which contains axons linking them. In humans, the

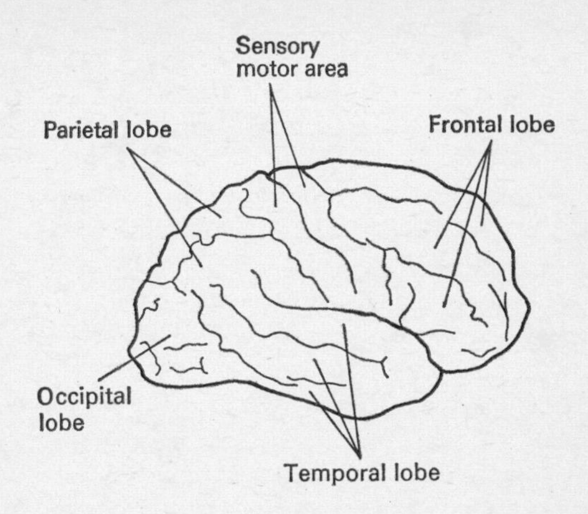


Side view of human brain.

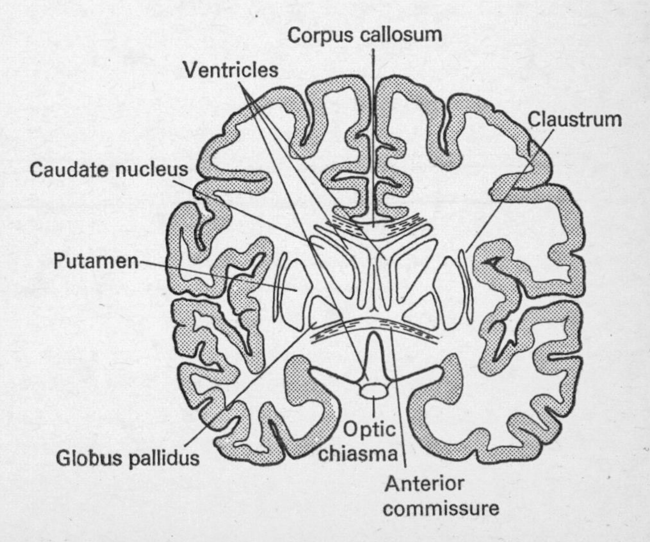


Coronal section; i.e. diagrammatic view through the centre of the brain cut through both ears.

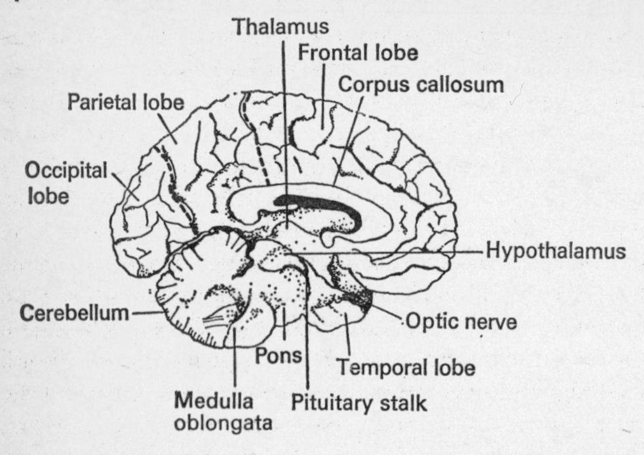


Medial section; i.e. diagrammatic view of the brain cut through the centre from front to back.

operation has been performed only to control the severe seizures of chronic epileptics who have not responded to less radical treatments. After the operation, the patient is usually much relieved. Neither his INTELLIGENCE nor his PERSONALITY are damaged, but he displays bizarre, if less serious, side effects. If he is shown a spoon so that he can see it only with his right eye, he can describe the spoon – long, round at one end, hard, shiny, and so on – but he cannot name it. If he is allowed to hold the spoon in his right hand, however, he can immediately say the word 'spoon'. His right eye, which is normally connected to both hemispheres, now signals only the right side, but his hand is still connected through the spinal cord and the brain stem to both hemispheres. He is much more successful at copying the drawing of a scene shown him through only his right eye, furthermore, than when the same scene is shown to his left eye. Information of this kind exemplifies the lateralization of hemispheric function, but it also shows that, though lateralization applies to the cortex, it does not appear to affect other parts of the brain.

Further evidence for the lateralization of function has come from the study of a form of reading disorder called deep dyslexia (see -LEXIS). In this condition, the patient makes frequent semantic errors; that is, shown the word 'table', he reads 'chair'. He may also find it easier to read concrete words – face, storm – than abstract words – origin, charm. And he may be almost totally unable to read prepositions and connectives – to, in, and, but. Max Coltheart, a British psychologist, has suggested that deep dyslexia occurs because the left cortical reading area is inoperative, for some reason. It is not connected to the visual system. Instead, the right hemisphere, which lacks the power of speech, comprehends the words in a semantic code which it transmits along nerve tracts to the left hemisphere. It can transmit only a semantic signal, not a syntactic signal, and even less, a phonological signal. The left hemisphere must then fit a word to the semantic signal. The theory has gained support from experiments with a Japanese deep dyslexic patient. Japanese is written in one of two different scripts: an ideographic script, like Chinese, and an orthographic script, more like a western alphabet. The patient is able to read ideographic script better than the orthographic. Since the right hemisphere deals with the ideographic script better than the left, and vice versa, the division of function between the cortical hemispheres is shown to be real.

Unfortunately, a mystique has grown up around the facts that are available. The left hemisphere is sometimes referred to as the rational side because it copes with symbolic language, and by the same token, the right hemisphere is non-rational, more primitive and possibly more artistic. It has even been suggested that western education trains primarily the left, rational half of the cortex, and that more attention should be paid to the right half. Some Oriental religions, Buddhism in particular, are said to perpetrate the opposite mistake. Until such fancies can be properly tested, it is well to remember that the normal brain consists of two halves functioning as a unit.

Across the top of the head, on the boundaries between the parietal and frontal lobes in both hemispheres, are two bands of the cortex which receive sensory data from touch, temperature and pressure RECEPTORS in the skin, muscles and viscera (see SENSATION), and help to regulate voluntary movement. Along the forward bands on each side, the sensory inputs are organized on a kind of body map or homunculus, with the feet at the top and the head at the bottom. Distortions in the map reflect the number of receptors in the different parts; the fingers, for example, are proportionately much larger than the

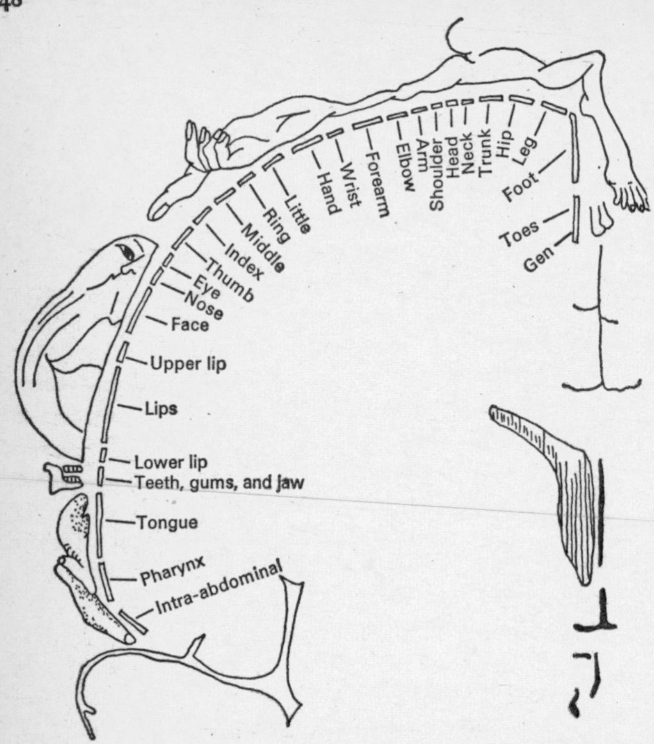


back. An analogous motor homunculus lies along each posterior band. Surface stimulation of appropriate points causes perception of sensation and movement in the connected body region. Secondary sensory and motor areas which may be more concerned with involuntary muscles, lie along the sulcus separating the temporal and parietal lobes. These areas, too, are organized as body maps. This logical arrangement of neurons is repeated again and again in the brain. For example, each retina is mapped in the neurons on both visual cortexes. By and large, the left half of the brain is connected to the right side of the body, and vice versa. The precision of these connections owes much to the environment of the developing individual, as well as to his inheritance (see BRAIN DAMAGE).

In the rat brain, about 85 per cent of the cortex can be mapped to show the location of sensory and motor functions. In the human brain on the other hand, about 15 per cent of the

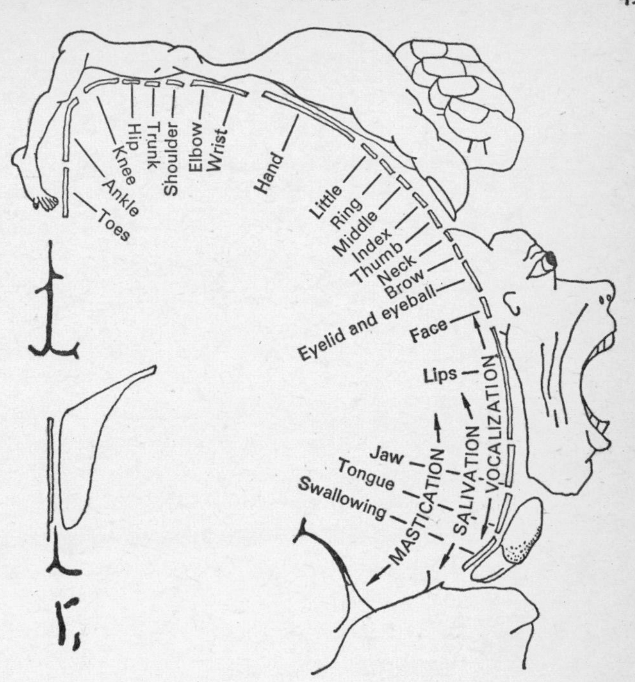


Motor and sensory Homunculi.

cortex is covered by such a sensory and motor map. The remaining 85 per cent, largely in the frontal lobe, is believed to be concerned with MEMORY (and therefore, with LEARNING) and with the coordination of memories and new sensory data.

At the front of the mid-brain is the olfactory bulb. In other animals, the bulb is in fact a lobe; out of it, the cortex evolved. Again, there are two olfactory bulbs, one on each side. Behind them is the thalamus, a major relay centre. It receives sensory data and distributes it to the appropriate cortical regions, and with the basal ganglia – the substantia nigra, putamen, globus pallidus and caudate nucleus – the thalamus sends motor instructions to both voluntary and involuntary muscles. Motor instructions also pass through the pyramidal tracts linking the cortex to the cerebellum, and thence through the hind-brain to the spinal cord and the limbs. This pathway is principally concerned with voluntary muscular movement.

Beneath the thalamus is the hypothalamus (*hypo*=below), a bundle of neurons amongst which are discrete groups controlling such phenomena as temperature, hunger, thirst, anger, fear and indirectly, sexual activity. Hypothalamic regulatory activity utilizes HORMONES called 'releasing factors', as well as nervous signals. Releasing factors are synthesized and secreted by neurons. They circulate in a local blood supply or, like TRANSMITTERS, they cross synapses to neurons in the pituitary, a tiny gland buried in the bony roof of the mouth. The gland responds by releasing at least seven hormones into the blood, regulating birth, growth, sexual behaviour and body chemistry.

Surrounded by the thalamus, at almost the geometrical centre of the brain, is the pineal body. Once called the third eye, and thought to be the seat of the soul, the pineal may, indeed, be affected by light and play a role in regulating sexual activity, at least in birds. At the side of the thalamus, the lateral geniculate bodies contain the endings of the optic nerve tracts and relay their signals to the visual cortex and the colliculi on top of the hind-brain.

Connecting the thalamus to the hind-brain are a series of neuronal bundles, including the amygdala, hippocampus and the reticular activating system. Together, they are called the limbic system. Like the hypothalamus, the amygdala is involved in the expression of anger, fear and satiation. The hippocampus (the word means 'horse field') is thought to be necessary for the transformation of short-term to long-term memory, and therefore, for learning. The reticular activating system regulates the state of wakefulness or SLEEP. If it malfunctions, the animal remains permanently more or less deeply asleep.

The reticular activating system runs into the hind-brain where it connects with the medulla oblongata, a region containing centres regulating heart rate and breathing. On top of the hind-brain are four small bundles of neurons, two on each side, called the superior and inferior colliculi (singular: colliculus). They receive and coordinate visual, auditory and feeling sensations independently of the main sensory areas of the cortex, and regulate ATTENTION reflexes.

The cerebellum sits on top of the hind-brain. The word means little brain. It is a remarkable organ, regulating fine muscular movements such as those required to play a musical instrument. The detailed functions of its clearly delineated neuronal layers are well understood. All but one of the several types of cerebellar neurons produce signals which inhibit the signals of the one excitatory type. The cerebellum obtains fine control by inhibition, a demonstration of the fact that brain function requires shutting down of output perhaps as often as excitation. There is also evidence that the cerebellum learns and remembers sequences of signals, and that fine control over movement is not a function of the cortex.

Literally dozens of anatomically-identified regions are not named in this entry simply because their functions are not known. In the cortex, for example, large areas may be lost due to accident or disease without permanent behavioural defects. The brain seems to be able to compensate for the loss of tissue despite the fact that no new neurons are formed in humans after the age of about 2. Providing that the person is younger than 15, he can overcome a serious accident damaging the left temporal language area, and may regain the power of rational speech. People in their twenties and thirties have lost the use of a limb following a brain injury, but in time they regain the function with almost the original efficiency. Other parts of the brain seem to take over the function of the damaged region. This excess capacity reflects the plasticity of brain tissue. Even after neurons are fully formed and no further growth takes place, functional remodelling continues. Learning itself is evidence of this astonishing plasticity.

The study of functional plasticity is one of the most important aspects of modern brain research. If the factors that permit fully-differentiated cells to take on new activities can be described, it will be possible to improve education along rational lines, and to re-educate those with mental or physical handicaps affecting their behaviour and intellects.

## BRAIN DAMAGE

Destruction of brain tissue by accident, nutritional deficiencies or disease. This entry is organized as follows:

1. Accident due to concussion and gunshot wounds
2. Anoxia (shortage of oxygen) due to foetal or birth accidents and cerebrovascular accidents (strokes)

3. Disease-based damage due to hydrocephalus, syphilis, tuberculosis and tumours
4. Minimal brain damage and cerebral palsy
5. Nutritional deficiencies
6. Other environmental causes

For brain damage due to drugs, see ADDICTION, ALCOHOL, AMPHETAMINE, BARBITURATE, OPIATE. For brain damage due to physical therapies, see PSYCHOSURGERY, SHOCK THERAPY. See also RETARDATION.

**1. Accident.** At about 4.30 in the afternoon of 13 September 1848, near the village of Cavendish, Vermont, a gang of workmen were building the new line, extending the Rutland and Burlington Railroad. The gang foreman was a likeable man of 25 named Phineas P. Gage. The men were ready to blast a rock that blocked the way, and Gage himself had taken charge of the delicate preparations. He poured gunpowder into the deep hole that had been drilled into the rock. Then he slowly lowered the tamping iron into the hole to compress the powder before covering it with sand. The massive bar, three and a half feet long, an inch and a quarter through and weighing thirteen pounds, struck a spark against the stone. The powder exploded, shooting the bar out of the hole and straight through Phineas Gage's skull. It entered just beneath his left eye, left through a hole in the top of his head and landed about fifty yards away.

To the astonishment of the work gang, to say nothing of the doctors who later attended him, Gage survived. The blow knocked him out, but within a few minutes, he had regained consciousness and the power of speech. The wound bled profusely. Infection set in, and Gage became delirious, but within three weeks, he was up and about. Then it began to be clear that the Gage who rose from what should have been his death bed was not the Gage who had placed the tamping iron in that fateful hole. That affable, energetic, responsible man had indeed died, but within the still-living, healthy body, there appeared a new PERSONALITY, irresponsible to the point of childishness, extremely strong and with a temper to match. For several years, Gage drifted around the United States and South America, a side-show freak exhibiting himself and the terrible tamping iron. When he died in San Francisco, someone had the wit to return his skull and the rod to the Harvard Medical School where they can still be seen, strong evidence of the first recorded frontal lobotomy (see PSYCHOSURGERY).

The tamping iron had effectively cut the main connections between Gage's frontal lobe and the rest of his BRAIN. The large frontal lobe of the brain cortex is involved in the development and perpetuation of the socializing and emotional faculties, but it plays little, if any, role in memory, sensation, movement, perception, breathing, heart beat or the thousands of brain functions essential to the maintenance of life. Gage's accident shows how, until recently, this kind of brain damage was the only source of information about the functions of different parts of the brain.

The permanent changes in Gage's personality occurred because part of his brain was damaged, but there had been another, less serious result of the accident. Concussion had knocked him out. Concussion means diffuse paralysis of brain function due to a blow on the head. The patient usually recovers from it quickly, without lasting injury. The most obvious sign of concussion is loss of consciousness, probably caused by the temporary increase in pressure at the point of impact. The blow compresses the cerebrospinal fluid and possibly the brain itself, but the effect is transmitted through the fluid to the brainstem. The brainstem passes through a narrow hole at the base of the skull to connect with the spinal cord. Compression forces it against the bone, and impairs the function of NEURONS in the reticular activating system which regulate alertness. AMNESIA may follow. The longer unconsciousness persists, the greater the danger that pressure or haemorrhage have caused lasting damage. Other signs that can indicate lasting damage are slowed breathing, erratic pulse (both symptoms can also indicate shock), an unusual appearance of the eyes and general lassitude. If any of these symptoms appear after a blow on the head, a doctor should be consulted.

Punch-drunkenness is a special case of concussion. Usually associated with boxing, it follows a series of blows to the head and is caused by pressure, localized haemorrhage or localized damage to neurons in the brain. Occasionally, a boxer dies suddenly after a fight when he has been knocked out, though he often regains consciousness first. The cause is probably concussion which has damaged irreversibly the brainstem centres regulating breathing and heart rate.

Gunshot wounds can be as dramatic as the accident sustained by Gage. The great Russian neurophysiologist, A. R. Luria, described a spectacular case in a book with the English title *The Man with a Shattered World*. In 1943 at the battle of Smolensk, a 23-year-old Russian officer named Zasetsky was hit by shell fragments which entered his brain, destroying part of his left parieto-occipital cortex. He did not lose consciousness, but obviously he was badly shaken and concussed. He always remembered the blood, the sharp pain in his head and how his breathing stopped so that he thought he was going to die. He could hear the voices of the doctors who were holding him, but their words had no meaning. As Zasetsky later wrote, 'I was killed . . . but because of some vital power of my organism, I miraculously remained alive.'

Indeed, that vital power was astonishing. He had been a brilliant engineer, devoted to his mother, who had struggled to make his education possible. After about three months, when he had recovered physically from his wound, Zasetsky could not visualize his mother's face. He had no memory of the streets and houses in his home town, nor did he know any engineering. At first, he could neither read nor write. He had lost the ability to see what lay to the right side of his nose, and his speech was limited to the simplest expressions. He could not add two single figures, describe a picture or produce the name of the month, without great effort.

It was then that Luria first saw Zasetsky. For 25 years, he kept in touch with his patient. His book is an edited version of the journal Zasetsky kept to record his struggle to achieve some semblance of life.

Because so much of the language area in his brain had been damaged, Zasetsky barely spoke, and it was hard for him to understand what was said to him. Partial blindness exacerbated the difficulty of remembering the first letters when he wrote a word, because he could not easily glance back without losing sight of the more recently written letters. Writing a sentence was that much more difficult. He found, at last, that if he collected a thought – an effort in itself – he could manage to write it. He had to allow it to appear automatically; that is, when he began a word, some persistent motor memory would carry it to completion independently of his weakened language-memory. Very slowly, a grammatical sentence would appear.

By the medium of this painfully-written journal, Zasetsky compensated in some small measure for his terrible disabilities. He tried to give medical science unique evidence of the workings of the damaged brain. In the face of odds so great that he often despaired, Zasetsky revealed not only intelligence but fortitude and courage.

**2. Anoxia (shortage of oxygen).** Though brain weight is only about 3 per cent of body weight, the brain receives some 20 per cent of the blood pumped by the heart, and therefore, about 20 per cent of the oxygen breathed. In the resting adult, moreover, roughly 20 per cent of the glucose in the blood is taken up by the brain. Glucose is a carbohydrate and the principle raw material out of which all cells obtain energy. The brain's continuous activity even in SLEEP, means that its energy requirement is constant. A brief or partial disturbance of the oxygen supply may kill some neurons. Their loss may not affect behaviour, but if the shortage is longer or more complete, the damage becomes apparent if it is not fatal. After as little as a minute without oxygen, brain damage is severe. After three minutes, the brain dies.

Anoxia can occur before or during birth if accident or disease impair the mother's breathing, or that of the foetus. Unless the mother has undergone some recognizable TRAUMA during her pregnancy, there is no way to predict nor indeed to diagnose anoxic brain damage in the infant until the effects reveal themselves in its behaviour. In adults, anoxic effects are easier to recognize. Anoxia can be brought about by paralyzing diseases, poisons, electric shock and other accidents, but the most common cause is a cerebrovascular accident, or a stroke. Either the heart fails to pump enough blood to the brain for a longer or shorter period, or the blood vessels no longer carry the blood to all cells. In either case, cells die. A stroke is the evidence of neuron death in the brain.

In the industrial societies, about one out of every five hundred people suffers a stroke. Damage to blood vessels in the brain can be caused by many diseases. For example, the walls of a large blood vessel may become weakened and swell, forming an aneurysm. Under pressure, the aneurysm can burst. Less widespread destruction follows a break in a smaller vessel, but damage that reflects haemorrhage as such causes only 18 per cent of all strokes. A much higher proportion are due to the death of cells caused by local anemia following obstruction, for example, by an embolism which may be a tiny fat particle or air bubble that blocks a blood vessel.

Strokes occur about equally in both sexes, but paradoxically, women are both more likely to recover and more likely to die as a result of stroke. Both the incidence and the proportion of people who die rise in direct relation to age. The longer the patient stays alive after the stroke, the better his chances of survival, though not necessarily of recovery.

The functional effects of a stroke indicate the part of the brain that has been damaged. Thus, anoxia in the left temporal lobe affects memory and language comprehension. Treatment depends on the cause of the accident. Inflammatory damage to cerebral blood vessels following bacterial infection, for example, may be reversible with an antibiotic such as penicillin. If no cause can be identified, and this is usually the case, little can be done either to clear up existing damage or to prevent more. Unfortunately, no direct connection between diet or exercise and healthy blood vessels has yet been demonstrated. High blood pressure or thrombosis causes cerebrovascular accidents, and a history of either is reason for concern. Certain drugs can control these conditions, but they cannot cure them. There is no medically-accepted way to prevent a stroke.

If the patient survives the stroke with impaired functions, will he recover? No answer is possible. The younger the victim, the better his chances. Yet given time, even those as seriously injured as Zasetsky find ways to circumvent their disabilities. Nervous pathways controlling movement that have been secondary, may take over a primary role. If ordinary speech has been impaired, the patient may find new gestures to convey meaning. In one study of functional impairment following brain damage caused by accidents, including strokes, it was found that patients might be severely handicapped as long as three years later, but that after ten years, three-quarters had experienced recovery. The doctors who undertook the study in Newcastle-upon-Tyne suggested that one influence on the time course of these disabilities may have been the fact that claims for compensation from industries in which accidents occurred took about three years to settle.

**3. Disease-based damage** (see also PSYCHOMOTOR DISEASE). Hydrocephalus is an abnormal increase in the volume of cerebrospinal fluid (CSF). The disease may be congenital or acquired, and appears in infants. It may be caused by a disturbance in the formation, circulation or reabsorption of the CSF, or by all three. Surgery will often relieve hydrocephalus, but if it continues, some damage is to be expected. A very small number of hydrocephalic infants also have deformed brains. Most of them die soon after birth, but cases have been reported of individuals with high intelligence who actually have no cortex (see BRAIN).

In adults, hydrocephalus can develop, but the causes are unclear. It leads to DEMENTIA and a wide range of related mental and behavioural disorders. In some cases, it may be relieved by diuretics; that is, drugs which increase the amount of urine, thus removing water from the body. Surgery can also reduce pressure from the CSF, but neither course stops the excessive formation of fluid. In some demented patients, moreover, hydrocephalus is a symptom of the underlying brain atrophy and cannot be corrected.

Syphilis and tuberculosis damage the brain (as well as other organs) directly, because of the activities of the infectious organisms. Syphilitic infection of the brain and spinal cord can cause deafness, dementia, psychomotor and visual disturbances, depending on the nervous tissue attacked by the organisms. Syphilis usually responds to treatment with antibiotics, but there is growing danger that the bacteria are resistant to the drugs. In any case, the degree of recovery from behavioural and mental deficiencies depends on the amount of destruction.

Tuberculosis bacilli may also grow in the brain and spinal cord as well as in the lungs, spine and joints. The disease can now be treated effectively with a combination of drugs – streptomycin, an antibiotic, and isoniazid – but recovery from mental and behavioural deficits again depends on the amount of nervous destruction left behind.

Tumours or neoplasms (the word means, new growths) appear as either primary or secondary growths in nervous tissue as in any other part of the body. They may be benign, in which case they are non-invasive and can be removed. Malignant tumours continue to grow. They displace and strangle healthy tissue, and they invade other parts of the body with secondary growths. Surgery, radiation therapy or drugs may be successfully used against primary malignant growths, but if secondary tumours have appeared, the outlook is poor. Unfortunately, a benign tumour may become malignant, so this comforting distinction is not absolute.

The behavioural effects of a tumour can be the same as the effect of a stroke or any other kind of accident. For example, a tumour on the left motor region of the cortex can cause paralysis on the right side. Tumours may arise from the distorted growth of neurons, or from glial cells. In both cases, the growth increases pressure on surrounding nervous tissue either directly or indirectly, through the CSF. Removal of the tumour rapidly relieves pressure and leads to recovery of the disordered function, but if the tumour was of neuronal origin, some loss may be permanent. As in the case of stroke, the patient's chance of recovery from a tumour declines with age.

**4. Minimal brain damage and cerebral palsy.** These conditions are distinguished, but their symptoms overlap. Cerebral palsy includes a group of chronic disorders of children which lack clearcut causes. In about a third of all cases, the child is also mentally retarded (see RETARDATION), but given time, some patients improve. Cerebral palsy is neither progressive nor fatal. It is usually associated with some specific area of brain damage. Movement disorders include weakness, spasticity and choreic or athetoid writhing movements (see PSYCHOMOTOR DISEASE). If the underlying nervous damage is not too severe, physiotherapy may be helpful. TRANQUILLIZERS are used to reduce spasticity. In a few more serious cases, cutting peripheral nerves or even surgery in the appropriate centre of the motor cortex may reduce excessive movement.

Minimal brain damage or minimal cerebral dysfunction has been diagnosed to explain clumsiness and minor speech defects in children with no sign of organic brain damage. Nor are the disabilities easily mistaken for autistic behaviour (see AUTISM).

Indeed, with attention and careful educational procedures, they may disappear as the child matures. In 1973, *The Lancet* wondered whether minimal brain damage was not 'an escape from making a diagnosis'. Some authorities believe that, like HYPERACTIVITY, minimal brain damage is diagnosed to explain indiscipline produced by incompetent parents who can afford to pay doctors to cover their own mistakes.

**5. Nutritional deficiencies.** There is now little doubt that improper diet during pregnancy adversely affects the INTELLIGENCE of the child as measured by IQ TESTS. Yet the exact relationship between any element of diet and intelligence – or organic brain development – remains unclear. Indeed, definitions of proper or balanced diet vary with climate, occupation and age, to name but three factors, and even the component elements of intelligence are undefined.

Effects of dietary deficiencies after birth are more clear cut. For example, children raised on a diet that is poor in protein show the mental dullness and diffuse body sores characteristic of kwashiorkor. The symptoms quickly improve if patients are fed protein-rich vegetables and milk, and such is the plasticity of the developing brain that the subnormality need not be permanent (see RETARDATION).

Pellagra is caused by a deficiency of vitamin $B_3$ (nicotinic acid or nicotinamide). The disease affects the whole body and can be fatal. Its major symptoms are growing lethargy, often associated with body sores, and a SCHIZOPHRENIA-like PSYCHOSIS. Though pellagra is happily uncommon today, it was once endemic in the southern United States. It is a disease of poverty and can be cured with milk, yeast, eggs, liver and yeast extracts. Advanced physical and mental symptoms may not be completely reversed, especially in older patients.

Beriberi is caused by a deficiency of vitamin $B_1$, thiamine. It, too, is seen as a general debility. Psychological symptoms are rare, although peripheral nerves may be affected, but visual and motor malfunctions, hallucinations and speech disorders characterize one form of the disease. It was identified in 1881 by Karl Wernicke, a German doctor, but more than fifty years passed before Wernicke's encephalopathy was recognized as acute beriberi. The evidence came from former war prisoners of the Japanese in Singapore who were victims of the encephalopathy but recovered with a diet rich in vitamin $B_1$. The major symptom of Wernicke's encephalopathy is a severe MEMORY deficiency which may also be caused by chronic alcoholism (see also Korsakov's SYNDROME). Although most beriberi symptoms can be reversed, the acute disease may leave permanent deficits.

Folic acid deficiency produces mental symptoms including dementia. It usually results from a failure to absorb the vitamin, another of the B family, through the intestine. Vitamin $B_{12}$ deficiency also occurs because of malabsorption. Its most common symptom is the blood disorder called pernicious anaemia, and the anaemia is frequently associated with degeneration of the spinal cord, vitamin $B_{12}$ neuropathy. Movement disorders and impairment of SENSATION are among the symptoms. If pernicious anaemia is recognized and treated, the danger from neuropathy is reduced. Whether the symptoms can be reversed depends on the seriousness of the damage.

**6. Other environmental causes.** Poisoning from organophosphorus insecticides is fairly common. Like the chemically-related nerve gases, the insecticides can be fatal. They act by inhibiting an ENZYME, cholinesterase, which is required to break down and remove from the synapse the TRANSMITTER, acetylcholine. The result is permanent excitation of the neurons or muscle cells receiving the transmitter signals. Domestic animals and live stock are affected in the same way as humans.

Tetanus and botulism are primarily rapid poisoning of the peripheral nerves, but the hind-brain may also become involved. Tetanus is poisoning by an excretion of the tetanus bacillus, *Clostridium tetani.* The bacteria are found in soil and quickly enter any open wound. They do not themselves leave the wound, but in the presence of some other foreign body such as a splinter, their toxin enters neurons and possibly the blood. The toxin disrupts muscular coordination and causes tetanic contractions that can be fatal. The best treatment is inoculation with the antitoxin, but failing this, a muscle relaxant such as curare must be injected to save life. Tranquillizers can help the patient, but they do not stop the seizures.

Botulism is the result of a poison produced by the organism, *Clostridium botulinum.* It is found in poorly-prepared food and damaged tins. The poison causes muscular weakening and paralysis by stopping release of the transmitter, acetylcholine, from pre-synaptic neurons. Death is caused by strangulation. If it is given early enough, guanadine will combat the toxin. Doses of the drug are continued until the poison has been eliminated from the system.

Manganese, mercury and lead poisoning can cause serious neurological damage. Because lead is a constituent of petrol, chronic lead poisoning is the most common mineral threat. Ninety per cent of ingested lead is excreted, but the remainder is stored in the kidneys, liver and bones. Only very small amounts enter the brain. All of us have some lead in our brains, but the normal range is a tiny fraction, between 0.1 and 0.5 per cent, of the lethal dose which is itself minute: about 10 micrograms per gram wet weight of brain tissue. Lead inhibits enzymes involved in both the synthesis and the breakdown of transmitters. Movement disorders are amongst the early symptoms of lead poisoning, followed by convulsions, delirium, coma and death. Children are especially sensitive.

To eliminate stored lead, a chelating or binding agent is used. One of the most effective is disodium calcium ethylene-diamene-tera-acetate (CaEDTA; Versene). An anticonvulsant drug (see PSYCHOMOTOR DISEASE) may also be necessary to treat advanced cases of lead poisoning. Some brain damage may remain. Between a fifth and a third of affected children continue to suffer from fits even after the lead in their bodies has been brought within the normal range.

**BRAINSTEM** See BRAIN

**BRAINWASHING**

Systematic, often forcible elimination of one set of ideas, usually political, from a MIND, and its replacement by another. The word was invented in 1950 by an American journalist to explain the apparent conversion to communism of American prisoners captured by the Democratic People's Republic of Korea. In fact, only a handful of American prisoners adopted communist ideas, no more than could be accounted for by normal educational processes under the circumstances. Although conditioning (see PSYCHOLOGY) takes place in humans as well as other animals, there is no generally-accepted evidence that it can change established value systems or moral or religious beliefs. The word is now often seen as an American propaganda effort to hide widespread doubts about the Korean and Vietnamese wars beneath a camouflage made of the enemy's demonic commitment. It was never admitted, for example, that the US Army tried to brainwash its communist prisoners, perhaps because such attempts were ineffectual.

Brainwashing may also be used as a synonym for mass suggestion, a phenomenon which is thought to describe, if it does not explain the response of crowds (see HYSTERIA). In this sense, the word has been applied to Hitler's acts (with or without the assistance of the Nazi hierarchy) which induced the German people to turn a blind eye to the killing of the Jews. Brainwashing has also been used to describe the persuasiveness of the Reverend Jim Jones, whose followers committed mass suicide in Guyana in 1978. Whether knowingly or not, those who use brainwashing in this way are making the word a substitute for powerful and bizarre socio-psychological phenomena such as propaganda, charisma and poverty – both economic and moral. There is still a need for theories to explain the relationship between leaders and led.

## BREAKDOWN, NERVOUS

1. sudden and rapid deterioration of the normal PERSONALITY amid symptoms of mental distress without overt psychological disease. 2. the acute period at the beginning of a mental illness.

The phrase 'nervous breakdown' is a popular expression which appears in general dictionaries, but it is not used in at least two textbooks, of psychiatry and neurology. The symptoms are too much like those of other mental disorders to be useful for separate diagnosis and treatment.

The suddenness of the breakdown varies greatly. Some patients undergo severe stress over a long period, for example, from the continual unfaithfulness of a marriage partner, before they collapse. Such a breakdown can sometimes be foreseen. The person is nervous, restless, insomniac or 'off his food'. In others, the breakdown seems to come out of the blue, perhaps because the person customarily hides his feelings. If there is a neurotic (see NEUROSIS) or neuropathic PERSONALITY, it is by definition more subject to nervous breakdown than normal personalities.

The symptoms vary according to whether the breakdown can be described as anxious, depressive, schizophrenic or as a prelude to any other mental disorder. Crying, sleeplessness, inability to work normally, AGGRESSION and PARANOIA are common. Whatever the symptoms, they are by implication unmistakeable. The patient is obviously and suddenly mentally ill. Any mental illness may begin with an acute phase which affords dramatic evidence of breakdown. Thus, the first symptom of DEPRESSION may be attempted SUICIDE. The doctor's task is to get the patient through the acute period, usually with a TRANQUILLIZER and as much SLEEP as possible. When the patient is quieter, PSYCHOTHERAPY or other forms of long-range treatment must be selected to deal with the underlying illness.

Yet the lay public, and doctors too, must be cautious with the phrase 'nervous breakdown'. A bad patch often leaves us depressed, unhappy and unable to work (see HEALTH, MENTAL). To label the behaviour 'a nervous breakdown' can make matters worse, especially if the person senses that the label hides lack of sympathy.

**BRIEF-INSIGHT THERAPY** See PSYCHOTHERAPY

**$B_{12}$ NEUROPATHY** See BRAIN DAMAGE

# C

**CAFFEINE** See ANALEPTIC

**CATATONIA** See SCHIZOPHRENIA

**CENTRAL NERVOUS SYSTEM (CNS)**
The BRAIN and spinal cord, including the spaces surrounding the cord inside the spine. Like the ventricles and the space between the brain and the cranium, the interior of the spine is filled with cerebrospinal fluid. All other nerves and groups of nerve terminals (ganglia; singular: ganglion) are called the peripheral nervous system (PNS).

The spinal cord consists of the long processes or axons of NEURONS originating in the brain, the periphery or the cord itself. These axons are myelinated and look white. The central portion of the cord also contains many neuronal cell bodies and interneurons linking those coming from or going to the brain with others coming from, or going to, the periphery. Cell bodies and interneurons are unmyelinated and look grey.

The senses of sight, sound, smell and taste are received directly into the brain (see SENSATION). Except for the head, the senses of touch, temperature and pressure are transmitted through the spinal cord. Although the cord is essentially a great nervous trunk containing a mass of neurons connecting the brain to the various muscles, glands and sensing organs from toes to neck, it is also the site of reflex actions. The simplest reflex action, like jerking a finger out of a flame, requires at least three neurons: a peripheral sensor in the finger which runs to the spinal cord, an interneuron and an effector running out of the cord to a cell in an arm muscle. The action takes place literally before the brain becomes aware of what is going on. Thus, we are seldom, if ever, aware of the component activities of a reflex, but in humans it is probable that the brain notes the event and assures the smooth continuation of any interrupted behaviour.

**CEPHALAGIA** See HEADACHE

**CEREBELLUM** See BRAIN

**CEREBROSPINAL FLUID** See BRAIN, CENTRAL NERVOUS SYSTEM

**CEREBRUM** See BRAIN

**CHOMSKY, N.** See LEARNING, PSYCHOLOGY

**CHOREA** See DEMENTIA, PSYCHOMOTOR DISEASE

**COGNITION**

(Latin: *cognosco*=know) the process of combining PERCEPTION and MEMORY in thought and understanding. The other inclusive mental activity, EMOTION, has been traditionally dealt with as distinct from cognition, but such a dichotomy is unrealistic and misleading.

Neither cortical location of cognitive processes, nor their

physiological description is yet possible. During the 1920s, an American psychologist, Karl Lashley, excised larger and larger areas from the brains of rats. He was interested in the effects of surgery on the animals' learning ability. He found that until he had destroyed the rat's capacity to sense and respond, the animal could still learn. Its intelligence seemed to be untouched by surgery until more 'basic' functions had disappeared. Almost 85 per cent of the rat cortex is devoted to functions such as smell and whisker movement that can be mapped, so perhaps Lashley's findings are not surprising. In the human brain, on the other hand, the cortex with identifiable functions is only 15 per cent of the whole; 85 per cent appears to be free for cognition. The problem of localization is enormous. It may be more reasonable to suppose that the cognitive process leaves no physical trace, but such a hypothesis only postpones the problem. Thought often becomes memory, and memory is probably localized.

Perhaps there are two more or less distinctive kinds of cognition depending on the means of giving the process expression. If words or numbers are used, the cognitive process is symbolic. If the expression is pure sound or form, music or colour, for example, cognition may be non-symbolic. Non-symbolic cognition also includes cognition based on form, for example, a lifted eyebrow and other kinds of non-verbal speech, or the restful content of trees in a summer landscape. The same perception and memory may participate in both kinds of cognition: thus, the lifted eyebrow can be described symbolically in words. It has been suggested that symbolic and non-symbolic cognition reflect the function of the two hemispheres of the cortex: the dominant language hemisphere (usually the left) and the second hemisphere which deals with colours and music. There is experimental evidence for this functional division (see BRAIN), but it should not be exaggerated. The normal brain operates as a single organ.

For the same reason, cognition cannot be separated from emotion. Everyone has experienced this interdependence. If I am happy, a tree in the winter garden reminds me of the silver lace surrounding an old-fashioned Valentine. If I am sad, the same tree recalls death and decay. If I am fearful, the numbers on the page refuse to add up whereas normally the sum takes less than a minute. Conversely, thought may alter emotions. Cognition is only one of many processes, all of them occurring in the same net of nervous tissue, if not in the same neurons.

**COMPLEX**

(Latin: *complexus*=woven together) a group of emotionally-labelled ideas or thoughts unconsciously associated with a particular object or event. The link between the ideas and the object is repressed so that a complex is often associated with mental disorders. Although the concept is psychoanalytic (see PSYCHOANALYSIS) and became an important part of FREUD's thought, the word was first used in the defined context by Freud's associate, JUNG.

**Inferiority complex** (see ADLER, PSYCHOANALYSIS)

**Electra complex.** The daughter's wish to sleep with her father is repressed because of the guilt it arouses. The association between the guilt and sexual desire damages her ability to make a normal transition to a suitable male love object.

**Oedipus complex.** The son's wish to sleep with his mother, being repressed because of the guilt it inspires, similarly cripples his normal striving to find a female love object. Freud introduced the Oedipus complex in 1913 to explain the manner in which many of his patients seemed to have become neurotic because of an abnormal relationship with their opposite-sexed parent. The phrase is based on the central events in the Oedipus legend, and was intended to dramatize and clarify a nexus in psychoanalysis which Freud believed was critical. He did not look upon the phrase as a scientific description of cause and effect. That is, the actual content of the Oedipus complex varied with the patient, according to Freud. The analyst was to use Freud's description for guidance, or as a symptom of illness which, like fever, does not always mean the same thing.

**COMPULSION** See OBSESSION

**CONCUSSION** See BRAIN DAMAGE

**CONDITIONING** See PSYCHOLOGY

**CONFABULATION**

(Latin: *con*=together+*fabulari*=to talk) fabrication, often without conscious intention to mislead, of imaginary experiences to compensate for loss of MEMORY. Confabulation is a symptom of organic BRAIN DAMAGE in DEMENTIA and alcoholism (see ADDICTION) and as a result of certain tumours.

## CONSCIOUSNESS

(Latin: *con*=together+*sci*=know+ness) 1. the totality of SENSATIONS, MEMORIES, thoughts (see COGNITION) and EMOTIONS which make up the self. 2. the conscious activity of the BRAIN.

The two definitions are not contradictory, but they emphasize different facts and have provided the foundations for opposing hypotheses. The first is dualistic; the second, monistic. Dualism holds that the self is more than the sum of its neurophysiological parts. Monism is the opposite argument. The hypotheses have long appeared as tendencies in philosophy and, more recently, they have moved into psychology. A resolution is no nearer today than it has been for centuries despite the vast increase in factual data about neuropsychology.

The dualist hypothesis was explicitly set forth in its modern guise by the seventeenth-century French philosopher, René Descartes. Descartes described mechanically the connection between the brain and the muscles. He supposed that the visible nerve trunks are tubes conducting fluid, and that changes in the fluid pressure cause alterations in muscle positions, an adaptation to biology of the contemporary interest in practical applications of hydraulics. In his search for first principles, moreover, Descartes recognized that the brain is the site of cognition, sensation and emotion. He also posited a separate, greater self, in part at least, because, as a good Catholic, he had to find a place for the soul.

More recent dualist explanations have avoided mysticism, but their physiological models also include a phenomenon, consciousness, that exceeds in some way the limits of the physical brain. For example, a simple reverberating circuit may be shown to exist in the brain; that is, a nervous signal moves around a set pathway, but because of the multiple connections amongst NEURONS, other pathways are also energized. It is suggested that consciousness arises when the signal creates such activity, which is autonomous. Underlying this model is an analogy to computers which can do more than store and use data according to their programmes but actually recombine the data in a manner reminiscent of thought. It is a fine philosophical point whether unprogrammed or apparently autonomous behaviour is really any different from behaviour which has not been predicted because of inadequate knowledge, or because the logic of the programme itself has not been carried through before it was introduced into the machine. Thus, if the 'wiring design' of the brain was fully understood, would dualism be a tenable hypothesis?

The problem with monism may also be a product of ignorance, but it is even more obvious. For example, supposing that every sensation, PERCEPTION, memory, thought and emotion are merely the electrical signal of a neuron. The question remains: how is that electrical signal converted into a psychological phenomenon? We know by observation that a flash of blue light causes an electrical signal to appear in a series of neurons, and much can be said about the properties of those signals. Yet an electrical signal is not the same as a flash of blue light. Nevertheless, 'I' sense the blue light, not the electrical signal. That being the case, it is hard to explain how all the signals in the brain at any time – arising from sensations, emotions and memories as they must – are somehow interpreted as consciousness.

Because the scientific explanation of consciousness always seems to open a Pandora's box, the concept is often avoided. Neurochemists and neurophysiologists argue that they have enough to do understanding the response of a neuron in a simple situation such as a flash of blue light. Consciousness cannot yet be 'observed' directly at the mechanical level.

The psychologists, especially the behaviourists (see EYSENCK, PSYCHOLOGY, SKINNER, WATSON), hold that consciousness is not a behaviour that can be isolated from other behaviours like LEARNING. Therefore, they suggest that it has no separate existence, and cannot be studied apart from other kinds of behaviour. Both of these arguments are reasonable. The scientific logic of postponing consideration of the complex until the simple becomes clear is impeccable. But each of us (and possibly the individual members of many other animal species) are aware of our own consciousness above all. To refuse to consider consciousness is at best to ignore what is perhaps the most interesting function of the brain.

With current knowledge, it is at least possible to identify the mechanical origins of aspects of consciousness. For example, consciousness includes selectivity, awareness and the sense of continuity in time. Selectivity occurs when we learn to drive. At first, it is necessary to find the correct sequence of movements for each situation that arises, but the necessary muscular coordination becomes automatic. Muscular coordination depends on neuronal coordination. We no longer select consciously in part because neurons in the cerebellum have learned a signalling-order. Similarly, awareness as opposed to unconsciousness can be assigned to the reticular activating system. The sense of continuity in time, of duration, is regulated by the cortex, but it may be more directly under the control of the hippocampus. If none of these aspects is consciousness, each of them is essential to it.

The existence of so powerful a psychological perception in each of us implies that consciousness must have a function in the economy of life which gives the individual an evolutionary advantage. In other words, organisms lacking consciousness have apparently failed to evolve. Ants and birds, for example, exist in a myriad individual forms; they are obviously well-adapted, but they have not evolved to the same technological level as man. Still, it is not possible to say that the individual insect or bird does not possess consciousness. Perhaps no evaluation of the evolutionary role of consciousness is possible until more is known about the machinery.

Consciousness can be seen in mechanical terms as the psychological equivalent of what the American physiologist, W. B. Cannon, called homeostasis: the struggle to achieve balance. Cannon meant that in order to survive, an organism must maintain a balance of internal physio-chemical forces in the face of constant environmental changes (see MOTIVATION, STRESS). The role of the brain is to regulate and direct homeostatic activity in the whole body. Perhaps consciousness is the most effective, if not the only, method of achieving homeostasis. See also MIND, PERSONALITY.

**CONVERSION HYSTERIA** See HYSTERIA

## CONVULSION

(Latin: *convulsio*=pull together) a violent, involuntary muscular contraction or series of contractions alternating with relaxations. Convulsion usually refers to contraction of the voluntary muscles and, therefore, can be seen as violent, irregular movement. Convulsions of involuntary muscles, such as those in the gut and bladder, also occur. Tetanic or tonic convulsion is a single muscular contraction. Clonic convulsion is a series of contractions alternating with relaxations.

Convulsions are most commonly associated with epilepsy (see PSYCHOMOTOR DISEASE) and tetanus, but they may also occur in many other diseases such as botulism (see BRAIN DAMAGE), malaria and poliomyelities, in deficiency states including ANOXIA, in the presence of drugs such as ALCOHOL and AMPHETAMINE, and of tumours, especially tumours of the motor cortex (see BRAIN). Convulsions may also be caused by high fever and electric shock.

A convulsion is always a symptom of something seriously wrong. It may indeed indicate the imminence of death. Treatment consists of first removing any physical cause, for example, reducing fever by means of a cool bath. An anti-convulsant drug and a tranquillizer may then bring quick relief.

**CORTEX** See BRAIN

**CREUZFELDT–JAKOB DISEASE** See DEMENTIA

# D

**DEATH** See BEREAVEMENT, SUICIDE

**DEFICIENCY DISEASE** See BRAIN DAMAGE

## DÉJÀ VU

(French: already seen) the illusion that one has already experienced the present situation. The phenomenon is experienced by perfectly healthy people, and it can rarely be associated with any specific state such as relaxation. Déjà vu is occasionally a symptom of a brain tumour (see BRAIN DAMAGE), especially a tumour of the temporal lobe (see BRAIN). It may also indicate an approaching epileptic seizure (see PSYCHOMOTOR DISEASE). In both cases, however, other symptoms are usually of more importance in diagnosis. Powerful though the illusion of déjà vu may be, there is, as yet, no physiological explanation for it.

In pathological states such as epilepsy, déjà vu may be experienced alternately with the opposite illusion, jamais vu; that is, never seen, or total unreality (see DEREALIZATION).

**DELIRIUM** See DREAM

**DELIRIUM TREMENS** See ADDICTION

**DELUSION**

(Latin: *de*=from+*ludus*=game) a false belief founded in logic which cannot be corrected, either by argument or by the evidence of the senses.

A symptom of many mental illnesses, a delusion may involve the patient alone, as in a delusion of grandeur, often seen in cases of advanced syphilis (see BRAIN DAMAGE). Conversely, the delusion may involve the patient's relations with others, as in a delusion of persecution sometimes experienced in paranoid SCHIZOPHRENIA. Depressive delusion is characterized by feelings of worthlessness and futility (see DEPRESSION). See also DREAM, OBSESSION.

**DEMENTIA**

(Latin: *de*=from+*mens*=mind) mental deterioration as a result of physical degeneration of the BRAIN. Dementia praecox, a group of PSYCHOSES characterized by splitting of the PERSONALITY, is not associated with physical degeneration of the brain and is now called SCHIZOPHRENIA.

Brain degeneration is a symptom of a number of diseases of which the most important are cerebral arteriosclerosis or hardening of the arteries in the brain, deficiency diseases, intoxications (see ALCOHOL, AMPHETAMINE, BARBITURATE, OPIATE), presenile and senile dementia, syphilis and tumours (see BRAIN DAMAGE). Presenile and senile dementia occur as the result of primary cerebral atrophy; that is, degeneration and atrophy the cause of which is not identified. Dementia caused by brain damage may be halted, and even reversed, if the underlying cause can be removed. Intoxications usually produce irreversible symptoms, but if the drug is stopped, the deterioration can be checked. Presenile and senile dementia, however, are progressive states which end fatally five to seven years, on average, after symptoms first appear. They are incurable. Presenile dementia differs from senile dementia only in that the symptoms appear before the patient is sixty-five, and life expectancy is, therefore, reduced by at least seven years. Presenile and senile dementia represent about 80 per cent of all cases.

Dementia is seen in the first place as a behavioural disturbance like ANXIETY or DEPRESSION. Only careful clinical tests and a case history can show that the origin is ORGANIC rather than FUNCTIONAL. The most common early symptom is loss of MEMORY. This memory deficit differs dramatically from the slow, partial loss often seen in older people. In dementia, the deterioration is sharp and global, effacing memories of the distant past as well as more recent memories. The patient may retain awareness of his forgetfulness at first and even be depressed by it, but this reflective capacity is usually soon lost.

The memory deficit may be aggravated and complicated by a growing dysphasia (see -PHASIS). The speech disorder can be hard to identify. Patients whose intelligence is conserved often appear to know what they are trying to say, but they cannot find the right word. Their speech may be sprinkled with 'thing', in place of the right noun, and the verb 'to be' may replace an exact action word. The speech disorder becomes worse as the disease progresses.

ATAXIA, akinesia (see -KINESIS) and other movement disorders may develop, and epileptic seizures (see PSYCHOMOTOR DISEASE) occur in a minority of cases. The patient becomes incontinent, slovenly and utterly lacking in self-awareness. A vegetative state intervenes before death.

Four diseases are thought to underlie the progressive brain degeneration in presenile and senile dementia: Alzheimer's disease, Creuzfeldt-Jakob disease (CJD), Huntington's chorea and Pick's disease. The most common, Alzheimer's disease, is thought to be the fourth or fifth most frequent cause of death in United States' citizens over sixty-five. Pick's disease may be a special case of Alzheimer's disease. Diagnostic differentiation between them requires physical examination of the brain by TOMOGRAPHY or post-mortem. Alzheimer's and Pick's disease occur slightly more often in women than in men.

Huntington's chorea is a psychomotor disease usually, though not always, first seen as the typical choreiform disorder of movement. Dementia develops as the disease progresses. It is a disease of younger people, presenting most often between the ages of 30 and 45. Symptoms may appear before 10, but rarely after 50. It is almost certainly an inherited disease caused by an as yet unidentified gene (see GENETICS).

CJD, once thought to be the rarest cause of presenile dementia, is now diagnosed more often. The most distinctive symptom is myoclonus, a peculiar jerking movement of one or more limbs. There is evidence that CJD is transmissible, that is, an infectious disease. A causative agent called a slow virus has been proposed (see also SCHIZOPHRENIA). In the usual virus disease, for example measles, a virus invades a cell, takes over the cell's biosynthetic machinery in order to reproduce itself, and destroys the cell in the process. A slow virus is thought to invade the cell, where it remains for months or even years, until some unidentified trigger causes it to reproduce itself and destroy the cell. Another very rare dementing disease, kuru, has symptoms almost identical to CJD. Kuru occurs only amongst members of one New Guinea tribe which practised cannibalism, eating the brains of its victims, as well as other parts of their bodies. When cannibalism was stopped, the disease began to disappear. In cases of CJD and kuru (and two related diseases of other animals), the slow virus invades NEURONS. The brain softens before it atrophies. Death usually takes place two to seven years after symptoms appear.

Since 1974, biochemical research, especially in British laboratories, has found changes in the activities of ENZYMES involved in the biosynthesis of TRANSMITTERS in the brains of patients with Alzheimer's (and Pick's) disease and Huntington's chorea. Whether directly or indirectly, these chemical changes may destroy neurons, causing brain degeneration which underlies dementia. In Alzheimer's disease, the change may affect neurons using acetylcholine as a transmitter, followed by changes in those using gamma-amino-butyric acid

(GABA). In Huntington's chorea, the sequence may be reversed. In the latter, the cause of the chemical disorder is presumably the inherited genetic error. There is also evidence of an inherited error in a few patients with Alzheimer's disease, but in most, the cause of the biochemical change is unknown. If it is the case that biochemical malfunctions cause dementia, there is hope that a drug may be given to control or correct the changes and halt the progress of the disease.

One major difficulty in the diagnosis of senile dementia could affect its treatment. The disease state is similar in many ways to normal ageing (see AGE). Some of the biochemical changes occurring in dementia also take place in senescence. As yet, there is no indication that senescence is a treatable condition, and there is a possibility, therefore, that whatever may be true of the presenile form, senile dementia is also untreatable.

**DEPENDENCE** See ADDICTION

**DEPERSONALIZATION**

The feeling of loss of identity or of the wholeness of parts of the body. In extreme cases, depersonalization may include a fear of the dissolution of the PERSONALITY.

Depersonalization may be a symptom of ANXIETY, DEPRESSION, HYSTERIA and SCHIZOPHRENIA. It may also follow the use of electroconvulsive therapy (see SHOCK THERAPY) and HALLUCINOGENS, but the feeling can occur in people who are mentally healthy. For example, it has been suggested that Wordsworth's '*Ode on the Intimations of Immortality from Recollections of Early Childhood*' originated in the poet's transient sense of depersonalization. It was a common experience of people arriving in Nazi concentration camps.

The feeling may include AUTOMATISM and DEREALIZATION. Inability to feel EMOTION is often part of depersonalization. It is hard to explain, but may be associated with fear. However, a 'primary depersonalization syndrome' relatively uncomplicated by other symptoms may occur in introspective (see EXTRAVERSION) young people. It is sometimes seen as a portent of schizophrenia, but there is no evidence that the disease follows the feeling. Primary depersonalization syndrome does not respond easily to treatment. As is often the case with mental disturbances, however, the condition can resolve itself in time without therapy. On the other hand, depersonalization which is symptomatic of other disorders must be dealt with by treating the underlying illness.

## DEPRESSION

(Latin: *de*=from+*premere*=to press) 1. a feeling of melancholy. 2. a disease, the most prominent symptom of which is extreme melancholy often accompanied by ANXIETY, self-denigration and disturbances of appetite, sexual activity, SLEEP and work.

The two definitions suggest that depression is an EMOTION that may range across a continuum from normal to abnormal, with a pleasurable melancholy at one extreme and severe psychotic (see PSYCHOSIS) depression at the other. Most people experience bouts of melancholy. The feeling may be associated with an obvious disappointment or loss, or it may accompany persistent ill health, even a bad cold that refuses to go away. Indeed, it could be argued that the reduction of emotional and physical activity during physical illness which is part of the lassitude characteristic of normal depression has definite survival value. Many of us may also experience depression which is not easily assigned to a cause, yet do not consider ourselves, nor are judged by others, to be ill. Looked at from the standpoint of depressive symptoms, there is no clear dividing line between health and illness.

Nor is there a fixed boundary between the accepted classes of depressive illness: reactive and endogenous depression. In both, the first symptom can be attempted SUICIDE. Whatever else this attempt reveals, it does demonstrate that at some point, melancholy becomes disease. In both reactive and endogenous depression, the melancholy passes beyond the power of the patient to control or overcome it.

In rare cases, the suicide attempt follows murder: the patient kills his children or his parents because he thinks he is saving them from the misery and despair he feels. Fortunately, the behaviour of most depressives changes more gradually. The patient feels dull and listless and is unable to work. At first, depression may be hidden by complaints about health which merge into HYPOCHONDRIA. Anxiety is a common symptom, often leading to delusional ideas (see DELUSION). The patient may experience DEPERSONALIZATION associated with a slowing of experienced events. His INTELLIGENCE and MEMORY are not impaired, but sleep disturbance is common, especially during the second half of the night. Bad DREAMS may be much more frequent than usual. ANOREXIA occurs along with a generalized dyspepsia. Even severely disturbed patients may deny that there is anything the matter, and others mock themselves and their feelings. One of the earliest symptoms may be silent weeping. An otherwise normal person cries copiously, but secretly, while washing dishes or sitting on a bus. Depression is a harrowing disease for the relatives and friends of patients, but for the sufferer it is painful beyond belief.

In general, reactive depression is associated with it if it is not brought on by some specific event – like normal melancholy. Endogenous depression, on the other hand, seems to have no environmental trigger. Yet the differential classification of a patient requires constant evaluation. Just as any one of us has our ups and downs, depressives also range from extreme despair, through a normal state to episodes of great excitement, even joy. This is MANIA. The cyclic or cyclothymic swing may last up to half a year. The period is about equally divided between despair, normality and mania. Manic depression is unlikely to be a reactive depression. The cyclic disorder seems to be more serious. But some cyclic patients do enter the depressive state in response to an environmental event which then carries them through the whole cycle. Other manic depressives display a regular seasonal rhythm. In creative musicians and artists, the cycle can be influenced by and in turn may influence the beginning or completion of a work.

So baffling and confusing are the symptoms of depression that it seems probable they will yield only to better understanding of underlying biophysical changes in the brain itself. For example, the fact that one class of anti-depressant drugs (see below) is useful in reactive depression while a second is preferred in endogenous depression implies that different biochemical disorders underlie the two groups of symptoms.

Depression can also indicate the development of DEMENTIA caused by hardening of the arteries, or by physical diseases the control of which will correct the depression. The true depressions are those which cannot be explained. They are classed as affective disorders because they are disturbances of AFFECT.

In general, women are more subject to depression than men. In the United States and Great Britain, about 1 per cent of all men and about 2 per cent of women risk becoming manic depressives. For both men and women, the risk increases with age, to a peak at about 60. All such facts can be explained environmentally. Thus, in advanced industrial nations, women tend to be more isolated than men, and age is less valued than youth. On the other hand, there is evidence that depression runs in families. GENETIC factors might explain both the sex difference and the age risk. Fraternal or two-egg twins of depressive patients are far more often depressives than is the case with people in the general population, and a massive 75 per cent of the identical (one-egg) twins of depressives are also ill. From the genetic standpoint, the closer the relationship, the greater the chance that both relatives will have the same disease. The evidence of such twin studies indicates that inheritance is more important as a causative factor in these cases than the influence of family background in which depression has occurred. Indeed, late in 1978, it was announced that a brain protein had been found in post-mortem examination of depressed patients which does not appear in the brains of normal people. The statistical frequency with which this variant protein is found is consistent with the existence of an aberrant gene triggered by an environmental cause. Thus, there is evidence of a connection between a genetic error and the environment in depression.

Because the basic emotional responses are mediated by the limbic system (see BRAIN), research has been directed to biochemical changes that may occur in this region. Many years ago, it was noticed that reserpine, a drug used to control high blood pressure, often brought on severe depressive episodes. One of the biochemical actions of reserpine is to cause a distortion in molecules of the TRANSMITTER, serotonin, which carries nervous signals between neurons in the limbic system. A second transmitter, noradrenaline (norepinephrine), also plays a role in the limbic system. Both serotonin and noradrenaline are affected by the older anti-depressant drugs.

Psychotic depression is probably evidence of biochemical disorders affecting the two transmitters, and the nature of the depressive illness may be determined by the balance between them. Smaller molecules such as tyramine (see below) have also been implicated. Mania is seldom relieved by any of the anti-depressants, but it responds to lithium carbonate, a salt which has no known effect on the transmitters.

Anti-depressant drugs fall into two classes: monoamine oxidase (MAO) inhibitors and tricyclics. MAO inhibitors are less often used today because the risk from undesirable side effects is significant, and patients may respond to less dangerous drugs, such as TRANQUILLIZERS, or to SHOCK THERAPY. The most frequently used MAO inhibitors are phenelzine (Nardil) and tranylcypromine (Parnate). They require days or even weeks to work, but undesirable reactions may appear much more rapidly. Because the drugs also act on neurons regulating the walls of blood vessels, they lower blood pressure and cannot be given to patients for whom this might be dangerous. Pargyline (Eutonyl), another MAO inhibitor, is prescribed to control high blood pressure. Conversely, acute high blood pressure and severe HEADACHE and palpitations will affect patients taking MAO inhibitors who eat foods containing tyramine, such as cheddar, camembert and stilton cheese, beer, wine, pickled herring, chicken liver, yeast, broad beans, tinned figs and coffee! If the drugs are given in too large a dose to hasten mood elevation, they may cause poisoning. The symptoms include hallucinations, fever and convulsions. A BARBITURATE is the best antidote. MAO inhibitors exacerbate the effects of ALCOHOL, barbiturates and OPIATES, and they are not given with the tricyclic anti-depressants.

The drugs were named monoamine oxidase inhibitors because they reduce the effective activity of the enzymes (there is more than one form of the molecule) called, collectively, monoamine oxidase. It normally acts in neurons and synaptic gaps to break down the transmitters, serotonin and noradrenaline. Inhibitors of the enzymes are thought to increase the amounts of the transmitters. Originally, it was assumed that this action by the drugs relieved depression, but two problems have cast doubt on the supposition: 1. the drugs also affect other enzymes and substructures within neurons. Their therapeutic value, as well as some side effects could arise from these poorly understood activities. 2. Supplies of both noradrenaline and serotonin are increased, but it is thought to be a disturbance in the balance between them which underlies depression rather than inadequate supplies as such.

The most commonly-used tricyclic anti-depressants are imipramine (Tofranil) and amitryptiline (Laroxyl; US: Elevil). Newer compounds include iprindole (Prondol) and mianserin (Bolvidon, Norval). The tricyclics have a better therapeutic record than the MAO inhibitors, especially for the treatment of endogenous depression. Imipramine is also used to control ENURESIS in adults as well as children.

The tricyclics are less subject to undesirable side effects than the MAO inhibitors, but they also require up to three weeks to affect mood, whereas unwanted reactions can occur within hours. About 10 per cent of patients who use them develop movement disorders which range in severity from tremor to convulsions. The disorders are more pronounced in older patients, but they can usually be controlled by lowering the dose and giving a barbiturate. An overdose of a tricyclic can cause acute poisoning manifested as high fever, high blood pressure and convulsions. Antidotes are a barbiturate and a drug that controls high blood pressure. In some patients, even small doses of a tricyclic may disturb heart action and *lower* blood pressure. Minor side effects such as palpitations and blurred vision, more often experienced by older patients, may decline as the body becomes accustomed to the drug. Indeed, after a course of imipramine extending over several months, a patient may experience a mild withdrawal when the drug is discontinued. Amitryptiline may produce fewer undesirable side effects than imipramine, but it is more sedative.

These drugs are called tricyclics because the atoms in their molecules are arranged in three rings. Imipramine is chemically related to chlorpromazine, a major tranquillizer often used to control anxiety and schizophrenia, but imipramine makes the symptoms of anxiety worse. The older tricyclics are thought to act by preventing the removal of transmitters from synaptic gaps, thus increasing transmitter effectiveness. (A similar mechanism has of course been proposed for the MAO inhibitors.) The newer tricyclics do not act in this way, however, and their molecular effect is not understood.

Both the tricyclics and the MAO inhibitors can work so effectively to elevate the mood in some patients that they become manic. Mania, and occasionally the depressive phase of cyclothymic depression, are often controlled with lithium carbonate. A few non-cyclic depressed patients are also helped by lithium. The metal is a poison, similar in atomic structure to potassium, one of the elements essential for the normal function of neurons. Lithium displaces potassium inside the cell, disrupting it, but no one knows why this toxic effect should have therapeutic value in manic–depression. It is possible that the salt has some other effect that is useful despite its disordering of nervous function. In any case, it too may take several days to work while undesirable side effects appear more rapidly. They include tremor, drowsiness, delirium, convulsions and kidney failure. The incidence of side effects increases with age. Lithium should not be given to patients with kidney or liver disease, or high blood pressure.

PSYCHOTHERAPY is of little value in reactive depression and may be positively harmful in endogenous depression. It is also a mistake to talk a depressed patient into a holiday or change of scene because of the risk of suicide. It is better for him to stay amongst people who know him. If he is admitted to hospital, it may be easier for him to have quiet and sleep. During the acute phase of the illness, manic depressives may also be hospitalized, but they are hard to manage. Every effort should be made to keep chronic depressives working normally within the community both because of the immediate benefit to the patient and to avoid the effects of institutionalization for as long as possible. A minority of depressed patients may be helped by occupational therapy.

Many psychiatrists believe the most effective treatment for depression is SHOCK THERAPY, especially if there is a risk of suicide or if the patient does not respond to drugs. Statistical evidence indicates that electroconvulsive therapy is more effective than any other treatment for the control of endogenous depression. Some doctors also recommend PSYCHOSURGERY for a minority of severely depressed patients, but the evidence that they have benefited is much more controversial. In order to prevent relapse, anti-depressant drugs are often given over long periods with a concomitant increase in the risk of undesirable side effects. In a majority of cases, shock therapy must also be repeated. Although some non-cyclic patients enjoy remissions from the symptoms, no existing treatment can guarantee a cure for depression. See also 'POST-PARTEM BLUES'.

## DEREALIZATION

Subjective distortion and alienation of the outer world. The term was coined by an English psychiatrist, E. Mapother, and refers to perceptions in which sizes, shapes and colours appear to be altered, often in a way that is frightening. Sometimes the world is very still, at others, merely purposeless. The sensation is less strong and less insistent than hallucination (see DREAM). Derealization may be a symptom of ANXIETY and DEPRESSION.

## DEVIATION, SEXUAL

(Latin: *deviare*=to turn aside) To define deviation, it is necessary to have a standard of normality. In sexual behaviour, such a standard might be: sexual activity which subserves reproduction. Yet how shifting are these sands. Note the effect that the practice of contraception has on otherwise normal sexual behaviour. No longer permitted to subserve reproduction, is it now deviant behaviour?

Textbooks of psychiatry still deal with the subject under the heading, 'perversion', presumably because patients as well as doctors associate deviant sexual behaviour with NEUROSIS or PSYCHOPATHY. That which is perverse, the reasoning implies, is evil, and therefore, cause for guilt which in turn leads to mental illness. On the other hand, it is now customary for textbooks to point out that such an association is unjustified. A majority of sexual deviants display no neuroses. Yet it is still true that sexual deviation is often looked upon as perversity by those who engage in deviant practices; such people may well suffer impairment of their sexual drives (see MOTIVATION, PSYCHOLOGY) and loss of sexual satisfaction, with a resultant increase in neurotic behaviour. It is also true that sexual deviation may be a symptom of disease, as for example, impotence coincident upon advanced syphilis, and satyriasis or nymphomania (in men and women, respectively) sometimes seen during manic episodes (see DEPRESSION, MANIA). In such cases, the deviation may cease when the disease has been brought under control, and the term 'perversion' has symbolic meaning at most. To describe any sexual practices as perverse, however, is a mischievous holdover from the intensely moralistic psychology enshrined by FREUD and his followers.

Sexual deviation takes many forms, but because all sexual behaviour is grounded in physiological attributes, it is necessary to examine the physical basis of SEXUALITY. There are two sex chromosomes in the body cells of every individual (see GENETICS). In accordance with their shapes, they are described as X and Y. Female body cells have two X chromosomes, one of which is normally immobilized and inactive throughout the life of the cell. Male body cells have one X and one Y chromosome, both of which function. Inasmuch as egg cells have only one sex chromosome, in ova an X and in spermatozoa an X or a Y, the sex of the foetus is determined by the father's contribution.

In the genetically-male foetus, the Y chromosome causes biosynthesis of male HORMONES. It has been said that these hormones carve the organs of masculinity out of an otherwise female structure, the reverse of the biblical story of Eve's birth from Adam's rib. The hormones alter not only the shape and size of muscles, the distribution of fat and hair and vocal timbre, but they work within the brain itself. Like the rest of the body, the brain is fundamentally female, in the sense that the Y chromosome must do something that changes the developmental pattern. Only the effect of male hormones during foetal growth, for example, reduces the capacity of hypothalamic NEURONS to respond to female hormones. Theoretically, the sex of the individual could be altered at the appropriate stages of foetal development by suitable hormonal manipulation. As the individual emerges, development shuts down the options. Cells become irreversibly specialized to play male or female roles. Thus, in 1974, a report described one of a pair of identical male twins whose penis had been removed accidentally during circumcision. Before the infant was a year old, the parents had decided to change his name and sex. The necessary operations were completed within the next year though some further plastic surgery will be required when the child matures. When the report appeared, she was 10 years old. Her behaviour was feminine, except that she possessed that abundance of physical energy usually associated with boys. Though she has been dressed as a girl and dealt with as a girl, and despite her physiological femininity, she will almost certainly be sterile because genetically she remains a boy. The inherited sex can be manipulated but not erased.

The most common forms of sexual deviation are:

1. Bestiality
2. Exhibitionism
3. Fetishism
4. Frigidity and impotence
5. Homosexuality
6. Masturbation
7. Paedophilia
8. Sado-masochism
9. Transexuality and transvestism

**1. Bestiality,** intercourse or other sexual activity with animals, is said to occur frequently amongst boys in farming communities. It may accompany mental defectiveness (see RETARDATION), and is sometimes a symptom of severe mental illness. Except in fiction, female bestiality has never been reported.

**2. Exhibitionism** is a curious deviation. In ordinary sexual activity, exhibition of the genitals is often an essential aspect of foreplay. In the deviant behaviour, the individual obtains satisfaction, though without ejaculation and sometimes without erection, from exposing his genitals to an unsuspecting person. Women are almost never guilty of this nuisance. PSYCHOTHERAPY is seldom helpful, and prison does nothing to prevent the act from recurring. A form of counselling which offers advice and support, in the manner of Alcoholics Anonymous, may help.

**3. Fetishism** is sexual behaviour aroused by, and focused on, some object other than the whole body: a foot, the breasts or a piece of clothing, for example. Perfectly ordinary people respond sexually to different objects, to the female leg or the male bottom, or even to satin surfaces. Their response seldom calls forth the accusation that they are deviant. The dividing line is uncertain, but the fetishist obtains satisfaction more or less exclusively from or with the fetish object. Fetishism can cause both legal and personal problems if the fetishist also commits a criminal act such as stealing in order to obtain the fetish. The fetish attachment can usually be shown to have originated in childhood as a kind of conditioned LEARNING. It can often be controlled, if not eradicated, by behaviour therapy (see PSYCHOTHERAPY).

4. **Frigidity** in women and impotence in men are sexual deviations only in the broad sense that they are not normal sexual behaviour. Both may be caused by the individual's preference, recognized or not, for another sexual partner, or indeed, for some other sexual deviation such as homosexuality. Frigidity and impotence are not uncommon in older people, though half of all men do not report impotence before the age of 75, according to the famous Kinsey report. Frigidity is more common, and may occur more often at an earlier age, perhaps because women are still made to feel more guilty about sexual behaviour than men. Lifelong impotence or frigidity are rare. When they do occur, they are often associated with a hormonal abnormality which could be corrected.

On the whole, these extremely trying conditions arise because of ignorance about sexual behaviour. It is important to remember that sexual appetite varies greatly not only from person to person but also from day to day. A husband worried about his job may lose his sexual urge more or less suddenly. A wife who is lonely and bored may refuse her body out of unconscious resentment towards an insensitive husband who is out at work all day. It is also important to remember that sexual routines can become just as stressful and unacceptable as sausage and chips or hamburger and french fries every night for supper. Frigidity and impotence may respond quickly to a little sexual inventiveness. Men, especially younger men, usually ejaculate before women reach orgasm. Simple awareness of this neglected fact can help to moderate the time difference.

Frigidity and impotence may also be symptoms of alcoholism and other kinds of drug ADDICTION. They are often seen during DEPRESSION and SCHIZOPHRENIA, and manic–depressives may become frigid or impotent after a deceptive burst of sexual activity which may itself be a source of complaint by those close to the patient. When frigidity and impotence are symptoms, they will respond to control of the underlying disorder.

**5. Homosexuality** means sexual attraction to the same sex. It is one deviation that is not unique to humans, being displayed by several of the higher animals. In the United Kingdom and the United States, between 2 and 5 per cent of the male population is exclusively homosexual. Estimates of the proportion of men who have engaged in homosexual relationships after the age of 16 range from 17 to 47 per cent. The estimates of female homosexuality are even less certain, but there may be about one-third fewer female homosexuals. No matter how uncertain the statistics, however, it is clear that the size of the homosexual minority is so large that, in the words of one leading British psychiatric textbook, it 'can hardly be regarded as a pathological variant in the ordinary sense' (Slater and Roth, p. 171; see *Further Reading*).

Twin studies have shown that a much higher proportion of the identical twins of homosexuals are also homosexually-inclined (37 of 40 pairs in one study) than is the case with the fraternal twins of homosexuals (3 of 45 pairs). These data suggest that homosexuality may have a genetic basis. If this is the case, there should be biochemical evidence of difference between homosexuals and heterosexuals. Investigations of male–female hormone balances have found no differences, nor have any other biochemical differences been discovered.

Theories of environmental causation are equally uncertain. Well-controlled studies do not support the popular notions that seduction by homosexuals or adolescent homosexual or masturbatory activity lead on to adult homosexuality. There is evidence to support the statement that homosexuals come from homes in which the opposite-sexed parent is strongly demonstrative and emotional whereas the same-sex parent is unattractive, autocratic or very weak. Yet no studies have been undertaken to demonstrate the opposite: that is, the frequency of heterosexual offspring produced by similarly ill-balanced couples. Nor are standards for judging demonstrative, strong, weak and similar traits very clear. Like the genetic hypothesis, moreover, environmental theories cannot account for the enormous individual variations in the psychological aspects of homosexuality.

The degree of homosexual exclusivity and the homosexual

personality itself fit no patterns. It is probably true that homosexuals of both sexes range across a continuum from femaleness to maleness (as do heterosexuals), and that there is also a continuum of sexual behaviour from activity to passivity. Neither amongst heterosexuals nor amongst homosexuals is there any correlation between these two continua. In other words, the most masculine of male homosexuals may obtain great pleasure by taking the female role during the sex act, and the reverse may also be true. No sharp distinction between activity and passivity, or between maleness and femaleness, holds water.

In the United Kingdom and the United States, some psychiatrists believe that homosexuals tend to be of above average intelligence, that the lower economic class tends to be under-represented, and that male homosexuals are inordinately successful in the arts whereas lesbians enter law and medicine. There is very little evidence for these beliefs. They may reflect observations which are misinterpreted. For example, educated people, if not those who are more intelligent, may seek medical advice when the less well educated try to cope on their own. In the United States at least, the lower economic class may find the cost of medical advice prohibitive. Those who enter the arts and professions, furthermore, tend to gain notoriety, especially if their success is in a field traditionally closed to that sex. Both psychiatrists and many homosexuals say that homosexual relationships tend to be short-lived, and that homosexuals are more promiscuous than heterosexuals. Given that homosexual marriage is at most a practice condoned only by certain fringe churches, and is in any event meaningless from the standpoint of reproduction, this is perhaps not surprising. Yet the permanent homosexual household is scarcely a rarity. The fact is that there is no good scientific research into any of these beliefs.

Since about 1960, liberalization of the laws against homosexual behaviour has reflected growing medical awareness that homosexuality is neither a disease nor a crime. In England and Wales and in 23 American states (1979), homosexual relationships between consenting adults in private have been removed from those areas defined as criminal. Courts have also tended to accept that neither psychotherapy nor hormone therapy can alter behaviour which is deviant only in a technical biological sense unless the patient is strongly motivated to become heterosexual. The heterosexual majority, moreover, have probably always been more tolerant than the law in this respect, providing that there was no hint of paedophilia (see below), and providing that the minority avoided outrages to the majority sensibilities. Thus, corruption of the English word 'gay', and the self-conscious assertiveness of some homosexuals of both sexes, occasionally produce a reaction against them which is both understandable and regrettable. If the homosexual individual accepts his or her predilection without fear or guilt, there is a good chance that he or she will be accepted by the community.

**6. Masturbation** is also a sexual deviation only in the technical biological sense. It is well-nigh universal amongst children and adolescents, and amongst young adults deprived of normal sexual relationships for an extended period. At worst, masturbation may perpetuate the kind of shyness and uncertainty that impairs the development of sexual partnerships. Of course, if it is surrounded by guilt, such a negative effect can be extended, but masturbation itself creates neither guilt nor any delay in normal sexual development. The traditional view that masturbation is a sin may have arisen in part from a misinterpretation of *Genesis*, xxxviii, where the Lord slew Onan because he did not impregnate his brother's widow. The bizarre notion that masturbation leads to madness may have originated in the uninhibited masturbation symptomatic of some mental disorders, and the notion is, therefore, a reversal of cause and effect.

**7. Paedophilia** means love of children. Perhaps the most famous literary example of paedophilic attachment is contained in Vladimir Nabokov's novel, *Lolita*, in which the hero's passion is strictly heterosexual. Public awareness of this deviation, however, is probably more often aroused by male homosexuals who have relations with prepubertal or socially immature boys. American and British law is forthright in declaring such acts criminal. The tiny minority who defend paedophilia insist that the boy is never forced, and indeed, that he is a willing participant. Even if this is true, the effect on the child cannot be calculated. Unfortunately, there is almost no relevant research. Nevertheless, paedophilia is condemned not only by the heterosexual majority, but also by most homosexuals. Psychotherapy, especially behaviour therapy, may help some paedophilics.

8. **Sado-masochism** is correctly two different personality deviations: masochism (Leopold von Sacher-Masoch, Austrian novelist, 1836–95) means behaviour in which cruelty gives satisfaction to the recipient. Sadism (Marquis de Sade, French diarist, 1740–1814) means the use of cruelty to gratify the user. The two are usually combined because a masochist is needed to satisfy a sadist, and vice versa. Note that neither form of behaviour is restricted to sexual activity. There is often an element of one deviation in the other, however. Cruel practices applied to sexual behaviour include whipping, burning, cutting and any other method of inducing pain. The deviation is commonly said to include the use of symbols of pain and cruelty such as chains and cords or the Nazi hakenkreuz. PSYCHOANALYSIS has broadened the definition of cruelty to include submission and AGGRESSION. Such usage blurs any difference between normal sexual behaviour and sado-masochist deviation, but it does emphasize the point that the border between normal variations in sexual behaviour and abnormality is shadowy. Psychoanalysis also identifies sadism with oral eroticism and homosexuality. There is no experimental evidence for this association. The fact is that sexually-motivated acts of violence make up a large part of all crimes against the person. Thus, rape might well be looked upon as a sadistic sexual deviation. In a minority of cases, Klinefelter's SYNDROME or another congenital anomaly underlies the behaviour, but most such acts remain largely unexplained outside the language of psychoanalysis.

9. **Transsexualism and transvestism** are interrelated deviations ranging from simple transvestism, in which the subject obtains gratification by wearing clothes of the opposite sex (called cross-dressing), but without genital excitement or homosexuality, to the profoundly-felt need to be physically changed, if possible surgically, to the opposite sex. Between these two states lie variations in which transvestism is in some measure symptomatic of homosexuality or fetishism and is a means of obtaining sexual gratification. It is wrong, however,

to assume that transvestism is always associated with either homosexuality or with transsexuality.

Both transvestism and homosexuality are more often seen in men than in women. Transsexual men, although they prefer to dress as women, may also marry and have children. Only a minority engage in homosexual acts. The much smaller number of transsexual and transvestite women are commonly the dominant partners in homosexual relationships.

The causes of the deviations are obscure. In some people, transsexuality is a congenital disorder, and transvestism has often been associated with Klinefelter's syndrome. There is no evidence that these conditions are inherited. It is said that transvestism may occur when the opposite-sexed parent is overwhelmingly dominant, but the evidence is impressionistic.

Simple transvestism often escapes the notice of psychiatrists. Even the marriage partner may be unaware of the deviation. Symptomatic transvestism or transsexuality, however, can raise medical problems. Adolescents will frequently respond to treatment because they feel isolation and shame. Aversive therapy (see PSYCHOTHERAPY) has been effective, but the older the patient, the less likely he will be to agree to treatment. It may be better to accept the patient as female in dress and role, but in such cases, the psychiatrist is sooner or later faced with a demand for surgical sex change. Some transsexualists have attempted self-castration. There is no easy answer to such a demand. The surgery is neither difficult nor dangerous, but little is known about the degree of psychological success which the patient can expect. At present, most psychiatrists discourage requests for sex-change operations.

**DIPSOMANIA** See MANIA

**DISEASE, MENTAL** See HEALTH, MENTAL

**DISSOCIATIVE HYSTERIA** See HYSTERIA

**'DOUBLE-BIND'** See SCHIZOPHRENIA

**DOWN'S SYNDROME** See SYNDROME

## DREAM

1. EMOTIONS, SENSATIONS and images perceived during SLEEP. 2. the act of perceiving during sleep. When dreams occur in the presence of disease or fever, during sleeping or waking, they may be called delirium. Dreams that occur on the edge of sleep-like changes in ELECTROENCEPHALOGRAM rhythms are called hypnagogic imagery. Dreams that fit none of these categories, and occur when the subject is awake, are called hallucinations. Whether all of these phenomena are subjective results of the same physiological events is not known, but they have in common the experience of emotions, sensations and images which are objectively or by common consent, not present. Day dreams, fancies or fantasies differ, in that the dreamer is both awake and aware that the objective world is there, even though it is not claiming his attention. Neither the physical origin nor the function of dreams is known. It has been suggested that they are the physical evidence that events experienced during the day are being permanently filed in the MEMORY with the necessary shuffling of existing data that such additions imply. According to this theory, sleep is needed to consolidate permanent memory, but there is very little evidence for it. All long-term memories are fixed within an hour after the event occurs. FREUD, on the other hand, wrote that dreams are 'the liberated excitement of the Unconscious.' A dream 'acts as a safety valve . . . and at the same time it ensures the sleep of the foreconscious at a slight expenditure of the waking state.' (*The Interpretation of Dreams*, pp. 457–82; see *Further Reading*). In other words, the function of the dream is to preserve sleep, more or less the opposite of the memory theory. Some primitive men believed that dreams represent the adventures of the soul which escapes from the body during sleep, a theory which has at least as much experimental backing.

It is probable that dreams are products of the same kinds of neuronal activity as occur during wakefulness with the difference that, during sleep, the sensory world is partially excluded. Thus, the increased proportion of random electrical activity is recorded subjectively as a dream (see NEURON). Drugs like BARBITURATES that produce sleep by depressing neurons in the reticular activating system (see BRAIN) also reduce the dream phase of sleep and the frequency of dreams. When the drug is withdrawn and sleep returns to normal, dreaming is for a time more frequent. The drug is no longer depressing neuronal activity which overcompensates at first before returning to normal.

Information about dreaming is usually obtained by observing a sleeping subject and awakening him for questioning when the rapid eye movements (REM) characteristic of dreaming are seen. Subjects report dreaming far less often if they are awakened when no eye movement is evident, but dreams do occur during these periods of deeper sleep.

Dreams may be very short, lasting microseconds, but the dream event will then also be measured in microseconds. The natural time span of the dream tends to be preserved in the dream events. Similarly, dreams are straightforward records of events far more often than is popularly believed. About a third of all dreams are located in the dreamer's home. Men dream more often than women about walking, driving, climbing and falling, but no other dream differences between the sexes have been confirmed. Two dreams out of three are said to be unpleasant, but there is no evidence to support the psychoanalytic theory that some dreams fulfil our wishes, suppressed or otherwise. A dream during one night that can be interpreted as an incest wish has been followed the next night by a dream that is explicit on the matter. Subjects starved for days in the interests of science, moreover, report gustatory dreams no more often than well-fed colleagues. Some 85 per cent of us are said to dream regularly in monochrome rather than in colour, but colour content has not been associated with any particular problem or personality type.

Although FREUD believed that dreams are one of the main avenues to the Unconscious (along with free association), he was not responsible for the proliferation of alleged dream imagery. JUNG and his followers elaborated the notion that certain dream symbols are common to us all, but no evidence has ever been adduced to support this view. A horse in one man's dream may well symbolize his sexuality, but in another's, it may represent a horse. Like memories, dreams are personal. The only person who can explain dream content is the dreamer.

Many people say they do not dream, but it is likely that all healthy subjects spend roughly the same amount of time dreaming. There may be some variation due to age, with more dreaming in later years. If you think you do not dream, say to yourself at bedtime: 'If I dream tonight, I intend to awaken immediately.' Even if you don't awaken, there is a good chance that you will remember one or two of your dreams in the morning. The more you practise remembering, furthermore, the more adept you will become. At the same time, you can begin to 'interpret' your own dreams. As soon as you awaken and recall a dream, try to grasp the whole thing at once, like looking at a picture. Note its general content and, especially your first emotional response to it. You can fill in the details later, because if you have captured your awakening response, the details should make sense. If some do not seem to fit, leave them and deal with those that do. The missing pieces will probably fall into place. You may find that they were not part of the dream in hand or, indeed, that the hard-to-place details are actually real memories from your recent life. Even if a piece refuses to fit, your first response to the dream – your first emotional response and overall picture of what happened – is almost certainly the 'meaning' of the dream. You may be surprised by the simplicity of the message in most dreams, but even more astonishing will be the unexpected insight into ordinary events that an occasional dream will give you.

Delirium is often peopled with bizarre and frightening distortions of things actually surrounding the patient. Thus, it can be akin to the ordinary dream which incorporates the ringing of a real telephone before it awakens the sleeper, but the delirious patient does not awaken. He may not be asleep. Delirium also contains distorted memories filled with emotional content. Though it is always associated with fever and illness, delirium is not easily distinguished from ordinary dreaming.

Much the same is true of hallucination. It can occur during both physical and mental illness, and it is produced by some drugs (see HALLUCINOGEN) and by isolation. Hallucinations also occur in the waking brain, however.

By applying microelectrodes to the cortex during brain surgery, neurosurgeons have induced hallucinations in their patients. The patient is seldom asleep because local anaesthetics can prevent pain caused by entering the skull, and the brain itself is not sensitive to pain. If the microelectrode is suitably placed on the cortical surface, a small current will elicit whole memories including sensations of sight, sound, smell, taste and touch. If the electrode is removed and re-applied at the same point some time later, the hallucination can often be reproduced exactly. Emotions associated with the memory are also evoked.

Hallucinations caused by drugs, isolation or illness differ in two important respects from these experimental experiences. They distort reality, more like dreams than like memories, and they are often filled with extreme emotions of joy, terror or hatred. Drug-induced hallucinations may be related to real objects or sounds, but the hallucinations of isolation are perforce entirely subjective. The subject is suspended in a bath so that he is cut off from all sensation. After about twenty minutes, he begins to supply his own by talking and singing. His imagination creates experiences which are at first under his conscious control, but as the control is lost, he becomes increasingly frightened. The core of self-awareness evidently fears that it will be trapped forever. The same fear affects some schizophrenics who hallucinate. Presumably, madness intervenes when the spark of the self goes out.

Though completely subjective, hallucinations reported by schizophrenics are related to their memories. In schizophrenia, most hallucinations are auditory, whereas in isolation and under the influence of drugs, they are more often visual. Both the sensory mode of the hallucination and its content may be useful diagnostic tools.

Hypnagogic imagery (hypnagogic means 'leading to sleep') is a fleeting, dreamlike experience reminiscent of DÉJÀ VU but without the sense of repetition. It occurs in moments of drowsiness between waking and sleeping, and is often mistaken for a dream. If the imagery contains a stumble or a knock, the appropriate muscles flex, awakening the subject. He can then observe this curious but distinctive phenomenon.

**DRIVE** See MOTIVATION, PSYCHOLOGY

**DYSKINESIA** See -KINESIS

**DYSLEXIA** See -LEXIS

**DYSPHASIA** See -PHASIS

**DYSPRAXIA** See -PRAXIS

# E

**ECHOLALIA**
(Greek: echo+*lalia*=talk) meaningless repetition of words and phrases. In children, echolalia is part of the normal process of learning to speak. It can become very irritating, but the child should be allowed to babble as much as possible. Echolalia is also a symptom of certain forms of speech disorder (see -PHASIS), AUTISM, DEMENTIA and advanced syphilis (see BRAIN DAMAGE).

**ELECTROCONVULSIVE THERAPY (ECT)** See SHOCK THERAPY

**ELECTROENCEPHALOGRAM (EEG)**
(Greek: *electro*+*enkephalos*=brain+*graphein*=to write) a recording of the electrical activity of the BRAIN through the intact skull. The recording is made by electroencephalography. Electrodes are placed on the hair or scalp, contact being improved by prior application of a waterbased grease. Up to 16 locations on the skull may be monitored at the same time. The electroencephalograph amplifies the signals and presents them as a pen-and-ink trace on calibrated paper moving around a rolling drum at a set speed, one trace for each electrode location. If the electroencephalograph is attached to a computer, traces over a fixed period of time may be averaged and then drawn out on calibrated paper. Interpretation of the traces requires skill and training and is often subject to controversy by experts.

There are four normal EEG rhythms. The alpha wave is the rhythm of inattentive, wakeful rest with the eyes closed. It disappears when the eyes are opened and is replaced by the beta rhythm which is faster. The beta rhythm is normally observed towards the front of the head. It may be accentuated by ANXIETY and by BARBITURATES. Infants display slow EEG waves called the delta rhythm, which is displaced by a theta rhythm as maturation proceeds. The theta rhythm in turn gives way at the age of 12 to 14, to the alpha rhythm. As we become drowsy and fall asleep, first the theta rhythm and then the delta rhythm return.

Delta rhythms may also be symptoms of certain diseases, such as abnormally low blood sugar (hypoglycaemia) and petit mal epilepsy (see PSYCHOMOTOR DISEASE). Both delta and theta rhythms may also be symptoms of focal epilepsy, which results in temporal lobe or grand mal seizures. If epilepsy is suspected, it is necessary to make several recordings on different occasions because any one may be normal. What is more, epileptiform rhythms occur in normal sleep, and may even appear in healthy, awake subjects.

Abnormalities in alpha and beta rhythms may be symptomatic of a blood clot or a tumour in the brain. At the site of the damage, the rhythm often disappears entirely.

The source of EEG activity is almost certainly the brain itself. There is evidence, however, that at least in the frontal region, the alpha rhythm is associated with electrical activity in the muscles of the eyes and eyelids. It has been argued that the rhythms originate in the cortex, but no wave-like activity can be found in cortical slices kept alive in cultures, though the NEURONS are still conducting electrochemical impulses. On the other hand, the theta rhythm measured by recording directly from the hippocampus of experimental animals appears to change in the course of LEARNING. This may be evidence that theta originates in the hippocampus. At this time, it is not possible to assign any brain waves definitely to a single source.

**EMI SCAN** See TOMOGRAPHY, COMPUTERIZED TRANSAXIAL

**EMOTION**

(Latin: *emovere*=to disturb; *e*=from+*movere*=to move) a mental feeling of excitement in excess of some subjective level. Emotional states are traditionally distinguished from cognitive (see COGNITION) states, but without justification.

A catalogue of emotions is surprisingly hard to construct. *The Oxford English Dictionary* lists pleasure, pain, desire, aversion, surprise, hope and fear. One might add rage or anger, love and hate, and possibly well-being and depression. But then is despair the emotional opposite of hope, and boredom, of surprise?

Only five emotions – pleasure, rage, fear, desire (in the sexual sense) and surprise – have some experimentally-based foundation in the physical structure of the BRAIN. No pain centre as such has been identified (see SENSATION).

Pleasure, rage, fear and sexual desire originate in NEURONS of the hypothalamus. The earliest identification of such a centre was made in the 1920s by P. Bard, an American, and W. R. Hess of Zurich. Hess showed that stimulation of a specific hypothalamic region by shocks delivered through an implanted electrode produced rage reactions in cats. When the electrode is moved to an adjacent group of neurons, in rats, their behaviour indicates pleasure. Given the opportunity to stimulate its own brain with a lever which sends a current into the 'pleasure' centre, the rat will press the lever until it is exhausted. Even though the animal has been starved and deprived of water, it will press the lever rather than eat or drink. In order to reach the lever, the rat will cross an electrified grid which normally deters its approach even to food. The stimulus is preferred to sex as well.

Fear and sexual desire can also be evoked by stimulating discrete hypothalamic regions. If their sexual centres are stimulated, monkeys and rats display erections and ejaculate frequently. Female cats become sexually-responsive, even though they may have just passed through the receptive period. Measurement of neuronal signalling in the hypothalamic sex centres in cats during normal sexual activity, moreover, reveals increased activity.

These hypothalamic centres do not operate alone. The amygdala, a structure near the hypothalamus in the mid-brain limbic system, may modify or inhibit signals coming from the hypothalamus.

Surprise reflects the appearance of an unexpected sensation. The structures which are first alerted are the colliculi. They receive signals from the eyes, ears and skin, and each mode is organized in the neurons of these small centres on the hind-brain as a map of the body, the three maps being juxtaposed. In animals, the colliculi control the attention reflex, for example, a response to a shadow at the edge of the field of vision. They may play a similar role in humans, but it is modified by the larger primary sensory regions of the cortex. Nevertheless, the colliculi may be said to mediate surprise.

The neurons which underlie emotional responses form parts of structures in the oldest parts of the brain, judged from the standpoint of evolution. Learning may change their activities as self-stimulation of the so-called pleasure centre vividly illustrates, but these neurons also function according to inherited patterns (see GENETICS). In humans at least, the lower right frontal cortex seems to contain learned emotional data. For example, a generalized rage reaction may be aroused by a culture object such as a Nazi hakenkreuz or a six-pointed Jewish star. Similarly, the music which gives us pleasure is determined by our education, personality and age. Learned emotions can be extirpated by damage to the cortex just inside the right temple. This may be one reason why cutting the connection between the frontal lobe and the limbic system in psychosurgical operations to relieve DEPRESSION profoundly alters emotional life.

**ENCOUNTER THERAPY** See ROGERS, PSYCHOTHERAPY

**ENURESIS**

(Greek: *enourein*=to void urine, to piss) bed-wetting.

About half of all two-year-olds have stopped bed-wetting. Three quarters of those aged three and 90 per cent of five-year-olds are dry throughout the night. On the other hand, 5 per cent of ten-year-olds still wet the bed. The average bed-wetter is not worried by it until the age of seven or eight, but of course it is a different matter for the mothers of these children.

A few children may wet the bed because of inflammation or some other physical irritation of the urinary tract. In most cases, however, enuresis is thought to be caused by an emotional disturbance. Punishment is worse than useless, if only because it makes the child anxious.

An electric alarm which delivers a mild shock when the first drop of urine wets the sheet helps about 80 per cent of those who use it. Tricyclic anti-depressants (see DEPRESSION), especially imipramine (Tofranil) and amitryptiline (Laroxyl; US: Elevil), are frequently prescribed to control enuresis, despite the fact that they work in only about 30 per cent of the children given them, and many of those children begin to wet the bed again within three months. The drugs are seldom effective before the child is seven or eight, but they are being prescribed much earlier. Unfortunately, the tricyclics are now the most common cause of fatal poisoning in children under five. It is true that some of those who are poisoned take drugs prescribed for depressive illness in another member of their family, but the *British Medical Journal* has warned doctors of the dangers inherent in prescribing potential poisons for children. In any case, the electric alarm is both safer and a more certain cure. Perhaps more important, given no more than the tolerant calm of their parents, most children will stop bedwetting in time.

## ENZYME

(Greek: *en*=in+*zyme*=leaven) an organic molecule capable of accelerating some change in another organic molecule without being permanently changed itself; that is, a catalyst. The most common chemical component of all enzyme molecules is protein, but minerals and vitamins form parts of many enzymes.

The first enzymes to be described were those in yeast that catalyze the fermentation of sugar (hence the name based on the Greek word for leaven). In humans, the earliest enzymes to be studied were the gastric and pancreatic juices which catalyze the digestion of proteins in food. Digestive enzymes act in the intestines. Of the several thousand enzymes that have been identified, however, the great majority function within cells.

The NEURON contains many of the enzymes which are common to all body cells, especially those catalyzing energy-producing processes. But the most important chemical distinctions amongst cells, the differences determining their distinctive functions, are the unique enzymes synthesized by each type of cell. Enzyme molecules are synthesized by the cell in response to the activity of genes and are, therefore, the direct chemical effect of inheritance (see GENETICS). Thus, only neurons transmit nervous signals (although muscle cells are also excitable (see EXCITABILITY)) and, as far as is known, only neurons synthesize the enzymes required to create and break down TRANSMITTERS. ALCOHOL, ANALGESICS, anti-convulsants (see PSYCHOMOTOR DISEASE), anti-depressants (see DEPRESSION), HALLUCINOGENS, OPIATES and TRANQUILLIZERS affect the structure and function of one or more of the enzymes involved in creation or breakdown of the transmitters. Indeed, the actions of these drugs are a significant element in the evidence that mental illnesses are associated with chemical disorders in the brain.

An enzyme facilitates a chemical change which could have occurred more slowly without it, under the conditions normally prevailing in the body. Yet, because of the immense number and speed of chemical reactions, life as we know it is impossible without these catalysts. Perhaps their most striking characteristic is their specificity: even small enzyme molecules contain several hundred atoms, and large ones may number thousands. Interactions amongst the atoms cause the molecule to fold upon itself so that the string of atoms resembles a piece of cord rubbed between the palms. Because of the convoluted structure, the enzyme can react with only one or at most, a few organic substances which fit into the enzyme molecule. Many enzymes indirectly regulate their own number by repressing or derepressing the gene which specifies their synthesis, an example of negative feedback within the cell.

**EPILEPSY** See PSYCHOMOTOR DISEASE

**ERGOTOMANIA** See MANIA

**EUPHORIA**

(Greek: *euphory*=well-being) 1. the sense of general bodily well-being. 2. exaggerated sense of well-being as in some manic states (see DEPRESSION, MANIA) or in epilepsy (see PSYCHOMOTOR DISEASE).

**EXCITABILITY**

1. susceptible of stimulation. 2. the quality of being excitable and of displaying excitation, seen in NEURONS and muscle cells. Excitability may also be used as a synonym for IRRITABILITY.

The excitability of cells is due to the ability of their membranes to regulate the flow of ions, charged atoms, into and out of the cells, thus causing them to become electrically-charged.

**EXHIBITIONISM** See DEVIATION, SEXUAL

**EXISTENTIAL THERAPY** See PSYCHOTHERAPY

**EXTRA-PYRAMIDAL** See BRAIN

**EXTRA-SENSORY PERCEPTION** See SENSATION

**EXTRAVERSION**
(Latin: *extroversio*; *extra*=outside+*vertere*=to turn) turning of one's interest and ATTENTION outward towards external things. Extraversion is one extreme on a continuum, the opposite end of which is introversion, the turning of interest and attention inwards towards self-contemplation.

The two types were described by JUNG in his book, *Psychological Types*. PAVLOV provided a physiological foundation for this typology when he referred to individuals who are more excitable (extravert) and less excitable (introvert; see EXCITABILITY), but he did not make the connection with the Jungian categories. EYSENCK has evolved TESTS which are designed to measure the PERSONALITY on the extraversion-introversion continuum. He has found a correlation between introversion and NEUROSIS, but the tests do not give firm support to the older belief that HYSTERIA is a disorder associated with extraversion.

**EYSENCK, HANS JURGEN**
Behavioural psychologist. Introduced the Eysenck index to measure EXTRAVERSION-introversion (see also PERSONALITY, TESTS) and advanced the theory that INTELLIGENCE is largely a heritable characteristic. b. 1916. Educated in Germany, France and England. University of London, BA, 1938, PhD, 1940, DSc, 1964. Senior research psychologist, Mill Hill Emergency Hospital, 1942–6. Director, Psychological department, Maudsley Hospital, 1946. Visiting professor, University of Pennsylvania, 1949–50; University of California, 1954. Professor of psychiatry, University of London, Institute of

Psychiatry, 1955–. *Dimensions of Personality*, 1947. *The Scientific Study of Personality*, 1952. *The Structure of Human Personality*, 1953. *Uses and Abuses of Psychology*, 1953. *The Psychology of Politics*, 1954. *Sense and Nonsense in Psychology*, 1957. *Dynamics of Anxiety and Hysteria*, 1957. *Perceptual Processes and Mental Illness*, 1957. *Crime and Personality*, 1964. *Causes and Cures of Neurosis*, 1965. *Fact and Fiction in Psychology*, 1965. *Smoking, Health and Personality*, 1965. *The Biological Basis of Personality*, 1968. *Personality Structure and Measurement*, 1969. *Race, Intelligence and Education*, 1971. *Psychology is about People*, 1972. *The Measurement of Intelligence*, 1973. *The Inequality of Man*, 1973. *Sex and Personality*, 1976. *You and Neurosis*, 1977.

# F

**FAINTING** See SYNCOPE

**FAMILY THERAPY** See PSYCHOTHERAPY

**FANTASY** See DREAM

**FEELING** See SENSATION

**FETISHISM** See DEVIATION, SEXUAL

**FOLATE DEFICIENCY** See BRAIN DAMAGE

**FOLIE DE GRANDEUR** See DELUSION

**FREUD, SIGMUND**

Discoverer of the Id and founder of PSYCHOANALYSIS. Perhaps the greatest literary stylist in the field of psychology. b. Freiburg, Moravia, 1856. d. London, 1939. Married 1886; 3 sons, 3 daughters. Educated Vienna. Salpêtrière Hospital, Paris, 1885. University of Vienna, MD, 1881. General Hospital of Vienna, 1882; Privatdozent, 1885. Originated psychoanalytic methods using hypnotism, free association and dream analysis, 1892–5. Invited ADLER, Max Kahane, Rudolph Reitler and Wilhelm Stekel to meet weekly at his house to discuss psychoanalysis, 1902, leading to formation of Psychological

Wednesday Circle and of the Vienna Psycho-Analytical Society, 1908. Professor of neurology, University of Vienna, 1902–38. Hon LLD, Clark University, Worcester, Mass., USA, 1909. Foreign member, Royal Society, 1936. *Studies in Hysteria* (with Joseph Breuer), 1895. *Interpretation of Dreams*, 1899, *Psychopathology of Everyday Life*, 1904. *Origin and Development of Psychoanalysis*, 1910. *Totem and Taboo*, 1913. *General Introduction to Psychoanalysis*, 1917. *Beyond the Pleasure Principle*, 1920. *The Ego and the Id*, 1923. *The Future of an Illusion*, 1927. *Civilization and Its Discontents*, 1930. *New Introductory Lectures on Psychoanalysis*, 1933. *Moses and Monotheism*, 1939.

### FUNCTIONAL

A mental disorder of behaviour or function with no known physical cause, such as ANXIETY, DEPRESSION, SCHIZOPHRENIA. The other major category of mental disorders is ORGANIC. Functional is used in this context because diagnosis is based on function; i.e. behaviour, rather than structure.

# G

### GENETICS

(Greek: *gennan*=to produce) the study of heredity. With the description of the deoxyribonucleic acid (DNA) molecule in 1953 by Francis Crick and James Watson, genetics shifted from the study and tabulation of physical characteristics (phenotypes) and the behaviour of chromosomes to the functions of individual atoms in the chromosomes. Before 1953, researchers into genetics had to guess at the genotype, the underlying chemical inheritance, by observing the phenotype. After 1953, the theoretical foundation existed for a science which can both explain how characteristics are transmitted from parents to offspring, and identify, select and control traits which are to become part of a new organism.

DNA forms the chromosomes, which are very long molecules in the nucleus of every living cell. (Bacteria and some other primitive organisms – primitive from the evolutionary standpoint that they came first – have no nucleus. Their chromosomes occupy the cell with other sub-cellular organelles.) With the exception of red blood cells which have no nucleus, and certain muscle cells with more than one, all human body cells have 46 chromosomes. Segments of each chromosome appear to be functionless, but interspersed along the molecule lie the genes, varying lengths of DNA, into each of which is coded precise instructions for biosynthesis of a related chemical, ribonucleic acid (RNA). No one knows how many genes there are on a chromosome, or the number of genes in a human cell.

The RNA from one gene leaves the nucleus and is then translated, again with astonishing chemical precision, into an entirely different compound, a protein. Most proteins are enzymes, but some are structural and form parts of cells. It is these proteins which determine not only what functions a cell will be capable of performing but also what phenotypic characteristics the organism may display. Blood type and eye colour are directly determined by the genes. Height, weight and INTELLIGENCE, on the other hand, are traits regulated in some degree by inheritance which depend also on the environment. Thus, cell function is circumscribed by the genes, but all cells in one organism contain exactly the same genes, the same 46 chromosomes. Yet man and all other familiar organisms consist of cells with a great variety of structures and functions. Two classes of events control which genes are transcribed and translated into proteins, governing the emergence of a specialized cell. Neither class of event is fully understood. Different kinds of cells – neurons, muscle cells, skin cells, blood cells – develop early in foetal life. This differentiation may be directed in the first instance by the positions of cells with relation to each other; this relationship is thought to activate one set of genes but not another.

The second class of controls is triggered by the conditions in which the fully-developed cell finds itself. For example, neurons normally derive energy from glucose, like all other cells, but if they are confronted with an oxygen shortage, they can temporarily make use of a substitute sugar, lactose. The use of lactose requires enzymes some molecules of which may have to be synthesized at short notice from otherwise inactive genes. Thus, even at the cellular level, genes set the limits but do not determine final structure or continuing function.

Nevertheless, DNA directly determines what the organism can be. As cell generations succeed each other during the life of the organism, DNA also determines, for example, that each successive skin cell or kidney cell will be like its predecessors, under normal circumstances. The chromosome reproduces itself exactly by building up a DNA mirror-image of itself within the nucleus, which is then passed on to the new cell. By a wonderful natural paradox, this astonishing exactitude underlies the individuality of each member of a species.

Under suitable conditions, the 46 chromosomes can be seen with a light microscope to fall into 23 pairs, 22 of which consist of partners that look alike. In women, the twenty-third pair are also similar in appearance, both being shaped like an X. In men, however, one of this pair is much smaller and looks like a Y. These are the sex chromosomes. Although the X chromosomes contain genes which underlie characteristics other than sex, the Y chromosome is apparently associated only with maleness. The egg cell or ovum and the sperm cell, furthermore, differ from body cells in that each contains only 23 chromosomes, one from each pair in the body cells. Because the mother always contributes an X chromosome, while the father may contribute an X or a Y, the father determines the sex of the child.

Every new individual receives 23 chromosomes, one of each pair, from each parent at random. Let us suppose that Mrs Brown contributes a chromosome containing genes for brown eyes, brown hair, above average height and possibly a tendency towards SCHIZOPHRENIA. Mr Brown contributes genes for blue eyes, brown hair and average height. Their son has brown eyes, brown hair and is 6 ft 2 in tall. But because the two chromosome decks have been differently shuffled, the Browns' daughter has brown eyes, blonde hair, is 5 ft 4 in tall, and, at the age of 21, develops schizophrenic symptoms. Despite the difference in the colours of the parents' eyes, both children have inherited Mrs Brown's brown eyes. Brown eyes is a dominant trait, whereas blue eyes is a recessive trait. Only if both parents have blue eyes will the eyes of the children probably also be blue. If the trait is recessive in one parent but dominant in the other (blue eyes and brown eyes), the children will be hybrids, and if two hybrids marry, the probability is, that of four children, one will be dominant/dominant (brown), one dominant/recessive (brown), one recessive/dominant (brown), and one recessive/recessive (blue). What makes one gene or group of genes dominant and another recessive is not known, but the dominant-recessive phenomenon can be important in the inheritance of mental RETARDATION.

Recessive traits determined by genes on the X chromosome are sex-linked. Thus, colour vision is in part dependent on a sex-linked gene. The absence of red-green vision (see SENSATION), or red-green colour blindness, is a recessive error in this gene. Unless she carries the same recessive gene on her second X chromosome, a woman will have correct colour vision. However, her husband with the same recessive gene lacks a second X chromosome, and will certainly be colour blind. He will pass the error on to a son, but a daughter will be hybrid and without phenotypic colour-blindness unless she inherits the X chromosome containing the recessive gene from her mother, a 50–50 chance for each girl in that family.

Reshuffling the genotypes is one way of assuring variation amongst individuals: a second is by mutation. Mutation may contribute a new enzyme, a new trait and possibly a selective advantage, which can, in the course of time – and if the mutation is dominant and breeds true – alter the species. Mutations are chemical changes in the DNA caused by accidents. Most of them are harmless and disappear after one generation. Some are lethal, almost always before the individual reaches reproductive age. An example is the enzymatic error that produces the symptoms of Tay-Sachs disease (see RETARDATION). Some mutations give a slight reproductive advantage in the environment of the individual in whom it originates which becomes a disadvantage if the environment changes. Thus, sickle-cell anaemia is a disease in which the red blood cells are less capable of carrying oxygen than are normal red blood cells. It is caused by a gene mutation which produces a distorted haemoglobin molecule. The gene is recessive. When it is inherited from both parents, the child dies. But when the parents are hybrids and the inheritance is mixed, only a proportion of the red blood cells are sickled, and the child will survive despite the disadvantage. In the tropics, principally in central Africa where the mutation persists, malaria is endemic, and the sickled red blood cell is resistant to attack by the malaria parasite. In these regions, therefore, sickle-cell anaemia confers a selective advantage on roughly half the children. But in the United States, where many of the descendants of sickle-cell anaemics live, malaria is not endemic, and the advantage is converted into a disadvantage. Were it not that modern medicine keeps alive some of those who might otherwise die, the mutation would die out.

On the basis of statistical evidence, all FUNCTIONAL mental disorders have been associated with inherited mutations. The most convincing statistics are produced by comparing identical and fraternal twins. Identical twins share genes which are either the same or very similar. Fraternal twins are likely to share more genes than unrelated individuals because they share a parent. Because the circumstances of their upbringing are usually similar too, they display similar phenotypes more often than ordinary siblings and unrelated individuals. Thus, the twin of a patient suffering from depression, for example, is examined. As might be expected if there is a genetic element in the disorder, the twin also suffers depressive symptoms significantly more often if he is identical than if he is fraternal. In depression, a variant brain protein has been found in post-mortem examination of depressed patients. Its statistical frequency is consistent with the appearance of a heterozygotic gene (that is, a gene contributed by one parent only) which is somehow triggered by the environment. The same protein appears in the brains of patients who have died with multiple sclerosis (see PSYCHOMOTOR DISEASE). In these very different conditions, there is physical as well as statistical evidence of the same genetic error.

Very few human genes have been identified and located, but this situation can change rapidly. By hybridizing human chromosomes with the chromosomes of another animal, a rat, for example – in the cells of that animal, it becomes possible to identify individual chromosomes and pieces of chromosomes. If the cell also produces a protein found in humans but not in rats (even homologous proteins have slightly different chemical structures in different species), the gene producing that protein may be located. Let us suppose that with such information, an examination of a few foetal cells should reveal that the gene is missing for an enzyme needed to synthesize the amino acid, phenylalanine, from another amino acid, tyrosine. The person with the missing gene has a disease called phenylketonuria, the symptoms of which include mental retardation. If the gene could be found in another, foreign cell and permanently inserted in the cells where it is missing, the disease could be cured. The technique to achieve this advanced form of replacement therapy is theoretically within reach. Phenylketonuria can also occur when the necessary enzyme is present but inactive or inefficient, but the replacement principle is the same.

A similar technique might be used to alter genes which result in traits that are looked upon as socially, rather than biologically, undesirable. Such traits might include unusual tallness or exceptional intelligence (assuming such traits have some genetic foundation). It is also possible to reproduce the chromosomes artificially; that is, asexually, without the intervention of sperm or ovum let alone man or woman. There is no known limit to the number of exact copies that could be made. This multiplication of identical individuals is cloning. It has already been performed with bacteria and with laboratory animals, such as mice. Since experimental work is well-advanced, it is only a matter of time before genetic engineering of specific traits in humans will be feasible. Some say the year will be 1984.

**GERSTMANN'S SYNDROME** See SYNDROME

**GESTALT** See PSYCHOLOGY, PSYCHOTHERAPY

**GROUP THERAPY** See PSYCHOTHERAPY

**GYRUS** See BRAIN

# H

**HALLUCINATION** See DREAM

**HALLUCINOGEN**

One of a class of drugs which produce hallucinations. They are chemically diverse and include cocaine, corticosteroids (see

HORMONE), and two ANAESTHETICS, ether and nitrous oxide. However, the most common hallucinogens are cannabis, lysergic acid diethylamide (LSD), and mescaline. Depending on the dose and the physical and mental state of the user, any of these drugs can cause ANXIETY, DELUSION, DEPERSONALIZATION, PARANOIA and other symptoms of PSYCHOSES, especially SCHIZOPHRENIA. Whereas the hallucinations experienced by schizophrenics are usually aural, drug-induced hallucinations tend to be visual. Anyone who has taken any hallucinogen must not drive for at least eight hours after using the drug.

Cannabis usually produces hallucinations only after high doses. Many users say that it helps them to sleep. Like BARBITURATES, it depresses nervous activity in animals, but cannabis, paradoxically, prolongs the stimulatory effect of AMPHETAMINE. The site and mechanism of its action within the brain are not known.

The drug is derived from the flowers and leaves of a variety of hemp, *Cannabis sativa*, which is easily cultivated in relatively poor soil and a wide range of weather conditions. Hashish, hash and charas are names for the resin extracted from the plant. Grass or bhang is the name applied to the dried leaves and flowers. Marijuana refers both to the whole plant and to the resin.

Cannabis in any form consists of a mixture of chemicals, the most active ingredient being 9-tetrahydrocannabinol (THC). Hashish is often eaten, but inhaling the smoke makes a given quantity three times more potent. The drug is said to have antibacterial activity, and it was once used as an anaesthetic. When it is taken, pulse rate, blood pressure and urination may rise slightly. High doses of THC have had teratogenic effects in rats. When it is smoked, cannabis causes changes in lung tissue similar to those produced by tobacco, but it has not been associated with lung cancer. The drug may diminish the ability of the heart to adapt to exercise. It is not addictive.

In humans, cannabis has almost no known undesirable side effects, but its psychological impact is usually unmistakable. People who have had no effect from the drug have either taken a very small dose, or a sample that has deteriorated because of age, and there are, of course, individuals who have an extremely high drug threshold. The common effects are dreamy, abstracted feelings, slowing of time, hilarity and heightened sensory awareness. Although sexual interest tends to fall, sexual pleasure is often increased. Violence and aggression while under the influence of cannabis are rare. Psychotic episodes such as paranoia have been reported, but they do not persist. Cannabis reduces short-term MEMORY while its psychological effect lasts, but it has not been shown that memory or LEARNING are impaired by long usage. No evidence supports the popular contention that the use of cannabis leads on to hard drugs such as OPIATES.

LSD is a simple chemical, part of which is similar to the brain TRANSMITTER, serotonin. Its hallucinogenic effect was discovered accidentally in 1939, and for a short time after the Second World War, it was used to mimic psychotic episodes in both animals and humans in the vain hope that such experiments would lead to a breakthrough in the understanding and treatment of psychosis. Unfortunately, too little is known about its chemical activity to make controlled experiments possible. LSD has been of limited value in the treatment of chronic alcoholism. Its most important clinical use, however, is to reduce the fear and pain of patients suffering from terminal cancer.

In most users, the effects are quickly manifested. At first, there may be tension, but this is soon followed by relaxation and slowing of time. A few users experience nausea and fever. The hallucinations begin about an hour after ingestion, and they last up to six hours. Most people retain full awareness, and know that they are hallucinating, but mood may range from excitement and pleasure, through neutral feelings, to acute anxiety and fear. LSD-induced anxiety should not be underestimated. The subject may at one and the same moment realize that he is hallucinating, but fear that he will lose control of himself and remain trapped inside the hallucination or even perform some dreadful act, possibly suicide. Suicide and murder have been committed under the influence of LSD, but just as in the familiar case of the misanthropic drunkard who is tense and unhappy when sober, psychotic reactions to LSD always reflect the undrugged personality. If the user becomes extremely frightened, friendly support by a trusted companion is essential. A barbiturate or a TRANQUILLIZER may also be useful, but the dose should always be specified beforehand by a doctor.

LSD has been associated with the occurrence of acute leukemia in users. It is not a poison. Although tolerance to it may develop, it is not addictive.

Mescaline is derived from the peyote cactus. It is a relatively weak hallucinogen. LSD is 4,000 times more potent on a molecule for molecule basis. Mescaline is also considered to be milder and more pleasant to use than LSD. For centuries, the peyote cactus was eaten during religious ceremonies by Indians of the American southwest and Mexico.

Mescaline is chemically related to amphetamine, the difference being that the mescaline molecule contains three methyl ($CH_3$) groups not found on the amphetamine molecule. Amphetamine psychosis may be accompanied by hallucinations and other schizophrenia-like symptoms. It has been suggested that they reflect the biochemical conversion of amphetamine to mescaline in the body. STP and several other hallucinogenic drugs are also synthesized by adding methyl groups to amphetamine.

LSD is also a methylated compound, chemically related not to amphetamine but to the transmitter, serotonin. Both serotonin and LSD are members of a class of natural organic compounds called indoleamines. Dimethyltriptamine (DMT), psilocybin and psilocin are indoleamines with hallucinogenic properties. Psilocybin and psilocin are the active ingredients of Mexican 'magic mushrooms'. How these drugs work in the brain is not known.

## HEADACHE

Perhaps the most common symptom of many physical and mental illnesses. Migraine is a severe headache, often periodic, one-sided and accompanied by nausea, but no clear distinction between migraine and ordinary headache is possible.

The immediate cause of headache is usually unknown. The BRAIN lacks nerve endings responsive to pain, but its surrounding membranes and the skull are extremely sensitive. Irritation or inflammation of the membranes which are symptoms of serious infections or even tumours will cause headache.

Worry and tiredness, especially eye strain, are perhaps the

commonest causes of ordinary headache. They may produce pain because of the tightening of small muscles in the eyes, face, scalp and neck.

The pain of migraine is believed to be due to swelling of arteries and possibly other blood vessels just before they enter the brain. No explanation for such a vascular malfunction can be given, but both emotional and allergic factors have been implicated. The treatment of migraine is difficult because the pain is so intense, and it is made more urgent by the periodicity of the headache. PSYCHOTHERAPY can occasionally help by locating emotional problems. Drugs are usually required to control the pain, but they are not cures. Antihistamines, a class of drugs used to control seasickness and some allergies, and ergotamine may help some patients. The most satisfactory drug has been propranolol (Inderal), a synthetic compound developed to treat heart disease (see also SCHIZOPHRENIA).

Less serious headaches should respond to rest or relaxation. If they persist, an ANALGESIC such as aspirin is usually helpful. If the headache is not relieved, it is important to consult a doctor.

**HEALTH, MENTAL**

Health is hard to define. According to *The American College Dictionary*, it is 'soundness of body; freedom from disease or ailments'. *The Oxford English Dictionary* also begins its definition with the phrase, 'Soundness of body', but it continues: 'that condition in which its functions are duly and efficiently discharged.' *Dorland's Illustrated Medical Dictionary* says: 'A state of complete physical, mental, and social well-being, and not merely the absence of disease and infirmity.' The first and last definitions implicitly contradict each other. Only Dorland's, moreover, at once distinguishes mental health from physical and social wellbeing.

This distinction is important for common usage, especially if the functions of the body are relevant to the meaning of health, as the *OED* states. It is simple enough to say that a man with a broken leg is not in perfect health. Even in the unlikely event that he should insist he is healthy, I do not need medical training to contradict him. Common sense is a reasonable guide to the interpretation of gross physical health. Yet even in this apparently simple example, questions obtrude: first, what is common sense other than a socially-agreed definition? Second, why should the man with a broken leg assert that he is healthy? (Of course, once the leg has been set and the pain has gone, he may feel well enough in other parts of his body.)

In matters of health as in any other aspect of nature, 'common sense' varies with time and place. In late Imperial China, it was a mark of status for women to have feet so deformed by having been tightly bound during growth that they could scarcely walk. Certain African tribes have accepted as a status symbol lips so enlarged by stretching as seriously to impair both eating and speaking. The greased pig tail worn by all British sailors two centuries ago could not have improved the health and function of the hair. Nevertheless, people who practised these anti-functional distortions acted within a rational social framework; for example, women with crippled feet were meant to be served. Their physical well-being was assured whatever the effect of footbinding on their functional well-being.

Distinctions between common-sense social criteria of health and physical criteria become even more significant in the definition of mental health and mental illness. Let us suppose that the man with the broken leg only believes that his leg is broken. By every physical standard, he has two whole legs. But he cannot stand. He suffers great pain in his 'broken' leg. The common-sense diagnosis is HYSTERIA; that is, the man is physically healthy but mentally ill. Certainly he has lost his sense of well-being, but has he not also lost the function of a leg? How then can he be accounted physically healthy?

Customarily, we answer such questions from one of three standpoints: that of society, that of the patient or that of the doctor. Looked at from the social standpoint, the hysterical patient is mentally ill but physically healthy, as noted. There is no point in applying a splint to his leg or confining him to bed. The malfunction in his MIND must be corrected.

Looked at from the patient's standpoint, however, the social answer is nonsense. His leg is broken. He feels physically ill. Anyone who disagrees with him is obviously mad, and it is the malfunction in that person's mind which must be corrected.

The patient struggles alone against family, friends and the doctor. Nor can his battle be dismissed as the ravings of a lunatic. The whole thrust of modern medicine (and of political democracy) sustains him: the patient's view outweighs the opinion of society. For this reason, the imprisonment of political dissidents on the ground that they are mentally incompetent is rightly looked upon as a perversion of medicine.

In theory at least, because of his specialized training, the physician recognizes a third viewpoint, intermediate between society's and the patient's. The fact that no bone is actually fractured must be given equal weight in his diagnosis with the patient's insistence that the reverse is true. Therefore, the doctor may look for less obvious physical causes, such as an obstruction in a major blood vessel in the leg, or a pinched or torn nerve trunk, either of which could destroy the function of a leg as effectively as a fracture. Often such an unmistakable physical malfunction does underlie an 'hysterical' complaint. No responsible doctor would diagnose mental disease before completing the most careful physical examination. Only if that examination reveals no recognizable physical cause will the doctor accept that the patient is suffering from a mental disorder. From that moment, the only important observation the doctor can make is the symptom of the patient's suffering. What he does to help will depend on the state of our knowledge rather than on an abstract philosophy of medicine. He may first try to engage and change the patient's mind by using words and other forms of communication, the method called PSYCHOTHERAPY. Though the example of the man with a bad leg makes it unlikely, the doctor might also use drugs or SHOCK THERAPY. But ultimately, if the patient is to be made healthy, his mind must be changed.

Physical treatments such as drugs imply that there is a physical malfunction underlying the mental disturbance which drugs can put right. Yet that is precisely what examination has failed to reveal in the case of the hysterical man. Without a physical malfunction, the doctor is sailing in the same boat as the rest of us: no matter how ill the patient feels, he is actually healthy. His dis-ease is only the extreme state of a continuum of behaviour conditioned by his social and environmental experiences. This is the argument used by anti-psychiatrists such as LAING or the American, Thomas Szasz. They have been frightened by the abuse of PSYCHIATRY and seek to counter the psychiatric belief that mental disease is just as identifiable as physical disease. Yet even FREUD recognized that PSYCHOANALYSIS is a stopgap form of treatment which doctors can employ until a treatable malfunction in the BRAIN itself has been identified. For examples of physical malfunctions that underlie mental disturbance, see BRAIN DAMAGE, DEMENTIA, PSYCHOMOTOR DISEASE, and medical science continues to search for causative physical errors in ANXIETY, DEPRESSION, SCHIZOPHRENIA and other FUNCTIONAL disorders. It is accepted, by and large, that whatever physical disturbances exist in the brains of mentally-ill patients, an environmental trigger may still be required to make the patient sick. At least the functional disorders cannot be said to exist without both categories of causation.

On the whole, modern psychiatry is premissed on the principle of dual causation. Until the putative physical causes of the serious PSYCHOSES have been discovered, however, the dispute about who is ill and who is well will continue: symptoms vary, and so do the interpretations of symptoms by doctors with different training and conflicting biases.

For the layman, especially the relatives and colleagues of mentally-disordered people, it is imperative to remember that there is an enormous range of behaviour which is perfectly normal. However annoying or provocative the disordered behaviour, one should try to avoid the accusation levelled against one psychiatrist by an opponent, on the nature of sexual behaviour: 'He thinks that anything he doesn't do is perverse.' Different people solve problems in different ways.

Even assuming that the body is responding within its limits of tolerance to environmental changes in temperature, humidity, food availability and the need for exercise and rest, the response of the mind cannot be guaranteed. One's PERSONALITY affects the way one's mind perceives and copes with everyday physical problems.

Indeed, living can be defined as the process of solving problems. Food, shelter, sexual release and procreation are the fundamental problems. On these foundations, complex hierarchies of problems grow, and people solve them in accordance with their age, education, income, social status, and their intelligence and mental health. Everyone has problems. Everyone solves problems.

Occasionally, we confront a problem for which there is no obvious answer. Where is the money to come from? Am I to go to bed with him/her? Most of us muddle through, but a few people can find no answer at all. They try; they hunt like a compass surrounded by steel walls, and find no way out. Finally, they give up. In extreme cases, they kill themselves. Such people are ill. But most of us get by. With occasional help from a parent, a friend, a priest and sometimes a doctor, we manage. However uncomfortable the problem makes us, we cope because we are healthy.

Perhaps the most mischievous error we make is to equate mental health, or indeed, well-being, with happiness. Happiness, one suspects, is an invention of modern industrial society: something that only a new car or the right toothpaste can produce. Mental health, on the other hand, probably entails a fair amount of unhappiness, a consequence of the perpetual need to solve life's problems. Death, as some nameless wit observed, is nature's way of telling us to slow down.

**HEARING** See SENSATION

**HEREDITY** See GENETICS

**HIPPOCAMPUS** See BRAIN

**HOMOSEXUALITY** See DEVIATION, SEXUAL

**HORMONE**

(Greek: *hormon*=impelling) a chemical secreted into the blood which acts on cells elsewhere in the body to produce an effect. Hormones are secreted by the endocrine glands: the Islets of Langerhans in the pancreas, the parathyroids, the thyroids, the gonads (ovaries in women and testes in men), the adrenals and the pituitary or hypophysis. (Exocrine glands secrete into a duct for local use where the duct emerges, e.g. sweat glands, the liver, which produces bile and the non-Islet cells in the pancreas, which secrete digestive enzymes.) The pituitary, located in a bony cavity above the roof of the mouth, is attached by a stalk of NEURONS and blood vessels to the hypothalamus and is a part of the BRAIN.

Although it is about the size of a pea, the pituitary secretes several hormones, two from the posterior pituitary (neurohypophysis) and five or more from the anterior portion of the gland (adenohypophysis). In some animals, but not in man, an intermediate lobe produces melanocyte-stimulating hormone which affects skin colour. All pituitary secretions are either directly or indirectly under the control of the hypothalamus. Those produced by the posterior pituitary are thought to be actually formed in hypothalamic centres called the supra-optic and paraventricular nuclei. With the possible exceptions of growth hormone and prolactin, anterior pituitary hormones are secreted in response to releasing factors, small molecules synthesized by cells in the hypothalamus and transmitted to the pituitary in a localized blood circulation. According to the definition, therefore, the releasing factors are themselves hormones.

One releasing factor controls each anterior pituitary hormone, and each releasing factor is in turn regulated by a feedback mechanism consisting of a hormone and a target organ. For example, the pituitary hormone, luteinizing hormone (LH), stimulates the ovaries which produce progesterone, one of the female hormones. Progesterone causes the hypothalamus to discontinue secretion of LH releasing factor. The names, functions and relationships of the releasing factors, pituitary hormones, target organs and 'feedback' hormones are summarized in the table on page 117.

Several of the anterior pituitary hormones, including ACTH, appear to originate in pituitary cells as a single larger molecule from which the active hormone molecules are somehow clipped off. The larger molecule may also contain additional hormone molecules which have not yet been described.

The Islets of Langerhans in the pancreas produce two hormones: insulin and glucagon. Insulin assists cells to utilize glucose, a form of sugar which is the most common source of cellular energy. Glucagon is secreted in response to decreases in blood sugar and balances the effects of insulin. However, it is somatotrophin (STH) which acts as the most important antagonist of insulin. STH mobilizes the constituents of protein, amino acids, by preventing their removal from the body as urea, for example, and it also mobilizes glucose and fats for

| Pituitary hormone | Hypothalamic releasing factor | Target organ(s) | Target organ hormone or control mechanism | Important function(s) |
|---|---|---|---|---|
| **Posterior** | | | | |
| ADH (vasopressin) | None | Kidneys, blood vessels, hypothalamic temperature centres | Amount of water in blood acting through hypothalamic receptors | Possible emotional associations; reduce urine formation; pallor in fear, anger; temperature regulation |
| Oxytocin | None | Breasts, uterus, gut | Not known | Stimulates smooth muscle; e.g. in labour |
| **Anterior** | | | | |
| Growth hormone, somatrophin (STH) | None known | Various | Not known | Normal growth |
| Adrenocorticotrophic hormone (ACTH) | Corticotrophin | Adrenals, outer layers | Corticosteroids | Fear produces increased output and palpitations, rapid breathing, sweating |
| Thyroid-stimulating hormone (TSH) | Thyroid hormone releasing factor | Thyroid | Thyroxine | Normal growth; response to cold: increased metabolism |
| Follicle-stimulating hormone (FSH) | Follicle-stimulating hormone releasing factor | Gonads | Oestrogen | Readying ova for release; in men, accessory to ICSH |
| Luteinizing hormone (LH); Interstitial-cell-stimulating hormone (ICSH) | LH releasing factor ICSH releasing factor | Gonads | Progesterone (female); testosterone (male) | Egg and sperm production |
| Prolactin (may not occur in humans) | Not known | Breasts | Oestrogen (from uterus) | Breast development and lactation |

conversion into sources of cellular energy. Insulin, on the other hand, promotes the storage of these substances. The balancing effects of the three hormones is not fully understood. Insulin secretion is not regulated by the brain, except incidentally to the secretion of growth hormone by the posterior pituitary.

The parathyroid glands produce parathyroid hormone which regulates the amount of calcium in the blood and the formation of bone. The glands are not directly under the control of the brain, but the amount of circulating growth hormone may act indirectly to influence parathyroid hormone secretion. Parathyroid output is also dependent on the availability of vitamin D.

The outer portion of the adrenal glands, the cortex, also produces aldosterone in addition to other corticosteroids such as oestrogen and testosterone. It should be noted that both of the sex hormones are produced in both sexes, though more oestrogen is secreted by the adrenal cortex in females, and more testosterone in males. Aldosterone regulates the amount of urine output and is in turn regulated by the kidneys. The inner portion of the adrenals, the medulla, secretes adrenaline (epinephrine), a hormone which plays a role in preparing the body to fight or flee. Secretion of adrenaline and aldosterone are only indirectly affected by the brain.

Thus, although there are important hormone systems which function more or less autonomously with respect to the brain, through the hypothalamus and the pituitary, the brain directly regulates the output of hormones affecting heart rate, breathing, urine output, the availability of protein and fat for energy and growth, and body responses to temperature changes. Disturbances in hormone secretion and regulation can have mental as well as purely physical effects. For example, excessive output of thyroid hormone, thyroxine, can cause excitement and excessive emotionality (see ANXIETY). Hormones are a second channel for brain-body and body-brain communication. They are slower than the nervous system, but more persistent, and they operate on the most fundamental functions: procreation, growth and defence.

**HORNEY, KAREN**

Psychoanalyst; taught that PSYCHOANALYSIS need not be a lengthy therapeutic experience, and that doctors should vary the form of treatment with respect to the social circumstances of the patient. b. Hamburg, Germany, 1885. d. New York City, 1952. Educated Germany, Austria. Migrated to USA, 1932. Teacher of psychoanalysis, Berlin Psychoanalytic Institute,

1920–32; New York Psychoanalytic Institute, 1934–41. Professor, New York Medical College, 1942–52. *The Neurotic Personality of Our Time*, 1937. *New Ways in Psychoanalysis*, 1939. *Self Analysis*, 1942. *Our Inner Conflicts: a Constructive Theory of Neurosis*, 1946. *Neurosis and Human Growth*, 1951.

**HULL, CLARK LEONARD**

Psychologist; mathematized theories of LEARNING; described behaviour in terms of hierarchies of stimuli and responses with reinforcements which operate a feedback to influence the beginning of the behavioural chain, a forerunner of operant conditioning (see PSYCHOLOGY, SKINNER). b. Akron, N.Y., USA, 1884. d. New Haven, Conn., 1952. Alma (Mich.) Academy, Alma College. University of Michigan, BA, 1913. University of Wisconsin, PhD, 1918. Acting professor of psychology, Eastern Kentucky State Normal School, 1909–11. Faculty of University of Wisconsin, 1913–29. Joined Institute of Human Relations, Yale University, 1929. *Evolution of Concepts*, 1920. *Aptitude Testing*, 1928. *Hypnosis and Suggestibility*, 1933. *Mathematico-Deductive Theory of Rote Learning*, 1940. *Principles of Behavior*, 1943. *A Behavior System*, 1952.

**HUMAN POTENTIAL MOVEMENT** See PSYCHOTHERAPY

**HUNTINGTON'S CHOREA** See DEMENTIA, PSYCHOMOTOR DISEASE

**HYDROCEPHALUS** See BRAIN DAMAGE

**HYPERACTIVITY**

Overactivity, a symptom of MANIA and of ORGANIC disorders such as DEMENTIA and thyrotoxicosis (see ANXIETY). Also called hyperkinesia.

Hyperactivity may also be diagnosed in children with behavioural problems who cause disruption in school and at home. The child cannot remain quiet, often shouts, moves inappropriately and awkwardly and is given to tantrums. The condition may be associated with 'trainable mental RETARDATION', a category of poorly-adapted slow learners who respond to special teaching, more often diagnosed in the United

States than in the United Kingdom. Hyperactivity is in fact diagnosed in half of all children taken to psychiatrists in the United States. Most of these patients are boys. In the United Kingdom, the diagnosis has been restricted to children with epilepsy, low IQ and 'recognizable neurological problems', according to the *British Medical Journal* (22/2/79).

Some American hyperactive children are said to have responded to dietary changes, especially a reduction in their intake of packaged foods. Trainable mental retardation has been treated with stimulants, especially methylphenidate (Ritalin), which acts like AMPHETAMINE, and theoridazine (Melleril), a major TRANQUILLIZER. Inasmuch as the symptoms themselves are controversial, however, the results of tests using these drugs must be accounted uncertain.

Many authorities suggest that the hyperactive child may be frustrated or bored. They hold that his behaviour is within the range of normal (see HEALTH, MENTAL). In other words, according to these doctors, hyperactivity is a syndrome invented by some of their colleagues. Most hyperactive children respond well to more varied exercise, discipline and the passage of time.

**HYPERKINESIA** See HYPERACTIVITY

**HYPNAGOGIC IMAGERY** See DREAM

**HYPNOTIC**

(Greek: *hypnotikos*=sleepy, narcotic) 1. that which produces hypnosis (see HYPNOTISM). 2. a drug which induces SLEEP. Technically, hypnotic drugs are intermediate between sedatives and narcotics, but the first two are now used synonymously, and narcotics are addictive drugs such as the OPIATES (see ADDICTION). However, the BARBITURATES, the largest class of hypnotics and the most frequently prescribed until they were displaced by the safer TRANQUILLIZERS, are also addictive. They may be both sedative and narcotic.

The first synthetic drug, chloral hydrate, is an hypnotic. It was discovered in 1832 by the great German chemist, Leibig, and is still in use. Indeed, it has one advantage over the barbiturates. Like some tranquillizers, chloral hydrate does not suppress REM sleep. However, on a weight-for-weight basis, it is more poisonous than the barbiturates, and it is also addictive.

## HYPNOTISM

(Greek: *hypnotikos*=sleepy, narcotic) the act of placing a subject in a trance-like state of responsiveness to the suggestions and orders of the hypnotist. It is probable that the subject can reject suggestions or orders that are repugnant to him in his normal state. The word 'hypnotism' was introduced in 1843 by Dr James Braid of Manchester.

Roughly four out of five people can be hypnotized, but with few, if any, exceptions, they must be willing subjects. It is not possible to hypnotize someone who resists the suggestion, and only rarely can a person be hypnotized who is unaware of the hypnotist's intention. About 5 per cent of responsive subjects will enter a deep trance; 35 per cent moderately deep; and 60 per cent can be only lightly hypnotized. Animals may be hypnotized, but in most cases, only by members of their own species. Occasional reports of interspecies hypnotism, as with the snake and the rabbit, are uncertain.

The degrees of trance are subjective judgments of the subject's behaviour made by the hypnotist and other observers. ELECTROENCEPHALOGRAM patterns in the hypnotized subject are similar to those of wakefulness rather than SLEEP, and they do not vary significantly between the trance states. The blink reflex in response to a flash of light may be absent, but the pupils contract. Otherwise, the subject seems to be aware only of the hypnotist, and to exclude all other stimuli, with some variation dependent on the depth of trance. His sensitivity to pain may be reduced or even eliminated. Indeed, hypnotism has been used for ANAESTHESIA during surgery, but it is not dependable. Even the deep-trance subject may respond unexpectedly to pain. Most subjects can be made to forget the entire trance period or to recall only specified parts of it. During the trance, it is possible to establish patterns of conditioned behaviour and to explore memories that had not been available to the conscious MIND. The ability to retain the MEMORY into the normal state, however, depends in part on the reason for its suppression (see PSYCHOLOGY, PSYCHOTHERAPY).

In the hands of a careful and experienced therapist and with the consent of the patient, the hypnotic facility for LEARNING and recall can be useful for treatment of NEUROSIS.

Prior information about the patient is important because the therapist may treat symptoms rather than the causes of the disturbance. The patient can then substitute another form of undesirable behaviour for the one that has been corrected. For example, a smoker who wishes to stop may be helped by hypnotic suggestion, but he may begin to eat excessively. Similarly, an anxious patient who fears spiders may find that he can tolerate the creatures after hypnotism. The fear of spiders has gone, but now he begins to experience a severe generalized anxiety. The therapist must decide with the patient how important it is to suppress the undesirable symptom in the light of such possibilities.

Hypnosis may be used to treat PSYCHOSOMATIC complaints such as asthma, but the results are not dependable. Rare congenital malformations, including disfiguring birthmarks, have responded to hypnotic suggestion, according to reports. In one test, ten patients with warts, a viral infection, were told under hypnotism that their warts would disappear, but only from one side of their bodies. It is said that nine patients recovered as directed, and the tenth lost all his warts.

Nothing is known about the physiological changes that underlie hypnotism. The subject's trust is essential, but the swinging watch is not. The subject needs only to focus his attention on the hypnotist; trance follows for no discernible reason. The time required depends on the subject.

Because hypnotism has no scientific explanation, it has been the bailiwick of charlatans for centuries. Though the technique is much older, it was popularized during the eighteenth century by F. A. Mesmer, a Frenchman. Mesmerism became a universal panacea for almost two hundred years. In our day, it has blended into BIOFEEDBACK, MEDITATION and other forms of alternative medicine. Because hypnotism can affect learning and memory, it should be used as entertainment only with the greatest care.

## HYPOCHONDRIA (or HYPOCHONDRIASIS)

(Greek: *hypo*=under, below+*chondros*=cartilage) intense preoccupation with one's own health and illnesses, real or imagined. Hypochondria is the plural of hypochondrium: the abdominal region covered by the lower rib cartilage in which the liver and spleen lie. These organs were thought to be the sites of biliousness and melancholia because they were said to produce the humours out of which these symptoms emerged.

Hypochondria may be a symptom of a mental disorder such as ANXIETY or DEPRESSION. More often, it is a complaint of people who are lonely or mildly neurotic (see NEUROSIS). Hypochondria may also be evidence that there was a serious disease in earlier life from which the patient has recovered physically.

Like any morbid preoccupation, the complaint can be annoying to others, but it is probably harmless as long as it does not lead the hypochondriac to experiment with drugs or nostrums which are, at best, expensive, and, at worst, dangerous.

**HYPOKINESIA** See -KINESIS

**HYPOTHALAMUS** See BRAIN

**HYSTERIA**

(Greek: *hystera*=uterus) a mental disorder in which the patient converts ANXIETY, often about some part of the body, into physical symptoms of illness which may be centred in the part of the body causing concern. For example, anxiety about cancer of the cervix, though unfounded, may result in cervical pain and frigidity (see DEVIATION, SEXUAL). As the name implies, hysteria is more often a female complaint. See also NEUROSIS, PSYCHOSOMATIC.

Although hysteria has been recognized in medicine for centuries, FREUD made it a part of the everyday language. His first book, *Studies in Hysteria*, written with Joseph Breuer, consists of case histories. In treatment, Breuer and Freud had used HYPNOTISM and free association (see PSYCHOANALYSIS). Freud proposed that hysteria represents clearcut Unconscious motivation, the Id dominating the Ego.

Despite the frequency with which it is diagnosed, especially when the cause appears to be obvious, hysteria is probably not a distinctive illness. It is recognized as a symptom of anxiety, but it may also be seen in DEMENTIA, DEPRESSION, epilepsy (see PSYCHOMOTOR DISEASE) and SCHIZOPHRENIA.

The cause of the symptom may be obvious, as in the case of a woman who has had a stillbirth, but hysteria takes many forms. The most common is a sensation of pain or some other sign of malfunction. Hysterical paralysis, like PSYCHOSOMATIC pain, occurs more often on the left than on the right side of the body. Multiple personality is sometimes an hysterical symptom. For example, a girl who is studious and quiet as Mary may be wilful, loud and gregarious as Margaret. Such a condition blends into schizophrenia. Hysterical AMNESIA may extend to a whole period of the patient's life, a condition known as hysterical fugue. It originates in fear or TRAUMA, but it is not usually associated with physical damage or accidents as such. One of the most familiar examples is the amnesia following shell shock. Trance states occurring for no apparent reason may also be hysterical in origin. Many of the saints are thought to have experienced hysterical trance.

The concept of mass hysteria is self-contradictory and derives from a misuse of the word hysteria. Apart from the pogroms in Nazi Germany, the most famous modern example of mass hysteria is probably audience reaction to the realistic radio play, *War of the Worlds*, by Orson Welles, which was broadcast in 1938. The excited over-reaction by many listeners revealed real fear that a cataclysmic interplanetary invasion was underway. Similarly, the mass suicide of the religious followers of the Reverend Jim Jones in 1978 grew out of the social conditions of the people involved. To discover in such sociological phenomena an element of neurosis begs the question. Poverty and ignorance are social problems and must be met with social and political measures. See also BRAINWASHING.

The diagnosis of hysteria is less common than it once was, in part because other mental disorders have become more fashionable. When the symptom exists but indicates some underlying problem, it persists in one form or another until the basic illness is controlled. Hysterical symptoms in isolation, such as shell shock, disappear spontaneously in about half the patients. A TRANQUILLIZER may be used to control the anxiety which contributes to hysteria. PSYCHOTHERAPY and psychoanalysis have no proven value, despite the work of Freud, but they may help some patients who need evidence that they have the support of a friend.

# I

**ILLNESS, MENTAL** See HEALTH, MENTAL

**IMPOTENCE** See DEVIATION, SEXUAL

**INDIVIDUAL** See PERSONALITY

**INFERIORITY COMPLEX** See ADLER, PSYCHOANALYSIS

**INHERITANCE** See GENETICS

**INSANE (INSANITY)** See SANITY

**INTELLIGENCE**
1. the ability to understand, comprehend. 2. the capacity of an individual to adapt mentally (see MIND). 3. that quality which is measured by intelligence TESTS.

These definitions reflect three different approaches to behaviour. The first is traditional; it focuses attention on the meaning of events or things rather than on the phenomena themselves. Thus, cause-and-effect is a sequential relationship arising out of events: for example, day and night are not just discrete happenings; they form a continuous pattern. A second example: the relationship amongst the three things – ice, water, steam – is to be found in both their molecular structure and in the causal role of a fourth phenomenon: heat. These patterns and relationships are discovered by abstracting one or more qualities from the phenomena themselves and giving those qualities a meaning which unites them. They are not experienced but learned. In its most abstract form, this kind of understanding creates symbols such as words which denote whole classes of events or things. To define intelligence in terms of this behaviour is to restrict it to the abstracting power of the mind. Because of the human command of language, the first definition gives intellectual supremacy to humans.

Definition two is also descriptive. It makes intelligence a particular example of a general attribute of organisms. Adaptability is that trait which permits one individual to survive whereas a lesser degree of adaptability may cause another to die in the face of environmental challenge. In this sense, intelligence gives its possessor an evolutionary advantage analogous to the advantage conferred by strength or speed. Physical adaptability is being able to run away from a predator; mental adaptability – intelligence – is knowing how to identify a predator. In comparison with the first definition, the second has the advantage that it includes behaviour which is not necessarily learned. Thus, instinctual recognition may be a part of intelligence along with the ability to learn.

Definition three takes a different course. It is functional or operational. That is, it attempts to measure a trait called intelligence by comparing certain acts by one individual with the same acts by many of his fellows according to standards set by the whole group of individuals. This group may be defined by age, culture or society. Definition three makes no attempt to say what intelligence is apart from a social consensus. It is a social definition, acceptable as long as most people agree with it, but problems arise when someone disagrees. Thus, if society says that intelligence is measured in part by the ability to write the English alphabet, the definition breaks down if the individual is illiterate or Chinese. Nevertheless, it is possible to develop sound tests which compare people's intelligence over a wide range of cultural differences, including the degree of literacy and nationality.

Note that none of the definitions attempts to relate intelligence to brain machinery or brain function. The facts needed to do so are unknown.

Each of the definitions is adequate as long as its limits are recognized. Mischief arises if an attempt is made to mix up the third definition with either of the first two definitions (or with the non-existent physiological definition of intelligence). Yet there is a school of psychological thought, exemplified by Dr Arthur R. Jensen, professor of psychology at Harvard University, and Dr Hans EYSENCK of the Institute of Psychiatry, London, which holds that intelligence tests can be used to say something about the mechanism of intelligence. In particular, they have found that a large number of tests given in the United States and the United Kingdom reveal that blacks have lower test scores on average than do whites. That is, if the black test scores range from, let us say, 50 to 150 with a statistical mean (not an average) at 96, then white test scores range from 50 to 150 with a statistical mean of 100. Thus far, the statistical operations, though complex, are generally accepted as valid. The problem arises because they argue that the tests reveal two further data: that intelligence is about 80 per cent an inherited trait, and therefore, blacks in the United States and the United Kingdom are in general less intelligent than whites. Note that neither Jensen nor Eysenck has suggested that individual blacks are less intelligent than individual whites. Rather, the reverse may well be true. Nor have Jensen or Eysenck argued that blacks should be offered fewer educational opportunities than whites. Unfortunately, however, their data have been used to promote such racist arguments.

Most biologists disagree with the Jensen–Eysenck extrapolations about the heritability of and the racial differences in intelligence. In the first place, tests based upon social criteria cannot be used to identify fundamental mechanical elements of a trait: its heritability, in this instance. Such elements can be elucidated only by research into the neurophysiological and biochemical activities of the brain. Jensen and Eysenck have confused two different kinds of data: socio-psychological and biological.

Perhaps even more serious, they have extended a social definition of race into biology where it has no place. Biological science recognizes no racial differences amongst humans. In the matter of skin colour, for example, there are gradations from pinkish blonde through yellowish to swarthy, light brown, reddish brown and black-brown. Amongst the four billion inhabitants of Earth, there is a continuum of skin colours, but no dividing line between brown and swarthy is detectable. In a community where the majority is light in colour, blacks stand out, and vice versa, but these are distinctions made within the social context and have no biological meaning. Apart from the dispute over the use of statistics by Jensen and Eysenck, therefore, biologists deny that comparison of blacks and whites has any fundamental validity.

However, these arguments do not answer one question. There evidently is a difference in intelligence test scores between the races as socially-defined in the United States and the United Kingdom. How much of *that* difference is inherited and how much is due to environment? This question has nothing to do with biological racial differences, because biological races do not exist. The question is only about the inheritance and environment of specific populations. Even so, Jensen and Eysenck have taken the wrong road to find an answer; that is, they have extrapolated from social data to biological data. Yet the degree to which intelligence is an inherited trait requires an answer. Long after irrelevant issues of race have at last ceased to vex humans, they will still be trying to increase the learning and adaptability of their children. To obtain the best results, it is desirable to understand the mysterious machinery of intelligence.

**INTOXICATION** See ALCOHOL, AMPHETAMINE, OPIATE

**INTROVERSION** See EXTRAVERSION

**INVOLUTIONAL MELANCHOLIA** See MELANCHOLIA

**IQ** See TEST

**IRRITABILITY**
(Latin: *irritabilitas*, from *irritare*=to tease) 1. the response of nerve and muscle tissue to stimulation. 2. abnormal behavioural response to slight stimuli.

At one time, the quality of irritability was held to be characteristic of living matter because mobile cells had been seen to withdraw from noxious stimuli. Plant cells are often not mobile, however, nor do red blood cells, for example, display this quality. On the other hand, the membranes surrounding NEURONS and muscle cells are specialized to admit or exclude charged particles in response to chemical stimuli such as TRANSMITTERS. As a result, these cells create and conduct electrical impulses. Thus, irritability is now seen as an electrochemical response to chemical stimulation.

It is more familiar as an abnormal behavioural response. Though irritability is a perfectly normal reaction when one is tired or hard-pressed, it may also be one of the commonest symptoms of both physical and mental disorders. As a symptom, irritability is often called over-reaction, but it should be remembered that the observer who uses this popular expression may be using it to hide his own discomfiture.

# J

## JAMES, WILLIAM

Leader of the philosophical movement called pragmatism, student of rational human psychology and analyst of religious behaviour. b. New York, 1842. d. Chocorua, New Hampshire, 1910. Medical studies at Harvard interrupted by journey to Amazon as assistant to Louis Agassiz, American naturalist, and by studies in physics and physiology in Germany, 1867–8; MD, 1869. Suffered from NEURASTHENIA. Instructor in physiology, Harvard College, 1872–6; continued on Harvard faculty, 1907. *Principles of Psychology*, 1890. Gifford Lectures, University of Edinburgh, 1901–02; *The Varieties of Religious Experience*, 1902. *Lovell Lectures, Boston*, 1906; *Pragmatism: a New Name for Old Ways of Thinking*, 1907. Hibbert Lectures, Oxford; *A Pluralistic Universe*, 1909. *The Meaning of Truth*, 1909. *Some Problems in Philosophy*, 1911. *Essays in Radical Empiricism*, 1912.

**JANOV, A.** See TRAUMA

**JENSEN, A. R.** See INTELLIGENCE

## JUNG, CARL FRIEDRICH

Psychoanalyst; introduced concepts of EXTRAVERSION-introversion and the collective unconscious. b. Kasswil, Switzerland, 1875. d. Zurich, 1961. University Psychiatric Clinic, Zurich. Staff of Berghölzi Asylum, Zurich (director: BLEULER), 1902. Collaboration with FREUD, 1907–12. President, International Psychoanalytic Society, 1911, but resigned to found a new school in Zurich with A. Maeder. Difference with Freud over theory of sexual basis of behaviour published in *Psychology of the Unconscious*, 1912. Professor of psychiatry, Federal Polytechnical University, Zurich, 1933–41. Professor of medical psychology, University of Basle, 1943. *Psychological Types*, 1921. *Modern Man in Search of a Soul*, 1933. *Essays on Contemporary Events*, 1946. *Answer to Job*, 1952. *Memories, Dreams, Reflections*, 1962.

# K

## -KINESIS

(Greek: movement, motion) movement, motion. Kinesis is a combining form used with prefixes to describe PSYCHOMOTOR disorders. (For telekinesis, see SENSATION.)

**Akinesia** is the inability to move or to move smoothly and efficiently. It is a common symptom of Parkinsonism, and it may indicate damage to the BRAIN region which regulates that movement (see BRAIN DAMAGE).

**Bradykinesia** means slowed movement, especially as seen in Parkinsonism.

**Dyskinesia** is a disorder of voluntary movements, but it is often used as a synonym for akinesia.

**Hyperkinesia** is HYPERACTIVITY.

## KLEIN, MELANIE (née Reizes)

Psychoanalyst, developed treatment of children. b. Vienna, 1882. d. London, 1960. Patient of FREUD's associate, Sandor Ferenczi. Settled in Berlin, 1919, and studied with Karl Abraham. Developed techniques of child analysis, 1921–34. Settled in London, 1926. *Psychoanalysis of Children*, 1932. *Envy and Gratitude*, 1957. *Narrative of a Child Analysis*, 1961.

**KLINEFELTER'S SYNDROME** See SYNDROME

**KORSAKOV'S SYNDROME** See SYNDROME

## KRAEPELIN, EMIL

Classified mental illnesses into a system which is still used. Applied experimental techniques to clinical studies. b. Neustrelitz, Germany, 1856. d. Munich, 1926. University of Würzburg, MD, 1878. Clinical position at Leipzig; studied with Wilhelm Wundt (see PSYCHOLOGY). *Textbook of Psychology*, 1883. Professor, University of Dorpat (Tartu, Esthonian SSR), 1885. University of Heidelberg, 1891. Distinguished manic depressive psychosis and dementia praecox (now called SCHIZOPHRENIA) in revision of *Textbook of Psychology*, 1899. Professor of clinical psychiatry, University of Munich, 1903–22. Director, Research Institute of Psychiatry, Munich, 1922–26.

# L

## LAING, RONALD DAVID

Clinical psychiatrist; explains SCHIZOPHRENIA as a disease of self-identity caused by socio-familial contradictions. b. Scotland, 1927. Educated Glasgow University. Central Army Psychiatric Unit, Netley, 1952–3. Department of psychological medicine, Glasgow University, 1953–6. Tavistock Clinic, 1956–60. Tavistock Institute of Human Relations since 1960. Principle investigator: Schizophrenia and Family Research Unit, Tavistock Institute. *The Divided Self*, 1960. *The Self and Others*, 1961. *Reason and Violence* (with D. Cooper), 1964. *Sanity, Madness and the Family* (with A. Esterson), 1965. *Interpersonal Perception* (with H. Phillipson and A. R. Lee), 1966. *The Politics of Experience and the Bird of Paradise*, 1967. *Knots*, 1970. *The Politics of the Family*, 1971. *The Facts of Life*, 1976. *Do You Love Me*, 1977. *Conversations with Children*, 1978.

## LEARNING

The process of acquiring new abilities, responses and COGNITIONS which are not the result of growth and lead to changes in behaviour. See also MEMORY.

That learning can occur separately from memory is contrary to common sense. Yet experiments on the neurochemistry of BRAIN regions thought to be involved in memory suggest that, providing the kind of memory is specified, the two activities may be separated. For example, an animal learns to perform an act in response to a stimulus. It is then given a drug which causes it to forget the act, but when it is retrained, the training time required for relearning is significantly less than the original training time. Apparently, although the memory of the task is wiped out, the learning remains. It may be argued that the drug blocks recall, leaving the memory intact, but then why should the most cursory retraining counteract the effects of the drug? Until memory is better understood, the question cannot be answered with certainty. The experiment remains a controversial curiosity suggesting only that there may be a rational basis in the machinery of the brain for treating learning as a separate phenomenon.

In 1898, THORNDYKE postulated the Law of Effect: an action

that leads to a desired outcome is likely to be repeated in similar circumstances. The law has been much studied and often modified, but the original formulation contains a functional description of elementary learning behaviour. On this foundation, an elaborate structure of learning theory evolved. Psychologists who rejected both inductive judgments about behaviour based on their own subjective experience and purely descriptive psychology, discovered in learning a behaviour which they could test experimentally, even using human subjects (see PSYCHOLOGY). When these behaviourists asserted that the proper subject of psychology is the measurable unit of learning, stimulus and response, they created an experimental form or paradigm. For years, it gave a focus for psychological research so that learning theory and psychology became almost synonymous. There was very little room in the field for such outmoded topics as value, self-image or MIND. It was not until certain kinds of essential learning, especially language acquisition (see below), were shown to resist the stimulus-response strait jacket that learning theory began to soften its approach to other aspects of behaviour. Nevertheless, the Law of Effect undoubtedly exists, and its identification has provided rationalizations for a great range of social activities including advertising, broadcasting, education and, indeed, PSYCHOTHERAPY.

The acquisition of abilities and responses may be largely explained by learning theory, at least in humans, but cognitions are learned only very indirectly if at all as a result of simple stimulus-response situations. Imprinting takes the place of stimulus-response in many animals, moreover, with respect to some aspects of their earliest learning. Konrad Lorenz, the Austrian ethologist, demonstrated how ducks, for example, will attach themselves to the first object they see on specific days after hatching. Lorenz's ducks were imprinted by him rather than their mothers and followed him about as though he was their mother. In a later experiment by other workers, rhesus monkeys were removed from their mothers soon after birth and were raised with two dummy 'mothers' made of wire and cloth. One, made of wire only, had a teat which gave milk to the suck. The other wire frame was covered by soft cloth but did not give milk. The infant monkeys spent more time with the soft 'mother' than with the wire frame even though only the wire frame gave them food. They seem to have become attached to the sensual stimulation of the cloth-covered frame despite the food reward offered by the wire 'mother'. This behaviour may not represent true imprinting, but it does suggest that rewards may be less clear-cut than had been supposed. It is sometimes said that rats become so bored by the experiments humans devise for them that they oblige just to get out of the cage. However that may be, imprinting has not been explained, and it does not seem to occur in humans.

The infant who stops crying as soon as his mother picks him up has identified her as a source of comfort, a learned response. He has begun the never-ending journey into a world of patterns, of this as against that, of objects within spaces and of creative thoughts which had not previously existed. Much of the experimental work on learning is now directed towards what is called developmental psychology. It is relevant to education and other aspects of socialization, and developmental learning also offers a new experimental paradigm: the relatively simple behaviour of infants, uncomplicated, for example, by elaborate language activity. One of the great pioneers of developmental psychology, PIAGET, has proposed four cognitive periods during the early years:

| Period | Approx. age | Description |
|---|---|---|
| Sensorimotor development | 0–2 years | Object permanence and actions that effect changes in the world |
| Pre-operational thought | 2–7 | Language development. Mental operations in place of actions; e.g. reasoning about location of lost ball. Limited to present events. Egocentricity |
| Concrete operations | 7–11 | Logical deductions from events. Child recognizes abstractions such as compensation; e.g. push and it falls. Less egocentric |
| Formal operations | 11–15 | Full adult logical apparatus |

Piaget has been criticized because these periods are generalizations based on anecdotal observations and lack objective experimental proof. Much developmental work is limited in this way, but on the other hand, experimental psychologists have found new ways to quantify and objectify their operations. For example, an infant can be seen to recognize his mother's voice within the first weeks of life. This was demonstrated by measuring the infant's eye movements in response to the voice of his mother broadcast through a speaker, so that she was not near him, and comparing his eye movements in response to other voices. By an equally simple counting operation, it has been shown that before the infant is two months old, he has taught his mother the meanings of his different sounds and body movements. In this case, the experimenter counted the endearments spoken by the mother. There is little more convincing evidence that an infant learns at the outset to manipulate his environment to assure his own protection and growth.

Piaget was among the first to recognize that language development marked a new period in human infantile growth. Learning to speak cannot be explained on the basis of physical development because many children who are slow to crawl and walk, for example, speak and begin to reason just as well and sometimes better than their physically-more-advanced peers. Is language development in some part innate? If it is, then it cannot be entirely the product of learning.

Theories of human behaviour based on innate qualities became unfashionable as a reaction against the religious belief in the role of inheritance, which dominated western thought and delayed the development of experimental psychology. For this reason, and because of the impossibility of testing innate behaviour with existing knowledge, behaviourists denied its relevance. They maintain that all behaviour is learned by means of the stimulus-response mechanism, including language. It was left to a brilliant young teacher of linguistics at the Massachusetts Institute of Technology, Noam Chomsky, to weaken the props beneath their hypothesis and to restore the notion of innate language behaviour to scientific respectability. In 1959, Chomsky reviewed SKINNER's recently published book, *Verbal Behavior*, in a technical periodical called *Language*. The book presented in great detail the behaviourist view of language learning. In a long article, Chomsky tore the book to pieces. He argued that stimulus-response learning cannot explain that which is interesting about language – the creative originality with which it is used by any two-year-old. He suggested and later elaborated the theory that the grammatical relationships underlying language are innate. Their syntactical expression – in English or Arabic, for example – are learned, perhaps largely by stimulus-response, but not the 'deep structures' which, he believes, give meaning to the arrangements of sounds we learn. Chomsky's early work has been criticized and revised, but its theoretical thrust has been widely accepted. Other behavioural capacities are now also thought to be inherited, but neither the degree to which behaviour is learned nor the machinery of learning, are well understood.

**LEUCOTOMY** See PSYCHOSURGERY

**LEWIN, K.** See PSYCHOTHERAPY

**-LEXIS**

(Greek: speaking) reading. A combining form usually used with one of two prefixes:

**Alexia.** Word blindness, a disorder of reading and writing due to damage, often congenital, to the reading and speech centres of the left cortex (see BRAIN).

**Dyslexia.** A disorder of reading and writing. In a minority of cases, it is due to congenital BRAIN DAMAGE. The disorder may also run in families, but in most cases, its origin and cause are unknown.

Dyslexia affects as many as one in two thousand London school children. These children are intellectually normal, according to IQ TESTS, and they may have unusually high visual imagery scores. Speech is also normal in most dyslexics, so that the disorder is not revealed until the child begins to read and write. Perhaps the most common symptom is mirror writing, writing from the left, in which case the child also reads from the left. For example, the word 'not' is written or read, 'ton'. This dyslexia may be associated with left-handedness, arising from damage to the left cortical hemisphere. In other words, the right hemisphere is forced into dominance by the damage, but the language skill remains in the left hemisphere.

Mirror writing can often be corrected by giving the child careful, individual instruction. It may be desirable to teach dyslexic children to read by phonetics rather than by the more common method in which the sound of the letters is taught first. Reading for amusement becomes of great importance. Dyslexic children should develop at least the essential basic skills if such special teaching techniques are used, but educational authorities must always be given the fullest information about the child's disability.

In adults, dyslexia is almost always the result of brain damage. Its treatment depends on the extent of the damage, the age of the patient and his responsiveness to special teaching techniques.

**LIBIDO** See PSYCHOANALYSIS

**LIMBIC SYSTEM** See BRAIN

**LOBOTOMY** See PSYCHOSURGERY

**LORENZ, K.** See AGGRESSION, LEARNING, PSYCHOLOGY

# M

**MALNUTRITION** See BRAIN DAMAGE

**MANIA**

(Greek: madness) mental disorder characterized by EUPHORIA, elation, HYPERACTIVITY and IRRITABILITY.

Symptoms which would now be diagnosed as SCHIZOPHRENIA were once included within the meaning of mania. The word is now associated with the euphoria characteristic of the cyclic form of DEPRESSION, manic depression. But mania may also be a symptom of physical disorders. Thus, dypsomania is associated with ALCOHOL poisoning. Ergotomania is a symptom of poisoning by ergot drugs, also called ergotism. It may be brought on by high doses of ergotamine given for the treatment of migraine (see HEADACHE). Epileptic mania is, of course, a symptom of epilepsy (see PSYCHOMOTOR DISEASE). Puerperal mania occasionally follows an otherwise normal childbirth and is the emotional opposite of the more common 'POST-PARTEM BLUES'.

**MASS HYSTERIA** See BRAINWASHING, HYSTERIA

**MASTURBATION** See DEVIATION, SEXUAL

## MEDITATION

A process of refreshment involving sustained reflection or contemplation. The word is often used with the adjective 'transcendental', because the practitioner believes that meditation enables him to transcend the physical tensions and anxieties imposed on him by his environment.

Meditation is in fact relaxation. Physical measurements of oxygen consumption, skin conductance and ELECTROENCEPHALOGRAMS during meditative states reveal no significant differences from the same measurements made during rest. Meditation often has a mystic, pseudo-Oriental flavour. The practitioner is in some degree abstracted from the surrounding world of stimuli and may be temporarily unaware of a crying child or a flashing light. Inasmuch as ordinary meditation and relaxation require self-abstraction, however, the distinction being made by those who believe in transcendental meditation is not clear. Perhaps in the latter, there is an element of auto-suggestion (see HYPNOTISM) which enhances the subjective value of the process.

Meditation may begin by focusing one's attention on an object such as a flower or a geometric figure. With practice the object can be internalized as a sensory image; for example, a mandala or sheep jumping over a fence. Some practitioners prefer to avoid all thought and imagery, to wipe their MINDS clean. Such homely devices suggest that meditation is one of several ways that people have found to relax. As such, it should be encouraged. Even trappings that are exotic, bizarre or mystical are preferable to sleeping pills (see HYPNOTICS), TRANQUILLIZERS or other drugs. See also BIOFEEDBACK, SLEEP.

## MELANCHOLIA

(Greek: *melano*=black+*chole*=bile) a symptom of severe DEPRESSION characterized by ANXIETY, DELUSIONS and HYPERACTIVITY. The word 'melancholia' reflects the notion that madness is caused by an excess of black bile, one of the four humours of medieval European medicine. It is perhaps most often used with the adjective 'involutional' to indicate that melancholia is a form of depression usually diagnosed in the aged. Involutional means retrogressive, returning to a more primitive state, shrinking.

The patient may slowly become more irritable (see IRRITABILITY) and hypochondriacal (see HYPOCHONDRIA). He worries more than usual about business or money. His expression becomes woebegone, and he wrings his hands, weeps and moans. His posture is bowed, even somewhat rigid. He believes that others are accusing him of crimes, of causing their own problems and of causing catastrophes, such as an economic crisis (see PARANOIA). Indeed, the patient accepts that he is responsible. He frequently demands attention and reassurance, placing great strains on the family or the nursing staff. Yet amidst this welter of self-recrimination and misery, the patient remains conscious of others, aware of his bodily needs and functions and amenable to treatment.

Like reactive depression, the condition may originate in some event such as menopause or BEREAVEMENT. Yet melancholia is a progressive deepening of the depression, so that it becomes an endogenous PSYCHOSIS. The prognosis is poor, and seems to grow worse, the older the patient. Treatments used for depression may help to control melancholia.

## MEMORY

(Latin: *memoria*=memory) 1. a change in a tissue enabling an organism to return to or re-enact a former state when the environment demands. 2. the attribute of MIND which allows storage and recall of COGNITIONS, EMOTIONS, PERCEPTIONS and SENSATIONS.

Memory has been called the most permanent change in protoplasm other than scar tissues. For centuries, it has been studied and classified. People who can remember logically-disconnected data are said to have mnemonic memory. Memory which seems to emphasize specific senses include aural, kinaesthetic, photographic and visual. Whether these kinds of memory are principally inherited or actually learned is controversial. In an attempt to improve memory and to treat diseases in which memory deteriorates, modern research has tried to come to grips with the nature of the physical changes that underlie the behavioural aspects of memory.

Thanks in part to computers which show that memory can be reduced to an on-off, yes-no mechanism, it has been recognized that the phenomenon is exhibited by tissues other than the BRAIN. The most important example is immunological memory. When a bacterium enters the body, cells of the lymphatic system respond by trying to immobilize and destroy the invader. If the same bacteria should then reappear, the response is quicker and more massive because the cells, or their descendants, have remembered the original invasion. This facility explains the effectiveness of vaccination: a light or slightly detoxified dose of the causative organism is given to 'teach' relevant cells in the lymphatic system how to protect the organism against a real invasion.

The machinery of this defensive memory is partially understood. It requires the creation in certain cells of special molecules called antibodies. When the invader, or antigen, first appears, a small number of cells synthesize the antibody against that antigen. The antibody may or may not be effective against other antigens. In any case, a colony of these educated cells grows so that many more of them are available to produce antibody against the antigen if it should reappear. The process by which antibody production is induced in the original cells is not yet clear, but a GENETIC capability must underlie this remarkable learning.

Whether brain memory functions in a similar way is not known, but it is probably more complex. The content of mental memory is more varied, and the responses required cover the spectrum of behaviour from defence to welcome acceptance. Yet three features of mental memory may well be identical to immunological memory: first, some physical phenomenon – a new structure or a change in an existing structure – records the event. This phenomenon occurs in the brain, and it is almost certainly a change in NEURONS, but glial cells may also play a role in the physio-chemistry of memory. Second, this change is made possible by a genetically-determined competence. Third, there is some mechanism for locating the new structure when it is needed. This is recall.

The nature of memory is further complicated by the

existence of two different stages in the process, called immediate or short-term and long-term memory. A third stage, intermediate or labile memory, may also exist between the short- and long-term stages. Evidence for intermediate memory comes from tests with drugs which either perpetuate or wipe out memory at various times after learning. Short- and long-term memory are revealed both by experiments with drugs and by behavioural tests. In one classical behavioural experiment, a list of twenty to thirty simple words is read slowly to the subject. After a prescribed interval which may vary from a few seconds to several minutes, the subject repeats as many of the words as he can recall. Depending on the speed with which the list has been read, the interval between reading and repetition, the distractions and other relevant conditions, but not on the length of the list, the subject will recall one or two words from the beginning of the list and three or four from the end. Over a number of such tests, his scores should average out to a curve like this:

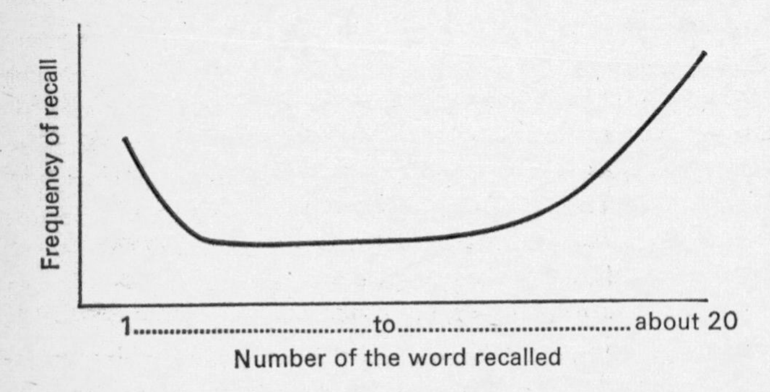


This kind of psychological experiment was devised in 1962 by an American, B. B. Murdock, Jr. It shows that there are two kinds of memory: long-term, up to about word twenty-five in a list of thirty, which works best for the first word or two. The interference from new words disturbs it. Short-term memory stores the last three or four words. This short-term memory is disrupted in Korsakov's SYNDROME; the patient's memory and recall for events prior to the onset of symptoms is more or less normal, but he is unable to remember new data. He may forget the beginning of his own sentence. He knows and greets his doctor when the doctor enters, but if he leaves and re-enters within a minute or two, the Korsakov patient will greet him again as though it was the first visit that day. Electroconvulsive therapy (see SHOCK THERAPY) interferes with short-term memory but rarely disturbs long-term. A drug such as marijuana (see HALLUCINOGEN) may impair short-term memory, but it has no apparent effect on long-term. Conversely, drugs which interfere with biosynthesis of proteins impair long-term memory but not immediate. It is possible to specify the duration of short-term memory by giving such a drug at different intervals before or immediately after training. The same technique is used to test intermediate memory. The problem is that the time seems to vary with the task, the experimental animal and perhaps with other experimental conditions. Nevertheless, there is now good evidence for the existence of at least two stages of memory, and possibly a third, which depend on different mechanisms in the brain.

Short-term memory is thought to require a change in the characteristics of the neuronal membrane so that the neuron becomes more easily excited. These changes probably occur in brain centres such as the hippocampus, and the resulting facilitation is temporary, persisting just long enough so that other neurons receiving the facilitated signals initiate the lasting changes underlying long-term memory. The permanent changes must be regulated by such attributes as ATTENTION and experience, but immediate memory probably depends on a temporary change in the electrical activity of neurons.

Long-term memory, on the other hand, is almost certainly associated with the biosynthesis of new chemicals by neurons. The nature of these chemicals is not known, but two substances have been implicated: ribonucleic acid (RNA) and protein. In all cells, biosynthesis of protein depends on prior formation of RNA which is in turn a copy of the genetic molecule, deoxyribonucleic acid (DNA). Thus, drugs have been used to prevent synthesis of protein or RNA. The experimental animals exhibit some impairment of memory. Another approach to the puzzle has produced even more dramatic results. Earthworms (planaria), goldfish, chickens and rats have been used for experiments in which the animal has been trained to perform a task. It is then killed, its brain is minced and a refined extract fed to naive animals. The results are controversial, but some workers have reported that the naive animals can perform the experimental task without further training. There can be no doubt that RNAs and proteins have been found in the brains of trained animals which do not exist in those of naive animals, and these new chemicals can be associated with the learning.

This fascinating research may help to reveal the nature of memory, but it can help only indirectly to answer two related questions: where is long-term memory stored, and what is recall? In fact, these questions may be different approaches to the same phenomenon. If it were possible to find a memory, it might be easier to suggest a device whereby the brain does the same thing. Brain surgeons have watched a patient respond to electrical stimulation of a point on the cortex by recalling in great detail a memory the patient had 'forgotten'. Yet if a disease such as epilepsy (see PSYCHOMOTOR DISEASE) requires destruction of that area, the patient may retain the memory undimmed. Where did it go, and how did it get there? In the 1920s, Karl Lashley, an American psychologist, trained rats to do various tasks. He then removed carefully delineated regions of their brains. When the animals had recovered, they were tested again for the behaviour they had learned. After performing brain surgery on hundreds of animals, Lashley concluded that only the removal of a substantial amount of the rat's brain adversely affected its memory, and by that stage, other aspects of its behaviour were also impaired. He could find no localized memory.

Broadly speaking, four generalized memory areas have been identified in humans. Three of them are in the cortex. Language-using ability, especially reading and writing, is dependent on the left parieto-temporal zone just inside and slightly above the left ear in most of us. Damage to this area reduces or destroys the memory for language, though not the ability to learn and use language based on pictorial signs and symbols.

The second human memory area is in the frontal lobe. The results of psychosurgical operations which disconnect the frontal cortex from the mid-brain indicate that the frontal cortex contains memories of social and personal responsibility. A third memory area, roughly inside the right temple, may contain learned emotions.

The fourth region is outside the cortex in the cerebellum. This remarkable structure regulates fine voluntary movements such as the fingering learned by a pianist. Damage to the cerebellum disorders or destroys such complex behaviour, and it cannot be relearned.

The great British anatomist, J. Z. Young, has proposed that memory formation is a negative rather than a positive event. If, for example, a sensory stimulus might take one of two different channels, the effect of repeated stimulation (as in the practice required for learning) is to shut down one of them, according to Young. Although the basic event is electrical, or rather, the loss of an electrically-excited pathway, it is possible that the inhibition reflects the action of some newly-formed chemical. But in Young's model, memory formation is irreversible. As he has said, 'I don't believe in forgetting.' The memory channel remains open, and the inhibited channel remains shut. Any failure of recall must be due to a block on the way to the memory channel. What this block might be, Young does not suggest. Otherwise, recall is automatic in his model because a new stimulus will excite a prepared neural pathway.

That human memory can be destroyed by brain damage has been noted, although Lashley's findings with rats imply the reverse. Degenerative diseases such as DEMENTIA impose a progressive memory loss affecting old as well as new memories. The slow decline, characteristic of ageing, reflects the death of brain cells with an inevitable effect on memory (see AGE). Yet the relationship is by no means simple. In normal ageing, the oldest memories and the recall mechanism are spared, but new memories are harder to lay down in the long-term store. For some reason, the transfer of immediate to long-term memory seems to become more difficult.

From time to time, press reports carry the glad news of a drug that helps old people to remember. So far, all such stories have been premature. Either the experimental results cannot be reproduced, or it has been demonstrated that the extra care and attention given the aged subjects could explain their improved performances on memory tests. On the other hand, psychological tests have demonstrated that memory continues to act efficiently into the sixties, and thereafter declines more slowly than had been suspected. Much depends on the motivation of the learner, as it does at any age, and on the framework of existing knowledge into which the new data is to fit. It is probably harder to learn a new language at sixty than it is at twenty, but the sixty-year-old Englishman who speaks French fluently will pick up new French slang with about the same efficiency as a younger person. The older learner has also often acquired techniques – tricks – which restore the balance with the younger, less experienced student. Some skills, such as bookbinding, may be learned more quickly by older people simply because they have more patience, or fewer distractions. Nevertheless, sooner or later the ability to acquire new knowledge declines.

The probable relationship between memory and the FUNCTIONAL mental disorders underlies all psychotherapeutic regimens. According to one theory, for example, SCHIZOPHRENIA is caused by disordered PERCEPTIONS. Perception may be looked upon as sensation modified by memory, but the question remains as to why perceptions should become disordered. Perhaps the connection between memory errors and mental illness is merely the obverse of normal memory in ordinary behaviour. Since memory is experience, future behaviour will be distorted by an abnormal or misperceived past.

**MENTAL HEALTH** See HEALTH, MENTAL

**MENTAL RETARDATION** See RETARDATION

**MIGRAINE** See HEADACHE

**MIND**

(Old German: roots, *min-*, *man-*, *mun-*=to think, remember) 1. the locus of CONSCIOUSNESS, PERSONALITY, the self. 2. the psychical being as distinct from the corporeal. 3. the MEMORY. 4. the name adopted to designate the National Association for Mental Health.

These definitions are based on the *Oxford English Dictionary*. They show how hard it is to find an agreed meaning for a commonly-used word, and indeed, how many meanings the word has. Perhaps the most important contribution by the brain sciences towards the clarification of the meaning of mind is the demonstration that the incorporeal conception of mind (definition 2) is no longer tenable. The idea of a soul or pneumen in man is at least as old as religion, but the modern notion of mind-body dualism is considered to have originated with the seventeenth-century French philosopher, René Descartes (see CONSCIOUSNESS). His influence has persisted because he approached the functions of the nervous system rationally. Nevertheless, we now accept that the mind could not exist without the brain which embodies it. Modern legal definitions of death centre on brain-death because with the disorganization and loss of function of the brain, the individual ceases to exist.

Having said as much, it is important to avoid the kind of sterile materialism which holds that the functions of mind are explained by the behaviour of NEURONS. Lest there be any doubt that this reductionism cannot solve all of the problems, consider the difference between an electro-chemical pulse in a neuron – the neuron's signal – and your PERCEPTION of a flash of light. Your perception cannot happen without the electro-chemical signal, but how is the physical event transformed into the psychological event? At present, the question cannot be answered. Although the eventual answer will no doubt reveal objective physiological events, the question suggests that the mind exists in the brain, but is more than the sum of its parts.

**MINIMAL BRAIN DAMAGE** See BRAIN DAMAGE

**MONGOLISM** See SYNDROME

**MONOAMINE OXIDASE INHIBITOR** See DEPRESSION

## MOTION SICKNESS

The nausea and general malaise felt by some people in vehicles and on swings, boats or aeroplanes. Also called air-, car-, sea-, travel-sickness.

The vehicle's motion upsets the organs of balance in the inner ear (see SENSATION). At the end of a sequence of nervous signals which pass through the BRAIN (though the eyes contribute to the effect), the vomiting centre in the hind-brain is triggered. Exactly the same sequence can be set off by squirting cold water into the ear, even in subjects who do not suffer from motion sickness. Animals and infants display the disturbance, indicating that it is physiologically-based. In fact, it is probable that with sufficient provocation, everyone with a normal sense of balance will experience motion sickness.

Nevertheless, there are certainly PSYCHOSOMATIC elements in the malaise. Motion sickness can become a conditioned reflex (see PSYCHOLOGY). There are people who become ill when they merely set foot on a boat. One experience of motion sickness creates ANXIETY in a similar situation, and the tension makes matters worse.

Car-sick children usually outgrow it. Games that take their minds off themselves and pass the time will help. Indeed, the same is true for adults. Trimming sails or just steering a small boat works wonders. On a large boat, it is better to stay on deck. The air and the visual space to the horizon seem to help, but it is important to keep warm. In planes and cars, the ears may be least disturbed by sitting in an upright position with the head tilted back against a seat rest.

Most authorities agree that small, frequent snacks are better than no food. Large, fatty meals should be avoided at all costs. Some recommend less liquid than usual. Alcohol may help by reducing fear, providing you are accustomed to drinking.

The most common motion sickness drugs are antihistamines. All of them tend to make you sleepy. The TRANQUILLIZERS may also help; certain major tranquillizers such as prochlorperazine (Stemetil) control the vomiting centre with less sedation than the antihistamines. However, people using car ferries must remember that they cannot drive safely for up to eight hours after taking any of these drugs. To be effective, furthermore, all remedies must be applied before the symptoms appear. Once motion sickness sets in, there is nothing to do but bear it.

## MOTIVATION

(French: *motif*=a motion) the internal stimulus for an action. Motivation may be either conscious or unconscious.

The similarity of the word 'motivation' to EMOTION is obvious. However, motivation is determined by cognitive (see COGNITION) as well as by emotional factors. It is a word beloved of psychologists who have used it in preference to the traditional concept of will which has religious overtones. Yet it is not easy to distinguish between motivation and will. Like motivation, the will injects purpose and meaning into behaviour. The behaviourists (see PSYCHOLOGY) have studied motivation in terms of the stimulus-response unit like all other behaviour. Motivations were converted to 'drives' which may be either inherited or learned (see LEARNING), but are revealed by and must not be read into behaviour. In other words, according to the behaviourists, the purpose of an act is inherent in it and is determined by the stimulus added to the learning experience and the behavioural repertoire available to the subject. For example, once overwhelming danger is recognized, birds can fly from it, but men can only run away. This mechanistic approach to motivation denies the importance if not the existence of a will.

PSYCHOANALYSIS, on the other hand, places motivation, especially unconscious motivation, in a central role. Far from being an attribute of behaviour, it conditions and determines thought and action. Motivation is thought to predate ongoing responses, and it bears many of the attributes of theological will.

Like other attributes of MIND, motivation exists in the machinery of the BRAIN. In common with other organs, the brain acts to keep the organism in a viable balance with its environment. Thus, there is a tiny region in the hypothalamus, stimulation of which causes the animal to display a rage reaction. In rage, the heart beats faster, to allow, among other advantages, more rapid exchange of gases required to increase energy formation in the muscles. The brain must locate the danger and coordinate the memories and muscles needed to combat it. A rage reaction to danger is an extreme example of a general, continuous balancing process exhibited by all organisms, which the American physiologist, W. B. Cannon, called homeostasis. The word applied originally to the behaviour of individual cells, and it may be objected that homeostasis in higher animals is qualitatively different, because animals learn and display a will, an attribute presumably not revealed by single cells (but see MEMORY). On the other hand, there is a scientific advantage in treating the complex behavioural kit consisting of inherited and learned motivations exactly like the biophysical forces that regulate a cell's behaviour. Ultimately, motivations must be understood in biophysical terms. They ought to be neither side-stepped as irrelevant, as the behaviourists do, nor obscured by psychoanalytic categories. If motivations exist, they can be related to neural machinery as in the example of rage. See also CONSCIOUSNESS.

# N

**NARCOTIC** See HYPNOTIC

**NERVE CELL** See NEURON

**NERVOUS BREAKDOWN** See BREAKDOWN, NERVOUS

**NEURASTHENIA**
(Greek: *neuron*=nerve+*asthenia*=debility) a NEUROSIS characterized by abnormal tiredness. Also called nervous prostration.

Neurasthenia is one of the first mental disorders to be described. In 1880, G. M. Beard, an American psychologist, outlined the main symptoms and associated them with a PERSONALITY type. For many years it was maintained that there is a neurasthenic physique: thin, small-boned, flaccid, infantile in appearance. The idea that neurasthenia occurs in oversensitive people probably grew out of the common observation that patients who feel tired when they are recovering from physical illness may also be unusually sensitive to emotional disturbances.

Like other neurotic reactions, neurasthenia is one extreme of a continuum of behaviour which includes the normal range of responses. Thus, the tiredness felt by someone recovering from pneumonia is normal and indeed, healthy. Similarly, emotional stress such as BEREAVEMENT is often accompanied by tiredness which disappears as the person comes to grips with his loss. The existence of mental fatigue as such is doubtful, but NEURONS become less efficient after transmitting frequent signals because the TRANSMITTER pool in the cell is temporarily exhausted. (This phenomenon is not the same as the refractive period displayed by all neurons immediately after they transmit an action potential.) Whether or not there is any connection between a decline in neural efficiency and a sense of tiredness, boring or tedious jobs make one emotionally tired.

Lassitude may also accompany the early stages of DEMENTIA, syphilis and other ORGANIC diseases which develop into serious PSYCHOSES.

Today, neurasthenia is infrequently diagnosed as a distinct disorder. It is more often a symptom, especially of those mental conditions associated with ageing (see AGE). Thus, an anxious patient may be both neurasthenic and insomniac (see ANXIETY). DEPRESSION is often accompanied by SLEEP disorders and lack of energy. In all such cases, the treatment is determined by the nature of the underlying disorder.

Monoamine oxidase inhibitors are useful if the patient is anxious. AMPHETAMINES may seem a logical antidote to lassitude, but in most cases, these drugs are unnecessarily strong. Not only are the amphetamines addictive, but they induce sleep loss which must be recouped. Where neurasthenia has been diagnosed as a separate condition, tonics or even placebos (sugar pills with no pharmacological effect) can be of great help.

## NEURON

(Greek: sinew, cord, nerve) a nerve cell.

In 1855, the great German physiologist, Rudolf Virchow, proposed that all living cells descend from other cells. He had built on the hypothesis that the basic unit of living matter is the cell. By the end of the century, microscopic evidence had confirmed these theories for many tissues, but debate still raged over the discontinuity of neurons, especially in the BRAIN. The staining and microscopic techniques then available could not reveal the double membranes separating one cell from another in nervous tissue. The major antagonists were a Spanish anatomist, Santiago Ramon y Cajal, who maintained that neurons are separated by gaps called synapses (=to clasp; so named by the English neurologist, Charles Sherrington in 1897), and an Italian physiologist, Camillo Golgi, who not only held the opposing view, but also invented the first stain which selectively picked out nervous tissue. Cajal used Golgi's stain to argue his case, the correct one, and the two men shared the Nobel Prize for Medicine and Physiology in 1906. They met for the first time at the award ceremony in Oslo and refused to speak!

The neuron consists of three parts: dendrites (dendrite=

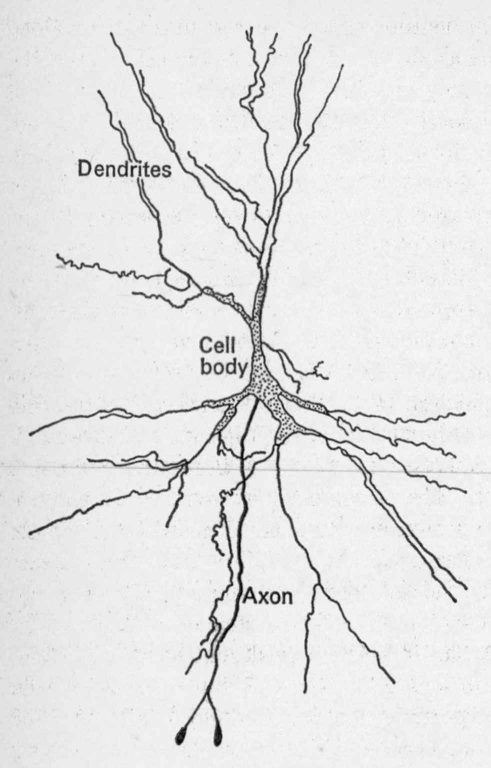


Diagram of a Neuron.

little finger), cell body and axon (=axle, axis). Dendrites are fine processes which taper towards their tips. They may form a dense arborization, like the branches of a tree, and they are studded with spine-like protrusions. The dendrites receive incoming signals from other neurons which form synapses at the spines. However, many CENTRAL NERVOUS SYSTEM (CNS) neurons also receive incoming signals on the cell body itself. The cell body may be bulbous or roughly pyramidal in shape. It contains the nucleus with its chromosomes as well as most of the energy-creating and biosynthetic machinery of the cell. Organelles in the cell body synthesize the TRANSMITTER which the neuron releases after stimulation to carry its signal across the synaptic gap to the next neuron. The transmitter, as well as other substances synthesized by the neuron, is conducted through molecular neurotubules for storage in the tip of a long process called the axon, the third part of the cell. Generally, each neuron has only one axon. Although it may branch, it does so less frequently than the dendrites, and it does not taper. Indeed, the tip of each axon branch consists of a swelling, the axon bulb, where the transmitter is stored in sacks or vesicles. In the peripheral nervous system, especially in the arms and legs, axons of single neurons may be up to three metres in length. Excepting at the point where it emerges from the cell body, the axon hillock, an axon does not itself receive incoming signals from other neurons. Thus, though it looks somewhat like a tree root of which the cell body is the trunk, and the dendrites, branches, an axon conducts away from the cell.

The function of the neuron is to propagate and conduct a signal. It is excitable (see EXCITABILITY) because it reacts to a suitable stimulus. The mechanism of reaction is electrochemical. Incoming signals in the dendrites and cell body are registered as changes in the electrical properties of the membrane surrounding the cell. The membrane acts like a resistor, preventing the flow of ions (charged atoms) into and out of the neuron. In particular, it retains a small number of positively-charged potassium ions inside the cell, but it excludes a far larger number of positively-charged sodium ions in the fluid outside the neuron. Because the ENZYMES and other proteins inside the cell are negatively-charged, and are too large to pass through the membrane, the inside of the cell contains a negative charge with respect to the external fluid. Without a physical barrier, the electrical charge inside and outside the cell would be the same, but the membrane maintains an electrical gradient. The excitability of a neuron is this charged state. It has a resting potential.

When enough excitatory stimulations have been received, the molecular constituents of the membrane at the axon hillock change suddenly. The membrane depolarizes allowing positive sodium ions to flow into the neuron along the electrical gradient. The result is an action potential, a signal, which is propagated along the length of the axon by a continuation of the same process begun at the axon hillock. A few microseconds after the membrane begins to admit sodium ions, however, it also allows potassium ions to leave the cell. Thus, a return to the resting potential begins. The influx of sodium ions is so great that at first the inside of the cell becomes positive with respect to the external fluid, but the outflow of potassium is soon followed by a reversal in the molecular constituents of the membrane, so that sodium ions are now 'pumped' out. After a brief refractory period, during which the cell becomes slightly more negative than normal, it returns to its resting potential. When it is visualized by a flow of electrons across the screen of an oscilloscope, an action potential looks like this:

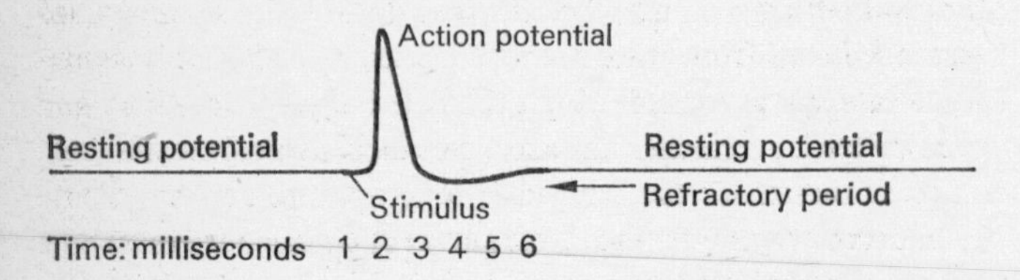


Many axons are myelinated; that is, they are wrapped along their lengths by concentric layers of a fat-like substance called myelin which is secreted by one type of glial cell (see BRAIN). The myelin sheath is interrupted by breaks, called nodes of Ranvier, after the anatomist who discovered them, where the axon itself comes into contact with the surrounding fluid. In myelinated axons, the action potential proceeds by jumps, or saltation, from depolarization at one node to depolarization at the next. It is a faster method of transmission, and all long axons are myelinated. In the periphery, the white, opalescent myelin of many axons together appear as nerves visible to the unassisted eye, and in the CNS, as white matter. Myelinated axons convey signals at speeds up to two hundred feet per second, whereas the smallest, unmyelinated axons conduct at about two feet per second.

When the axon potential reaches the axon bulb, it causes the release of transmitter into the synaptic gap where it diffuses to the dendritic spine, or cell body of the post-synaptic neuron. The number of transmitter molecules released is not known, but it is the same, or very nearly the same, in response to each action potential. There seems to be no reduction in the responsiveness of the neuron membrane over time. In normal circumstances, it continues to depolarize and repolarize without fatigue, no matter how many action potentials it transmits, but the transmitter reservoir in the axon bulb is finite. When it is exhausted, the neuron stops functioning, although it may continue to conduct signals, until more transmitter has been synthesized.

Three extremely important characteristics follow from these properties. First, the neuron is a summing machine. It is not just a relay device, because it must decide when the incoming signals warrant the sending of its own signal. Not only does the neuron add together incoming excitatory messages, but it must subtract incoming inhibitory signals. These negative signals, conveyed by means of inhibitory transmitters, cause the membrane to become hyperpolarized so that it is less responsive to depolarizing stimuli. The molecular nature of this change is not understood. The astonishing summing power of the neuron means that each one plays an active role in determining what happens to a signal.

Second, once an action potential has been propagated at the axon hillock, it cannot be reversed. It is an all-or-nothing response which proceeds inexorably to the axon bulb. Its form and voltage is always the same. Like the on-off state of a unit in a digital computer (or of a light switch), the neuron is either resting or signalling. The frequency with which it signals depends on the intensity of the stimulation. Thus, a brighter light causes more neurons to signal and also causes some of them to signal more rapidly. How much, therefore, is an aspect of the on-off nature of the action potential.

The third characteristic of the neuron concerns not how much but what, where and what is to be done. All neurons send the same message, whether they are recording data from the senses or sending instructions to muscles or glands. Incoming signals from the eyes and ears, as well as outgoing signals to the arms and legs are coded in the same way, as an action potential. All distinctions between sight, hearing and instructions to arms or legs depend on the existence of specific neural pathways. It is the wiring rather than the signal, which carries information about light as against sound, and about running as against striking.

Each neuron is a decision-making unit in a functional pathway, but many neurons also provide links between one or more pathways. In the brain, these linking neurons and a substantial number of those forming pathways either come into existence or take up their fully-developed shapes and positions after birth. In humans, new neurons are not formed after roughly the second year of life, but the actual location of many interneurons and the number of dendrites they develop depend on environmental stimulation, as well as on GENETIC instructions. Thus, both the decision-making behaviour of the neuron and the formation of pathways are plastic in some degree, at least during the early years.

LEARNING, therefore, plays a role in the physical development and interconnections of brain neurons, along with proper food, adequate oxygen and the absence of traumatic phenomena such as atmospheric lead (see BRAIN DAMAGE). The effects of environmental conditions on neural development are still imperfectly understood, and it is not possible to specify optimal conditions for development. Yet there can be no doubt that the efficiency of neurons depends in an important degree on environment.

## NEUROPATHY

Any disorder affecting structures or functions of the peripheral nervous system (see CENTRAL NERVOUS SYSTEM).

Encephalopathy and myelopathy are corresponding words designating disorders of the brain and spinal cord, respectively. Inflammatory disorders of the peripheral nervous system may be separately designated by the term, peripheral neuritis.

Neuropathy is most commonly caused by pressure which impairs neural conductance (see NEURON). For example, a slipped disc (actually, a myelopathy) refers to a cartilagenous disc separating two vertebrae which has swollen, shrunken or otherwise shifted so as to press on the spinal cord. Pressure can lead to localized paralysis as well as pain. Other conditions causing neuropathies include diabetes, circulatory disorders (which reduce blood supply to neurons), poisons such as lead, and various vitamin deficiencies. Thus, pellagra, caused by vitamin $B_3$ (Niacin) deficiency, is in part a neuropathy.

## NEUROSIS

(Greek: *neuron*=nerve+*osis*=disorder) a FUNCTIONAL disorder of the MIND ranging in severity from a state of MENTAL

HEALTH, on the one hand, to PSYCHOSIS, on the other. The patient is said to recognize his illness and to be willing to cooperate in carrying out therapeutic measures.

From the medical standpoint, the term may have only historical interest. FREUD, for example, said that PSYCHOANALYSIS could be used to treat neurosis, but that it was useless against psychosis, because the psychotic patient lacks the power of reason. Conversely, LAING argues that the schizophrenic is behaving rationally within a logical structure, which it is necessary for the therapist to penetrate. Medical literature is surprisingly averse to the definition of neurosis or, indeed, to the differentiation of neurotic conditions. The *Glossary of Mental Disorders*, based on the International Statistical Classification of Diseases, Injuries and Causes of Death, published by the General Register Office in 1970, makes no attempt to define neurosis. Nevertheless, the word is used by doctors to designate a collection of symptoms, including ANXIETY, reactive DEPRESSION, HYSTERIA and NEURASTHENIA. Psychotherapists refer to a person who suffers chronically from one or more of the symptoms of these conditions as a neurotic personality. Familial studies have found evidence of a GENETIC element in neurosis, despite the uncertainty of definition. The range of possible psychosocial causes revealed by studies conducted over eighty years (since publication of *Studies in Hysteria* by Breuer and Freud) is all-embracing. No causal relationships have been demonstrated or agreed, however. In fact, the word neurosis has little more than a vague popular meaning.

Most psychotherapists admit that by and large the neurotic illnesses they treat are conditions about which the patient himself complains. In a significant respect, they are performing the role of a priest. Given that in many cases, neither the disorder nor its treatment can be precisely described (as might be done, for example, with measles), EYSENCK's claim that more neuroses are cured by general practitioners than by psychotherapists is reasonable. In the opinion of Anthony Clare of the Institute of Psychiatry, London, 'the distinction between neuroses and psychoses, while often convenient, is without substance'. (*Psychiatry in Dissent*, p. 66, see *Further Reading*.) It might be added that the distinction between neuroses and mental health, like beauty, is often in the eye of the beholder.

# O

## OBESITY

(Latin: *obesitas*=fat, stout, plump) the condition of having an excess of fat. Note that obesity is not the same as corpulence. A small-muscled person may not be overweight according to statistics for his height and age, but he may be obese because his weight consists of too much fat in relation to the other major body constituents, protein and carbohydrate. Conversely, a weight lifter may have developed muscles which make him overweight, according to statistical averages, but he is not obese. (It is doubtful whether the word corpulence would be applied in this case either.) About 25 per cent of the male body and 30 per cent of the female body should consist of fat. If the body contains more fat as a percentage of body weight, the person is obese. Corpulence is a subjective judgment.

The psychosocial reasons for obesity include the western diet, rich in fats and sugar, and the pressure of advertising, but obesity may also be a symptom of a mental disorder. As such, it is the opposite symptom from ANOREXIA NERVOSA. It is, then, almost always the result of obsessional overeating. The patient knows he is eating more than he needs; he may also be aware that he is eating more of the 'wrong' foods.

Whatever its cause, obesity can seriously shorten the patient's life. Not only does his heart have to work harder, but his blood vessels tend to become clogged by fat-like deposits, adding to the burden on the heart. He becomes more subject to diabetes, degenerative kidney conditions and arthritis.

Like anorexia nervosa, therefore, neurotic (see NEUROSIS) obesity contains the threat of self-destruction. One explanation holds that the problem is emotional. The patient eats because he is unhappy. Yet others refuse to eat under circumstances which appear to be similar, and for a third group, unhappiness has little effect on their food intake. The third group is of course the largest, and is labelled, normal. Statistics on neurotic obesity are extremely unreliable.

It has been suggested that the fault may lie with overweight parents who fatten their children because of their own self-images. Such children then learn to see themselves as 'pleasingly plump', whereas they are actually obese. If the children later become mentally disturbed, the argument suggests, they try to overcome their problem by eating.

It is scarcely surprising that treatment for obesity is difficult. If the patient is so overweight that there is a danger from heart failure, drugs may be used to reduce appetite. AMPHETAMINE or a derivative is still used, but the danger from ADDICTION or a severe psychotic response to the drug may be greater for an obsessional patient than for a person who is not mentally disturbed. Newer drugs such as fenfluramine are safer. Once the acute danger has passed, however, it is necessary to cope with the underlying problem if it can be identified. Traditional PSYCHOTHERAPY, behavioural therapy and HYPNOTISM help some patients. There is always a risk with behavioural therapy and hypnotism that some new symptom will replace overeating. In order to control their food intake, it may be desirable to hospitalize obese patients.

Obesity caused by errors in HORMONE output is not unknown, but it is far less common than is sometimes supposed. There is also new evidence that overeating is accompanied by excessive biosynthesis of a substance chemically related to the natural OPIATE, enkephalin, but it must be admitted that the significance of these data is not clear. A difference in one type of fat in obese patients has also been tentatively identified. It may be that obesity will eventually be treatable with specific drugs. In any case, a doctor will look first for a physical cause of obesity before prescribing any treatment. The great majority of us, however, know what we are doing when we eat too much. We retain self-control, but allow it to slip so often that we endanger our health. Reasonable diet, reasonable exercise and good sense should suffice.

Yet a reasonable diet is admittedly almost as hard to define as MENTAL HEALTH. Individual needs vary over a wide range of body types and environmental conditions. Nor do nutritionists agree about the balance of fats, proteins and carbohydrates which comprise an optimal diet. The body can convert each of the three major food constituents into the other two, and it does so in order to maintain a balance of its own. Given this scientific uncertainty, one is forced to fall back on the dictates of common sense. For example, someone who is fat ought not to eat cream cakes. Carrots, on the other hand, contain almost no fat. They are filling and cheap, raw or cooked. But they do lack protein, and it is possible to get too much of the vitamin A, the visual vitamin (see SENSATION), they contain. Eggs are also cheap and easy to prepare. They contain large amounts of protein, as well as some fat and vitamin A. Add something green for minerals, and you have a reasonably balanced meal. This is not the place for directives on dieting, but rational food consumption is obvious if not easy. Thus, if tea or coffee must be sweetened, one teaspoon of sugar well-stirred will do the work of two that have been poured in. Whether margarine is or is not better for the blood vessels than butter, and there is no scientific agreement on the issue, they are equally fattening. Try to use less. Some people even accept plain yoghurt as a spread. (Plain yoghurt has almost no calories, but the flavoured yoghurts are all sweetened, often with sugar.) Contrary to the common wisdom, the stomach does not shrink, though one's subjective desire for food may decline. But faddist dieting can be expensive, boring and silly. There is no reasonable excuse, for example, for a mother of small children to try to lose ten pounds in a week. A body geared to a certain food intake will suffer a shock from sudden reduction of food not unlike the shock of a road accident.

Exercise is also good for most of us. Again, common sense should be an adequate guide. For example, to lose just one pound by walking, it is necessary to walk 25 miles without eating. Thus, the old saw: the best exercise is pushing yourself away from the table three times a day. If that is too glib, perhaps it might be possible for you to walk around outside for ten minutes after lunch while the others are eating a sweet. Most of us are not accustomed to herding sheep or ploughing a furrow, but we do dodge traffic, walk the dog and play with the children. Exercise is not just push ups or jogging to work; it can also mean climbing the stairs two at a time and hoisting the kids above your head. If you enjoy exercise and games, by all means participate, but eat sensibly afterwards. Obesity is one disorder most of us can cure.

## OBSESSION

(Latin: *obsidere*=to sit down before, besiege, occupy, possess) preoccupation with an idea, EMOTION or movement which compels expression despite subjective resistance. In the absence of subjective resistance – that is, when the patient is not self-critical – the compulsive behaviour (see below) is delusional (see DELUSION).

The typical obsessional patient is middle aged with a history of mental disturbances. He usually complains of ANXIETY, DEPRESSION or NEURASTHENIA, and the obsessional behaviour is one of his symptoms.

Obsessions are classified on the basis of clinical experience into several flexible categories. Compulsive rituals such as handwashing are less complex than *folie de doute*, in which doubt that he has properly fulfilled the ritual leads the patient to reiterate it endlessly. Obsessional phobias, such as the fear of disease or death, differ from the phobias of anxiety because the obsession may shift from one object or idea to another, whereas the phobia associated with anxiety is fixed. Obsessional ruminations may also involve phobias, but they tend to be focused on HYPOCHONDRIA or some emotionally-neutral subject, such as numbers. For example, a patient may write down car registration numbers, or the numbers on bus and train tickets. In rare cases, obsessional symptoms occur independently of any other FUNCTIONAL disorder. They may then come and go in cycles.

If the obsession is symptomatic of anxiety, PSYCHOTHERAPY and social adjustment to reduce stress may bring an end to the symptom. When obsessional behaviour is associated with SCHIZOPHRENIA, the prognosis is good, but treatment is ineffectual. If the patient is depressed, the obsession may be harder to eradicate. Indeed, the treatment of choice is SHOCK THERAPY. The true obsessional state, when it does occur, also has a poor prognosis. As FREUD recognized, PSYCHOANALYSIS is useless. Tricyclic anti-depressants may give some relief, and PSYCHOSURGERY has been used for severe cases.

Note that obsessional symptoms are never associated with HYSTERIA. The two disorders appear to be antithetical, perhaps because of the PERSONALITY traits which underlie them. For example, the hysteric tends to be mercurial and superficially adaptable whereas the obsessive is inflexible and relatively less capable of adaptation.

Once again, the borderline between a normally neat, disciplined and principalled person and one who suffers from a compulsive obsession is not easy to draw. Little progress has been made in understanding the psychosocial origins of such traits, and despite slight evidence of familial histories of obsession, GENETIC influences are doubtful. Obsessive behaviour is too subjective to permit of easy analysis and study.

**OCCIPITAL** See BRAIN

**OCCUPATIONAL THERAPY** See PSYCHOTHERAPY

## OPIATE

One of a class of narcotic (see HYPNOTIC) ANALGESICS, drugs which control pain by dulling CONSCIOUSNESS. All opiates are natural or synthetic substances chemically related to extracts of the opium poppy, *Papaver somniferum*. The oldest and still the most widely used, morphine, was extracted in 1803 by Sertürner, a German chemist. Codeine, also a derivative of *P. somniferum*, is much weaker. Synthetic opiates include methadone (Physeptone; US: Adanon, Dolphine), pethidine (Pamergan, Pethilorfan; US: Meperidine, Demerol), and dextropropoxyphene hydrochloride (Distalgesic, Doloxene, Doloxytal; US: Darvon). Heroin is diacetylmorphine, a semisynthetic compound which is stronger than morphine.

Sir William Osler, the Canadian physician, called morphine 'God's own medicine'. The great British surgeon, Joseph Lister, claimed that he had never seen ill-effects in any of his patients from the use of morphine, but most doctors acknowledge that it is addictive (see ADDICTION), like all opiates. Continued use increases the possibility that the patient will become dependent, but there is rarely any danger from one or two doses. Large amounts of the opiates may depress the hind-brain centres which regulate breathing and heart rate, and can cause coma and death.

An opiate does not eliminate awareness of pain, but it makes pain subjectively bearable. The drugs both sedate and tranquillize. For that reason, they are often used prior to ANAESTHESIA to relax the patient. Heroin may also be used to control the acute pain of terminal cancer.

It has long been recognized that the opiates function in the brain. They do not impair the transmission of pain signals from the periphery. Synthetic drugs which antagonize the effect of morphine, such as nalorphine, tend to make pain worse. The efficiency of the opiates as pain killers suggests that they act by altering the function of NEURONS. The existence of antagonists, moreover, points to the presence of molecules in the neuronal membrane called RECEPTORS, which are employed by the opiate and blocked by the antagonist. (See also TRANSMITTER.) But if the neuronal membrane contains receptors for a drug, which is, after all, a foreign substance, they are probably there to receive some naturally-occurring substance. In 1975, Dr John Hughes and his associates at the University of Aberdeen announced the isolation of an analgesic chemical synthesized in the brain which they called enkephalin. Enkephalin is an inhibitory transmitter. It acts to reduce the response of neurons involved in the sensing of pain.

Though it acts like them, enkephalin differs chemically from the opiates. Because it is a natural substance, furthermore, it should not be addictive, but it should be as effective as morphine or heroin. Research is now being directed towards the use of enkephalin, or a synthetic chemical similar to enkephalin, as a pain killer in place of the opiates. The natural substance may also provide a better understanding of opiate tolerance, dependence, withdrawal and addiction. For example, opiates preempt the enkephalin receptors. Either enkephalin performs some function in addition to analgesia which the opiates cannot do, or the opiates distort the receptors as well as the neuronal response. In either case, and they are not mutually exclusive, the distortion caused by the opiate may require increasing amounts of the drug to maintain the subjective psychological effect it produces. If the distorted neurons are deprived of the drug, they are left without chemical support, as it were, and become subject again to the action of enkephalin. Return to normal chemical inhibition could be the source of the subjective experience of withdrawal. Thus, the opiates are not only amongst the most useful drugs in the doctor's bag, but they are also a key to understanding the subjective experience of pain.

## ORGANIC

1. related to organism, originating in life. 2. a mental disorder caused by or arising out of a demonstrable physical cause such

as DEMENTIA or dyslexia (see -LEXIS). The other major category of mental disorders is FUNCTIONAL.

**OVERREACTION** See IRRITABILITY

# P

**PAEDOPHILIA** See DEVIATION, SEXUAL

**PAIN** See SENSATION

**PAIN KILLER** See ANALGESIC

**PARANOIA**

(Greek: *para*=beside, beyond+*nous*=mind) a mental disorder in which a permanent DELUSION of persecution or grandeur, developed in logical form, coexists with clear thinking and behaviour and without hallucinations (see DREAM).

When the condition was first described in clinical terms by KRAEPELIN about 1920, it was almost immediately argued that paranoia was only seen as a symptom of SCHIZOPHRENIA. Controversy still surrounds the issue, in part because the case notes describing symptoms are inevitably the subjective observations of the doctor.

Paranoia may originate in a physical disease, however, as when a patient recovering from an infection develops the fixed idea that he smells. Occasionally, paranoid symptoms are displayed by patients with ORGANIC BRAIN DAMAGE, due, for example, to alcoholism (see ADDICTION). These patients may become demented (see DEMENTIA). It seems probable, however, that most paranoia is a symptom of schizophrenia or will develop into schizophrenia. Such delusions rarely disappear unless the underlying schizophrenia goes into remission.

Some paranoid delusions, particularly those that originate in middle age, seem to emerge logically from the pre-morbid PERSONALITY of the patient. Others display little, if any, logic. Suppose that an unhappily married man evolves the delusion that his wife is determined to murder him. If this delusion is logical because the man is already dissatisfied with his marriage, then a similar belief held by a happily married man is illogical.

Some psychiatrists hold that paranoia is a manifestation of guilt because of repressed homosexuality (see DEVIATION, SEXUAL), but there is little objective evidence for the theory. The distinction between a common, natural belief that someone has it in for one and paranoia, furthermore, is never easy to make.

**PARIETAL** See BRAIN

**PARKINSONISM** See PSYCHOMOTOR DISEASE

**PAROSMIA** See ANOSMIA

**PAVLOV, IVAN ILYITCH**

Physiologist, best known for his identification of the conditioned reflex (see PSYCHOLOGY). b. Ryazan, Russia, 1849. d. Leningrad, 1936. Theological student until 1870, when he began to study chemistry and physiology at University of St Petersburg. Imperial Medical Academy, St Petersburg, MD (graduand, 1879, dissertation, 1883). Studied in Leipzig and Breslau, 1884–6. Research into cardiac physiology and blood pressure, St Petersburg, 1888–90. Professor of physiology, Imperial Medical Academy and Institute for Experimental Medicine, 1890–1924. *Lectures on the Work of the Principal Digestive Glands*, 1897. Nobel Prize for Physiology, 1904. Worked on laws of conditioned reflex, 1898–1930. Proposed use of rest and quiet for treatment of PSYCHOSES. Introduced theory that language LEARNING is a sequence of conditioned reflexes.

**PELLAGRA** See BRAIN DAMAGE

**PERCEPTION**

(Latin: *perceptio*=a gathering together) awareness of a stimulus.

Perception differs from SENSATION in two respects: with a perception, the sensation actually registers in the CONSCIOUSNESS. We are all continuously flooded with sensations – sights, sounds, feelings, tastes and so on – but not all of them enter awareness. For example, how often do you notice the feel of the air on your face, or the sound of traffic? Perception also differs from sensation because it enrols sensations in a context provided by MEMORY and MOTIVATION. This can be best exemplified if you will close your eyes and imagine paper. Now, what kind of paper have you visualized? Is it newspaper, a book page, writing paper (which kind!), toilet paper, paper towelling? Your perception of the word 'paper' is much more than the sensation 'paper'.

The fact that you could imagine paper in order to perceive it indicates another important aspect of perception. Although we normally mean by the word 'perception of an external phenomenon' it need not be so. We can speak of perceiving a dream or hallucination or an image, without in any way sounding odd. Perception may also be an insight. Consider the perception of the modern Dutch artist, Escher, and indeed, your own perception of his impossible topological world. Thus, any painting is the artist's perception of a subject (i.e. his *in*sight), and it is also an external phenomenon perceived by the viewer. This dual nature of perception underlies an important question in eighteenth-century philosophy: whether a thing exists when it is not perceived. We can recall one famous answer:

> There was a young man who said, 'God
> Must think it exceedingly odd
> If he finds that this tree
> Continues to be
> When there's no one about in the Quad.'

To which the Reverend Ronald Knox added:

> Dear Sir:
> Your astonishment's odd:
> I am always about in the Quad.
> And that's why the tree
> Will continue to be
> Since observed by
> Yours faithfully, GOD.

Today we are more interested in the machinery of perception.

If perception depends on memory and motivation, very little of the mental machinery involved in the process can be inherited. Perhaps only in the case of language has a case been made that perception is in some important degree a function of genetically-determined wiring. Even with language, however, learning and motivation play a massive role. For instance, ordinary speech projected on to the screen of an oscilloscope tube shows up as a continuous wave of light. But it is heard as a sequence of separate syllables, words, phrases and sentences. Consider how hard it is to distinguish words in the speech of a foreigner whose language you have just begun to learn. As to motivation, its effect on language perception can be illustrated by the 'cocktail-party' effect. If you are chatting in a crowded room, you may have difficulty hearing what is said to you in reply. But let someone ten feet away from you speak your name, and there is a good chance you will hear it clearly. This kind of perceptual selectivity extends to all the senses.

In the absence of biophysical information about the machinery of perception, research has been largely behavioural. Broadly speaking, perceptual theories fall into two categories. They are either selective and analytic or constructive and synthetic. The theories are easy to illustrate, but the case for either is almost impossible to prove. Let us first give two illustrations of the selective, analytic hypothesis.

Visual perception depends in the first instance on the machinery of visual sensation, about which a great deal is known. Cells in the visual cortex (see BRAIN) respond selectively to contrasts between light and dark, in the shape of lines that are either still or moving in a specific plane and direction. With such machinery, the brain must select certain lines from the incoming visual data by analyzing the data; for example, — and / are removed from other sensory inputs. With them, it analyzes the letter Z. According to data from experiments with subjects who look at quickly-flashed groups of letters, the Z is seen more rapidly when it is surrounded by Os and Ss and Cs than when it is surrounded by Ts and Xs and Ms. The selection and analysis is facilitated by the distinctive ground.

Or consider the illusion of the Grecian vase published in 1915 by the Danish psychologist, Edgar Rubin. First it is a vase, and then it is faces, or vice versa. This visual reversal depends on neither motivation nor learning, but on whether one selects the figure or the background for analysis.

Greek vase illusion.

These examples illustrate the analytical theory of perception, but could they not also be evidence for the constructionist hypothesis? Whether it is learned or inherited, this theory holds, there is a pattern in the brain into which sensory data fits. As Ulric Neisser, an American psychologist, has written, 'the whole is prior to its parts'. Thus, the letter 'Z' cannot be perceived, despite the fact that visual cortical neurons see — or / lines as a result of genetic determinants, until a Z pattern has been learned. The earliest pattern theory of perception was that of the gestalt (German: form) psychologists (see PSYCHOLOGY), but it was too naive to explain the facts. The gestalt for a Z would also have had to include a z, 𝔷 and 𝒵. Modern pattern theory has generalized such a concept by showing how context – or background – can carry some of the weight. For this, the Greek vase illusion seems to offer evidence.

In fact, Neisser and other cognitive (see COGNITION, PSYCHOLOGY) psychologists have carried their analysis of perception further by postulating the theory of 'analysis through synthesis'. Motivations select the synthesizing patterns into which are fit data from analytical neurons, such as those in the visual system. This theory has been tested by building robots designed to select plastic parts for the construction of model buildings and cars. Either because the sensing and motion mechanisms are not adequately refined or because the theory itself is wrong, such experimental machines have scarcely surpassed the abilities of a two-year-old. Much more success has been obtained with chess-playing computers, but in these situations, the perceptual problems are minimal. Both the board and the pieces are recorded as digital symbols; e.g. on-on =black; on-off=red; off-off=king; on-on-off=queen; and so on. The space relationships and movements of pieces raise logical and memory rather than perceptual problems. Like the illustrations of perceptual behaviour, the computer evidence suggests that the analytical and the synthetic theories of perception are simply two ways of looking at the same phenomena.

It is also possible to analyse perception from the standpoint of how the brain might construct a perception on the basis of the sensory data it receives, and to test the resulting model on a computer. Thus, a visual image might be built up if the brain selected an axis of a figure either in relation to the force of gravity or in accordance with relative length. Using that axis as a preliminary pattern for a figure in space, the brain decomposes the figure in successive steps to obtain finer and finer detail in relation to a new axis of orientation at each step. It would also build in the concave and convex angles formed by the successive axes. This modern form of pattern theory sounds complex, but it can be shown by computer testing to give fast and accurate results. It has the added merit that it excludes for the time being the complicating issue of whether patterns are learned or inherited. (See figure on page 168).

Apart from an understanding of the nature of perception in general, the relevance of physical sensation may have immediate clinical value. Thus, it is known that the ear hears some 16,000 wavelengths or tones, but the brain learns to perceive meaning in the most frequently heard median wavelengths without the extremes. This fact has been applied by the British psychologist, Richard Gregory, to the development of a new kind of hearing aid. Instead of magnifying all sound equally, the new device magnifies only the median wavelengths and tends to eliminate the extremes. The noise background so

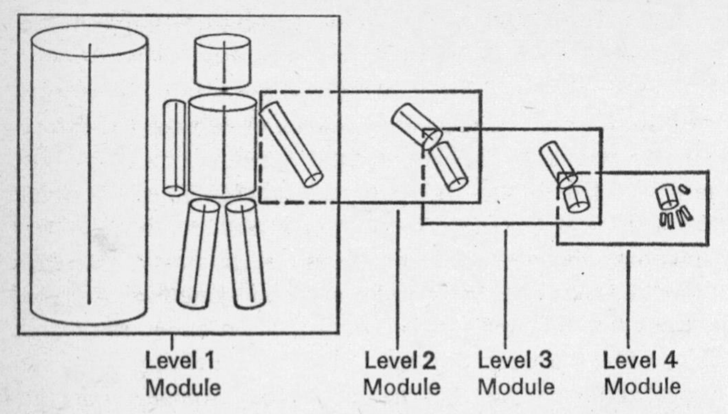


Theoretical decomposition and reconstruction of an image. Within each rectangle is shown on the left the 'model axis' for that level of description and on the right the way in which the model is broken up into component parts. The level 1 module represents the whole object, and the finer details of the arm, forearm and hand are represented respectively at levels 2, 3 and 4. At each level other than level 1, there would of course be many other modules representing for example the decomposition of the head, the nose and so on. (*Nature, Vol. 278, 29 March 1979*)

disturbing to the user of older hearing aids is much reduced. The device is now being manufactured for the British National Health Service. Physical aspects of visual perception are also being used to direct the treatment of squint in children and to help the blind to read. In addition to such practical clinical considerations, moreover, the nature of perception has theoretical importance, for example, in the understanding of SCHIZOPHRENIA. The schizophrenic patient gives ample evidence that he suffers from distorted perceptions, but to isolate the causes of distortion, it may be necessary to know more about perception itself.

**PERIPHERAL NERVOUS SYSTEM (PNS)** See CENTRAL NERVOUS SYSTEM

**PERSEVERATION**

Repetition of an activity without adequate external stimulus. The behaviour is usually a symptom of ORGANIC brain disease such as DEMENTIA or epilepsy (see PSYCHOMOTOR DISEASE), or a speech defect (see -PHASIS).

Thus, perseveration may occur in speech or in movement. It indicates that the patient has run up against a barrier imposed by his illness. For example, dements may reply to the question, 'How are you?': 'Didn't sleep well.' All later questions in the interview will then be answered with the same words. Movement perseveration may sometimes be broken into if the task is approached from a different angle. For example, if the patient perseverates in the process of sitting down in a chair, turning the chair slightly may permit him to complete the movement successfully.

## PERSONALITY

(Latin: *persona*=a mask used by an actor, an actor) the collection of characteristics and behaviour that distinguishes one animal from another of the same species. The word is a popular synonym for CONSCIOUSNESS and MIND, but it is perhaps more significant as the embodiment of difference, uniqueness.

In the history of PSYCHIATRY, the meaning of personality has become restricted to include only emotional and motivational aspects of the mind; intellectual aspects have been excluded because it is held that mental disease, distinguished by emotional and motivational disorders, ought to be differentiated from mental subnormality arising out of congenital or accidental causes (usually grouped as psychopathy; see HEALTH, MENTAL; RETARDATION). Thus, idiocy and mongolism are not treatable conditions within the overall context of psychiatry, and they are characterized by subnormal intellect. This distinction between disease and subnormality has been of great importance from both social and psychological standpoints; for example, an idiot is no longer mistaken for a malingerer, on the one hand, or a psychotic, on the other. Yet EMOTION and INTELLIGENCE are facets of the same brain, and if the word 'personality' has any meaning, it must include both.

Psychiatrists such as LAING and the American, Thomas Szasz, question the reality of mental illnesses as diseases with physiological aspects, thus confirming the tendency to set them apart from psychopathy. In doing so, they draw attention to the baffling fact that the patient has succumbed to environmental pressures which most people manage to withstand. This is the central problem of psychiatry, and it seems to be soluble only in terms of a physical mind. In other words, the most useful model is one which supposes that FUNCTIONAL disorders occur when an experience triggers an ORGANIC malfunction. For example, research into the biochemical changes underlying organic disorders such as DEMENTIA and Parkinsonism (see PSYCHOMOTOR DISEASE) reveals information about chemicals that may also be abnormal in a functional disorder such as SCHIZOPHRENIA. The value of drugs and other physical treatments, like SHOCK THERAPY, moreover, has brought the majority of British and American psychiatrists to accept that psychopathy differs from personality disorders only in respect to the balance between the environmental and the organic factors which cause them. Most psychiatrists no longer seek to separate intellect from emotion and motivation, but treat the patient's personality as a whole.

Doctors, including psychiatrists, are concerned with personalities which seem to be subject to mental disorders. If there is a psychopathic personality, it must have been shaped by inherited or congenital physical characteristics. Mental diseases are studied from the GENETIC standpoint to determine whether there is a discoverable error in the genes which can be controlled or perhaps even corrected. (Prospective parents whose children may be at risk from the defective genes could also be advised accordingly.) But so far, most mental disorders lack clear genetic components. Either such genes do not exist, or not one but several gene-determined traits are operating to increase the risk. That is, such people are more at risk from environmental circumstances – for example, a socially-disadvantaged family background – than people who lack some or all of these gene-determined traits. People who are at risk, according to this reasoning, have personality characteristics which might be observed before symptoms of disease appear. Indeed, there is evidence that abnormal personality factors are to be found in neurotic (see NEUROSIS) conditions such as ANXIETY, reactive DEPRESSION and MELANCHOLIA, and in psychoses such as endogenous depression and schizophrenia. There may also be addictive (see ADDICTION) and even epileptic personalities. It is not just the functional disorders which are thought to occur more frequently in personalities at risk, but organic diseases such as dementia may also be predicted from personality traits, which appear superficially to be irrelevant. The existence of personalities which are subject to mental disorders seems likely, but the characteristics of such personalities are at best controversial.

Trait differences are founded in both genetic and environmental circumstances, but their relationship to mental health is not clear. For example, it is said that tall, thin, fair people are more anxious than short, fat, dark people, but there is no good evidence for such a classification. Nor is there support for the popular view that sensitivity, nervousness and an artistic bent more often characterize actors than sports persons. But such ideas are not just the product of the popular imagination. ADLER made the inferiority feeling central to his psychoanalytic system. EYSENCK says that he can distinguish between extraverted and introverted personalities (see EXTRAVERSION, TESTS), and that the latter is more subject to neurosis. Many of their colleagues, however, have not found these classifications useful for the treatment of their patients. The possibility that there can be a prophylactic psychiatry based on recognition of a psychopathic personality remains remote until the physical bases of personality are better understood.

**PERVERSION** See DEVIATION, SEXUAL

**-PHASIS**

(Greek: speech) a combining form meaning speech, writing and language use in general, used with one of two prefixes.

**Aphasia:** impairment or loss of one or more linguistic capabilities such as the ability to speak, to write (also AGRAPHIA), to read (also alexia or dyslexia; see -LEXIS) and to understand speech or signs.

**Dysphasia:** impairment of speech, including the ordering of words, usually due to physical damage to the dominant hemisphere of the BRAIN. The word 'aphasia' is now more commonly used to designate speech disorders both of expression and of understanding. Disorders of writing and reading are designated separately, as are impairments in the use of non-verbal symbols such as numbers (ACALCULIA) and musical notation (amusia).

Speech disorders are so noticeable that they have been of great assistance in the diagnosis of disease. For example, a patient may suffer either from a poverty of speech sounds, or he may find it impossible to understand the meaning and significance of spoken words. In the former instance, the patient knows what he wants to say but is unable to say it. There is little or no failure of understanding. The damage underlying the disorder is in the forward portion of the language zone, known as Broca's area. Occasionally, the patient may be almost completely dumb, in which case the damage probably extends into the white matter (see NEURON) connecting Broca's area to the motor cortex. Instructions to muscles controlling the mouth and throat cannot get through. Physical examination of such patients usually reveals a tumour or damage caused by a stroke (see BRAIN DAMAGE). Dements often display this impoverishment of speech early in the development of the disease (see DEMENTIA).

In the second kind of aphasia, the patient may display no speech impairment, but his speech is, nevertheless, without sense because he is failing to understand what has been said to him, or indeed, to remember and understand what he himself has said. Thus, his short-term MEMORY may also be impaired. The damage affects a region called Wernicke's area, behind Broca's on the cortical surface. In rare cases, the patient seems to be unable to understand even the words he produces, a kind of deafness which may be due to damage deeper in the cortex. Conduction aphasia is similar to Wernicke's aphasia, in that speech is often inappropriate, though it is only slightly impaired. The patient also finds it hard to repeat words and to read aloud. His comprehension of verbal and written language is normal, however. Conduction aphasia is caused by damage to the nervous connections between Broca's and Wernicke's areas.

Aphasia may also be global, due to more extensive damage to the language hemisphere. Both speech and understanding are impaired. Partial losses of expression and comprehension reflect more diffuse damage to the connection between the language areas and other less clearly-defined cortical regions, the association areas, where COGNITION and PERCEPTION may occur. For example, the patient understands and produces speech normally, except for the naming of objects and people (anomia or amnestic aphasia). He retains the ability to write names, showing that his memory is not affected, but the links between memory and speech seem to be disconnected.

Even severe aphasics may be retrained if the patient is determined to recover. The prognosis is best if the damage is in Broca's area, affecting expression, and poorest if Wernicke's area is involved, when there may have been loss of comprehension. Even adult patients who have lost all power of expressive speech can be trained to use a new language, such as the American Sign Language, which is based on the hand language of the deaf-and-dumb. One severely wounded American war veteran quickly learned the American Sign Language, though he showed no recovery of the ability either to use or to understand English. Retraining children who have speech disorders is normally simpler and faster because the child's brain is more plastic.

**PHOBIA** See ANXIETY

**PIAGET, JEAN**

Psychologist whose work on child development has identified major stages and phases of growth (see LEARNING). b. Neuchatel, Switzerland, 1896. Article on albino sparrow published, 1906. Article on molluscs published, 1911. University of Neuchatel, DSc, 1918. Research in psychology, Sorbonne, 1919–20. Director, Institut J. J. Rousseau, Geneva. Professor of psychology, University of Geneva, 1929–54. Director, International Centre for Epistemology, University of Geneva, 1955. *Language and Thought of the Child*, 1926. *Judgment and Reasoning in the Child*, 1928. *The Origin of Intelligence in Children*, 1954. *The Early Growth of Logic in the Child*, 1964. (For a review of Piaget's writings and theories with an introduction by Piaget: J. H. Flavell, *The Developmental Psychology of Jean Piaget*, see *Further Reading*).

**PICK'S DISEASE** See DEMENTIA

**PITUITARY** See BRAIN, HORMONE

**'POST-PARTEM BLUES'**

DEPRESSION experienced by women soon after childbirth. More properly called post-natal depression.

The condition is common and may be accompanied by silent weeping and ANXIETY. Mothers of later children may express dislike for the newborn infant.

Most post-natal depression reflects an emotional reversal: the quiet hospital routine following the tension and excitement of delivery. The new mother understandably feels emotional as well as physical relief, especially if she has been secretly fearful of childbirth. In such cases, the depression lasts a few hours and then disappears. A few women suffer from more serious PERSONALITY problems, however, which seem to crystallize around the newborn infant. The father's sensitive and affectionate response is always important to the rapid relief of post-natal depression, but it is imperative if there are underlying difficulties. The patient may then also require PSYCHOTHERAPY. In any case, post-partem blues should neither be laughed at and dismissed nor over-dramatized.

**-PRAXIS**

(Greek: action) a combining form meaning action or purposeful muscular coordination, used with two prefixes.

**Apraxia:** the inability to carry out suitable and purposeful movements in the absence of paralysis, sensory loss or failure of muscular coordination (ataxia). Thus, the patient cannot stick out his tongue on command. He may open his mouth and make inappropriate faces, and then after the passage of time, he does stick out his tongue with no effort. APHASIA is a special example of apraxia.

**Dyspraxia:** partial loss of the power to coordinate movement. The term is not often used because ataxia or apraxia are preferred.

Either understanding of the desired movement or the capacity to perform it may be impaired. In the latter case, either the body fails to sense the position of limbs (see SENSATION), or the BRAIN is unable to make use of the data. Strokes and tumours (see BRAIN DAMAGE) are the most frequent causes of apraxia, but it may also follow diffuse degeneration of brain tissue, such as that which takes place in DEMENTIA.

**PRESENILE DEMENTIA** See DEMENTIA

**PRIMAL THERAPY** See TRAUMA

**PSYCHE** See MIND

**PSYCHIATRY**

(Greek: *psyche*=organ of thought+*iatreia*=healing) the branch of medicine concerned with prevention and treatment of diseases and disorders of the MIND.

For the purpose of defining psychiatry, disease differs from disorder in the matter of cause: the causes of disease include some physical malfunction, for example, damaged NEURONS or a biochemical imbalance. The causes of a disorder are apparently social and lack known physiological factors. In these terms, reactive DEPRESSION is a disorder and endogenous depression, a disease. The distinction is fluid and highly controversial, but it is introduced to make room for the range of mental illnesses (see HEALTH, MENTAL) that makes up the psychiatrist's practice.

Because of this uncertainty about causes, psychiatry itself is riven by argument. One group of psychiatrists holds in contempt another with a different interpretation of mental illness, and the debate often descends to name calling. The pages of *The Lancet* reveal that as recently as the 1860s, before the germ theory of disease began to explain the causes of the abscesses and inflammations doctors often saw, general medical disputation was also conducted at the same level of invective.

Although the treatment of mental illness is of course much older, psychiatry as a branch of medicine came into existence less than a century ago after the classificatory work of KRAEPELIN identified two diseases: manic depression and dementia praecox (SCHIZOPHRENIA). Thenceforward, physicians could deal with these diseases as entities rather than random symptoms. It is not surprising that so young a discipline should still be subject to controversy, and the uncertainty in psychiatry is still essentially about whether Kraepelin's classifications were justified!

The controversy originally involved four more or less distinctive schools: Kraepelin's, the so-called localizers, the psychobiologists and the psychotherapists. The localizers, led by Karl Wernicke, a German neurologist (see lateralization of

BRAIN function, -PHASIS) and the great British doctor, Hughlings Jackson (see epilepsy under PSYCHOMOTOR DISEASE), sought to identify parts of the brain responsible for specific behaviour. For example, Jackson discovered the epileptic focus and suggested that the seizure resulted from a spreading of energy around the focus – a remarkably accurate description. These workers were much closer to neurology than to psychiatry, in that they tried to identify the neuronal (see NEURON) source of mental disorders. Thus, they were well ahead of their time.

The psychobiologists looked to Adolph Mayer, an American psychiatrist, who held that the individual is unique. They opposed all attempts to group symptoms under the rubric of a disease name as Kraepelin had proposed. In effect, they argued that each patient had a different disease and required a singular treatment. This approach denies the existence of a medical field called psychiatry, a grave weakness if the laudatory objective of helping many patients is to be possible. Psychobiology is the spiritual origin of contemporary 'anti-psychiatry'.

PSYCHOTHERAPY originally meant only one thing, PSYCHOANALYSIS. However, at about the same time that FREUD and his followers became international figures, in the Soviet Union the great PAVLOV introduced a system of psychotherapy based on his work with the conditioned reflex. Its principle elements were rest and a primitive form of behaviour therapy which aimed to retrain the mentally-ill patient by restructuring his reflexes. The system is still the foundation for Soviet psychiatry, and of course it is increasingly influential in the west.

All of the early psychiatric schools have their followers today, but most practitioners in Great Britain and the United States are eclectic. The same doctor may treat an hysterical patient with HYPNOTISM, free association and dream analysis in a manner of which Freud would have approved. He may treat an anxious patient with rest and behaviour therapy, a manic depressive patient in terms of a disease entity which requires rest, psychotherapy, drugs and SHOCK THERAPY. He will almost certainly treat all three patients as individuals with unique environmental and GENETIC histories. Psychiatrists are trained as doctors before they specialize. Psychiatry is grounded in physical medicine, but our relative ignorance about the brain as compared with the heart or the kidneys forces psychiatrists to use techniques which lack rigorous scientific proof of their efficacy.

Because of this fact, and because many psychiatrists are less honest with themselves and their patients (or the families of their patients) than they should be, psychiatry is sometimes dubious and often misunderstood. The most sustained attack, and in the long run, probably the most effective, has come from inside the field. Anti-psychiatry is led by men like the Scot, LAING, and the American, Thomas Szasz. They insist that the patient is not ill unless he believes himself to be ill, as is normally the case in physical medicine. They attack the identification of diseases by doctors when the patient denies that he is ill, and above all, they attack the use of therapies, especially drugs, shock treatment and PSYCHOSURGERY, without the patient's consent. In effect, they deny the existence of the most serious psychotic conditions because in these conditions, the patient is incapable of reasoned self-awareness. In their view, it is up to the doctor to understand the symptoms and not to impose his own will. Thus, Szasz's phrase 'the myth of mental illness', refers to what he considers to be improper and unethical behaviour by psychiatrists who invent a disease entity such as schizophrenia in order to explain and treat a unique collection of symptoms. Mental disease is a construct of the psychiatrist acting on behalf of the community which is embarrassed, annoyed or frightened by certain of its members. In the Soviet Union, such people include political dissidents. In the United States, one thinks of such former convicts as Patti Hearst. According to the anti-psychiatrists, people who measure above average on intelligence TESTS sense the hostility about them, and those who are less intelligent respond to contradictory and inimical behaviour. In either case, they behave abnormally, but unless there is a clear ORGANIC complaint, the patient is not ill. Thus, Laing says that a patient does not *have* schizophrenia. He *is* schizophrenic.

The role of the therapist is to win the patient's trust by taking him seriously. He must enter the schizophrenic's tortured and divided world. There, his training may enable him to unravel the tangled web of the patient's warring personality. With this knowledge, the doctor may be able to lead the patient to a point where the self recognizes the subsidiary selves with which it has become entangled and assigns each of them a role in his new adjustment to life. The patient is never wrong. He may be misguided, confused, fearful, unable to perceive the distinction between common reality and his own, but he is not mad.

Laing, who is a brilliant stylist, has described one 26-year-old schizophrenic patient:

> 'The fact that her self-being was not assembled in an all-over manner, but was split into various partial assemblies or systems, allows us to understand that various functions which presuppose the achievement of personal unity ... could not be present in her. ...
>
> In Julie, each partial system could be aware of objects, but a system might not be aware of the processes going on in another system which was split off from it. For example, if, in talking to me, one system was "speaking", there seemed to be no overall unity within her whereby "she" as a unified person could be aware of what this system was saying or doing.
>
> In so far as reflective awareness was absent, "memory", for which reflective awareness would seem to be prerequisite, was very patchy. All her life seemed to be contemporaneous ...' (*The Divided Self*, p. 197; see *Further Reading*)

The anti-psychiatrists have taken the logical, rational element so essential to psychoanalysis and elevated it to dogma. Laing's later inclination towards the mystical may be a result of his own over-involvement in the lives and disorders of his patients, because it is totally absent from his earliest and most influential writing. Similarly, the critique of psychiatry by Szasz achieved its force from its commitment to the Hippocratic position that doctors must treat only with the informed consent of their patient. Neither Szasz nor Laing, curiously, make allowances for the undeniable fact that medicine is an art grounded in science. Amongst the most intuitive of men, they deny the essential role of intuition in treatment. Thus, even the general practitioner must intuit the degree to which his patient's stomach ulcer is PSYCHOSOMATIC. The weakness of anti-psychiatry is precisely its laudatory commitment to rationality. Yet it has fortunately influenced all of psychiatry by forcing doctors to re-examine their shibboleths. In a field where treatment and improvement are not only empirical, but often extremely relative, dogma has no role.

Like the psychobiologists before them, the anti-psychiatrists throw the baby out with the bath. Hundreds of thousands of very sick people – one out of five hospitalized patients in Great Britain and the United States – need help now. Even Laing and Szasz practise psychotherapy, and most of their colleagues refuse to exclude from their armouries the whole range of therapeutic weapons.

Psychobiology has, however, provided a framework for a new approach, orthomolecular psychiatry. The name means 'the correct molecule'. It was coined by the great American biochemist, Linus Pauling, in 1968 to describe a therapy based on discovering the biochemical error underlying mental disease and correcting it with drugs. Pauling and many others have been impressed by the confused but mounting evidence that schizophrenia has a physical cause, like epilepsy. Pauling's own work on the value of high doses of vitamin C fits into experiments with vitamin therapy of schizophrenia, although the effectiveness of the treatment is at best controversial. Orthomolecular psychiatry attempts to supply the clear distinction between mental disease and psychosocial disorder which anti-psychiatrists and psychobiologists have implicitly demanded.

## PSYCHOANALYSIS

A system of treatment based on the ideas of the Viennese physician, Sigmund FREUD and his associates and followers, which aims to reveal the unconscious experiences and MOTIVATIONS that have disordered the patient's EMOTIONS and behaviour.

The existence of an unconscious MIND is the core of psychoanalysis, for it is the content of the Unconscious which treatment will reveal. The remarkable force of Freudian psychology, however, arose from the imaginative structure which Freud elaborated to explain the function of the Unconscious, the origins of mental illness and his treatment methods.

The idea of an unconscious mind directing our energies

existed long before Freud. Indeed, the widespread notion of demonic possession is no more than an early attempt to understand and explain the dark powers that cause us to disregard God's ordinances – to swear, steal, fornicate and murder – and occasionally, to go mad. According to the Roman Catholic Church, the practice of dispossession is part of the treatment a priest may use to guide and protect his flock.

Freud was a rationally-oriented Viennese Jew, immersed in the prevailing Judaeo-Christian ethics and trained as a doctor. He replaced the ancient devils with a nineteenth-century conception allegedly amenable to reasoned analysis and manipulation. It was left to one of his most important associates, JUNG, to emphasize and elevate the dark non-rational element underlying Freud's vision of the mind.

In addition to the Unconscious, the mind contains the Conscious and the Preconscious. The Conscious is the ordinary, waking mind that perceives SENSATIONS, engages in thought and reasoning, utilizes MEMORY and emotion and directs action accordingly. The Preconscious is a kind of antechamber between Conscious and Unconscious containing elements emerging from the Unconscious but not yet apparent in the Conscious. Thus, dream thoughts, the actual aural and visual content of dreams, exist in the Preconscious. They have escaped from the Unconscious when the Ego lets down its guard in SLEEP.

The Ego is a part of the PERSONALITY, the part that we and others recognize as the identifiable 'I'. It normally controls the personality, determining the motives that direct mental and physical action. The Ego contains the censor which restrains or, when necessary, represses the second element of personality, the Id. Again, Freud has taken for the Id a complex and ancient phenomenon – the belief in spirit, extra-sensory perception and primitive instincts – which he has redefined rationally so that he can manipulate it. That is, the Id must be forced to reveal its mysterious cargo under controlled circumstances, so that its hold over the disordered personality can be weakened and the Ego restored to power.

The third element of the personality, the Superego, contains the body of moral precepts which the individual learns from his parents, teachers and religious instructors. If the Id is the instinctual, pre-learning element of the personality, the Superego is the social element, and appears as the child becomes a reasonable being. Its role is to advise and assist the Ego to censor the Id and regulate conscious behaviour.

Thus, there are three elements of the mind and three facets of the personality, but they are not exactly conterminous. The Ego is aware of the Conscious, the Preconscious and at least the more proximal layer of the Unconscious. The Superego is primarily to be found in the Preconscious, but it is apparent in the Conscious, and in so far as certain moral precepts such as self-preservation are practically instinctual, the Superego also exists in the Unconscious. Only the Id is entirely submerged in the Unconscious, isolated from the world of experience and dependent entirely upon thoughts and experiences repressed into the Unconscious for its awareness of the avenues open to it to assert its dominance over the Ego. Thus, the Id is represented as struggling to escape, like volcanic magma, and the Ego fights to prevent the eruption of irrational forces so as to maintain the stability of the personality.

Throughout his life, Freud continually redefined these concepts. The elements of the mind were not to be seen as spaces filled with contents, and yet he could never disperse this mechanical image they evoke. Similarly, the three elements of personality were attempts to characterize the different classes of motivations and activities in the brain; despite their distinctions, however, they were never meant to be separate elements, much less entities with their own functional rules. Yet Freud's model was beset by the nut-and-bolt rationalism that had built the machines underpinning the prosperity of his world.

Nevertheless, the driving force of the Freudian psyche is instinct. Prior to 1910, Freud enunciated the pleasure principle, the instinct to achieve satisfaction, especially sexual fulfilment. At first, the infant is polymorphously perverse; that is, he obtains gratification from sucking, bowel movements, body warmth and all other tactual experiences. Only as he grows does the gratification of sexual urges become distinguishable from the satisfaction of hunger, for example. At the same time, the normal child learns that sexual gratification is limited to the genital regions. Like Freud's mechanistic mental model, the word 'perverse' and the physical delimitation of sexually-sensitive regions of the body reflect the values of the world in which he worked.

Too often, however, the child's development is not normal. Perhaps because he is compelled to accept restrictions, to abandon polymorphous sexuality, it never is. But if the process is made difficult by traumatic (see TRAUMA) experiences that threaten his sex, security or safety, the damage may be serious. The forbidden experience is repressed into the Unconscious where it becomes a part of the Id and threatens the normal activity of the Ego.

The notion of the Oedipus COMPLEX came later in Freud's life. It is a special case of sexual frustration leading to neurotic impairment. Instead of losing his infantile attachment to his mother, the child maintains it and becomes sexually jealous of his father. This forbidden emotion henceforward distorts his ability to fulfil himself sexually.

Freud considered that the pleasure principle is a rational instinct in the Darwinian sense that it contributes to the adaptability of the individual and the perpetuation of the species. However, he also saw in his patients evidence of a self-destructive urge. Depressed patients threatened to kill themselves, and some did. Perhaps it was the horror of the world war that drove Freud to enunciate the death wish, a second instinct which is also universal. Normally, it is caged by a healthy Ego, but if the bars are lowered, the death wish may escape.

This sketch of the Freudian psyche demonstrates that psychoanalysis seeks to treat mental disorders by restoring the strength of the Ego, the power of reason. The object of the patient's self-revelation is abreaction, an emotional as well as an intellectual reliving of the trauma that had distorted the psyche. To obtain abreaction, Freud had to catch the Unconscious unaware, to force it to let slip the aberrant content hidden within it. Hypnotism, the first technique he used, never satisfied Freud. He said he did not do it well. He substituted free association. Within the first decade of his practice, moreover, he perceived that dreams might also have significance. Thereafter, Freud used dreams and free association in tandem. Although he held that some dream symbols may be widely-shared, their significance for therapy still depended on the patient's experiences. It was left to Jung to develop the elaborate structure of a universal dream language often mistaken for Freudian.

As his clinical experience grew, Freud realized that abreaction might seem to be just within the analyst's grasp only to slip away out of reach again. The patient's Unconscious seemed to find some totally unexpected dodge to avoid revelation of the repressed memory. Thus the patient would at first transfer his neurotic object to the analyst, or he might develop some block to the therapeutic process which took the form of a physical illness (see PSYCHOSOMATIC). He might project his ambivalent (see AMBIVALENCE) behaviour on to some other person (possibly the analyst) or thing. Freud devoted much of his later life to the attempt to understand the subterfuges of the embattled Unconscious.

What Freud never seemed to realize was that his search for these subterfuges hid the failure of psychoanalysis as a therapeutic technique and, by implication, the inadequacy of his elaborate psychic model. If it is always possible to explain failure by finding some new device in the patient's mind which prevents abreaction, then the psychoanalytic system is infinitely flexible. But science is based on the principle that the shortest distance between two points is a straight line: if it is necessary to make too many amendments to a theory of NEUROSIS, then there is probably something wrong with the theory. Psychoanalysis, moreover, demands of the patient that he participate willingly in the long, painful and often expensive process. Freud recognized that for this reason, PSYCHOSIS could not be treated psychoanalytically. Typically, he found yet another stratagem to explain this shortcoming. He suggested that psychosis must be physically-based illness, and that it does not originate in repressed memories from infancy. In this at least, he may have been right.

Yet Freud knew that all mental illness had to be physically grounded in the brain. He assumed that psychoanalysis could cope with neurotic illness, but explicitly stated that his therapy was a stopgap. When a better understanding of the brain permitted, Freud believed that physical medicine might cure all mental disease. The brilliance and the strength of his imaginative system derived from its grounding in the rational, mechanistic beliefs of nineteenth-century medicine.

Freud's two most important associates, Adler and Jung,

respectively exploited the rational and the irrational elements in his psychic model. Adler's enunciation of the inferiority feeling led him to the conclusion that mental illness was chiefly caused by the patient's misapprehension of his own skills and capacities. The Unconscious might play a role in this mistake, but it was far less important than the patient's Conscious self-image. It followed that sexual repression was of far less significance, and that dreams had little role in Adlerian psychoanalysis (see also PSYCHOTHERAPY).

Jung, on the other hand, elevated the Unconscious to a force of such prominence and generality that every Unconscious was said to be linked somehow with every other. Jung believed that there is a race consciousness embodied by the individual Unconscious. Although he had travelled in Africa, his patients were almost entirely Zurich burghers and their wives and children. How he managed to draw from so restricted a sample knowledge of the minds of blacks and Orientals, Eskimos and Red Indians remains one of psychology's great unsolved mysteries. Nevertheless, he found in the collective Unconscious symbols of the crimes of incest, murder and general devilment which beset mankind. Libido is a Freudian term referring to the energies and emotions relating to love and sexuality. Jung broadened its meaning to include striving and creativity, thus associating aesthetic expression with the most primitive motivations in the human personality. It is hardly surprising that although Freud regretted Adler's defection, they remained professional colleagues, whereas the break with Jung was total.

Of course psychoanalysis still has its practitioners, but criticism of the system has forced them to become more eclectic. They have always resisted statistical evaluation of their practice, claiming that each patient is so different that their therapies have had to vary accordingly. Nor is it easy to see how independent evaluation would be possible. Psychoanalysis requires the exclusive and lengthy contact of patient and analyst in silence and secrecy. Perhaps of equal importance in the decline of psychoanalysis, however, is its expense. Psychotherapy offering faster treatment and amenable to group practice is often preferred.

**PSYCHOBIOLOGY** See PSYCHOLOGY

**PSYCHODRAMA** See PSYCHOTHERAPY

**PSYCHOLOGICAL ADDICTION** See ADDICTION

**PSYCHOLOGY**

The study of the MIND by observing, classifying and generalizing from the behaviour of the organism. The history of psychology consists of the different ways in which psychologists have looked at behaviour, only one of which is labelled Behaviourism (see below).

The science of mind, as psychology is sometimes called, began to differentiate out of the broader fields of physiology and philosophy during the nineteenth century. At first, some physiologists studying the nervous system became particularly interested in the functions of sensory apparatus. Thus, the German scientists, Herman Ludwig von Helmholtz, G. T. Fechner and Ewald Hering investigated the mechanisms underlying sight and hearing. Helmholtz's assistant at Heidelberg was Wilhelm Wundt (1832–1920; see KRAEPELIN) who approached the study of SENSATION from the standpoint of why we perceive in the way we do (see PERCEPTION). Wundt's first book, *Contributions to the Theory of Sensory Perception*, appeared in 1862. Thenceforward, he worked largely by introspecting his own perceptions, aiming to elucidate a full-scale philosophy of human behaviour. Because he recognized that the individual's cultural background influences the way he perceives, Wundt is often credited with laying the foundations of social psychology.

Wundt's contemporary in the United States, JAMES, began work as a doctor, but like Wundt, his interest was more philosophical than medical. James directed his attention to human systems of beliefs, beginning with rational consciousness and including religions. He also based his observations largely on his own introspective power rather than on clinical experience or experiment.

The monumental studies by these two figures established psychology as a new field of research. Their successors turned to memory and movement, among other brain functions which are less easily identified and assessed than sensation. Hughlings Jackson (1835–1911) and Sir David Ferrier in England sought to localize functions of the human brain by observing the effects of brain injury and surgical intervention on behaviour. In the United States, THORNDYKE and R. M. Yerkes (1876–1956) experimented with animal behaviour. They watched animals in mazes or boxes or other conditions of confinement, and counted their responses to different stimuli. Whereas Wundt and James had accepted data from introspection in place of or even in opposition to experimental data, the next generation made experiment the core of their work.

As a result of his experiments with cats in puzzle boxes, Thorndyke proposed two laws of LEARNING. The Law of Exercise states that repeating a given situation to produce a given response strengthens the association between stimulus and response. In other words, practice makes perfect. The Law of Effect added to the Law of Exercise the dimension of satisfaction: if a specific response produces a good effect, it will tend to be repeated; if an adverse effect, it will not. The laws are the foundation of associationism, the forerunner of behaviourism.

At about the same time, PAVLOV published his famous experiments with dogs. Like other animals, dogs salivate when they are given food. The salivation is an unconditioned response. Pavlov rang a bell as he presented food to an experimental animal. After several such presentations, he rang the bell but did not give the dog food. He measured the saliva in the dog's mouth and found that it increased in the same amount in response to the bell alone as it had in response to the bell with food. Thus, the bell produced salivation in what Pavlov called a conditioned response. The dog had learned that the bell meant food was coming. Later, Pavlov measured the time required to extinguish the conditioned response as the dog learned that the bell did not necessarily signal the advent of food. He also experimented with intervals between bell and food, and with patterns of repetition of the bell and the food stimuli. By presenting the conditioning stimulus, the bell, at long intervals, and by giving food erratically, he could make the experimental animal behave as though it had grown anxious. Eventually, the dog entered a condition similar to a nervous BREAKDOWN. By stopping the experiment and removing the animal from the laboratory, Pavlov found that he could produce recovery. He utilized this discovery as a foundation for PSYCHOTHERAPY.

Thorndyke's associationism and Pavlov's conditioned response set the stage for Behaviourism. In 1913, WATSON published a seminal article in which he eschewed the introspective psychology of Wundt and James, and called for an objective science of psychology founded on observable behaviour. The unit of behaviour is the stimulus-response association. S-R became to psychology what the electron is for physics – an indivisible and irreducible universal phenomenon, the functions of which can be measured and counted. Variations in the behaviour of different animals or in the behaviour of an animal at different times could be evened out by the frequent repetition of carefully-designed experiments, the results of which could be treated according to the newly-emergent laws of statistics. Thus, the behaviourists offered to make psychology an exact science.

During the next two decades, HULL developed abstract mathematical theories of behaviour. He was particularly concerned with the strength of the S-R connection: how firmly it became fixed and how long it took to break. He and his associates returned frequently to human subjects for their experiments. Because they are free of associations, and therefore neutral to the subject-learner, the experimenters used nonsense syllables as stimuli. They measured the accuracy of subject responses, believing that with the neutral stimulus, the subject would respond with the same passivity as Pavlov's dogs.

Obviously, such an experimental situation is artificial in the extreme. SKINNER revolutionized Behaviourism by showing that objectivity could be retained while accepting that memory influences later learning. He substituted operant conditioning for the classical conditioning of Pavlov. Using Thorndyke's Law of Effect as his theoretical guide, Skinner rewarded or punished the experimental subject – animal or human – immediately in response to *its* response. Thus, if the rat pushed a pedal when the bell rang, it received a pellet of food. The more often the animal responded correctly, the more food it received. It controlled or operated the conditions of its own learning. Note that in terms of the experimental conditions, the question whether the animal is conscious or aware of its operant behaviour is meaningless. The implications of Skinner's invention are indeed profound. It suggests that all behaviour can be understood in terms of operant conditioning. What is more, all behaviour is subject to almost limitless manipulation by the experimenter – or the social planner. Perhaps it was the failure of social planning which first pulled the plug on Behaviourism. Nevertheless, the approach has dominated psychology during the first two-thirds of the twentieth century, and its experimental techniques continue to be immensely valuable. Despite the dominance of Behaviourism, gestalt (German: form) psychology developed principally in Germany and Austria in the interwar years as a significant counter force. It concerns itself with formal or patterned aspects of learning, and maintains that the brain contains forms or maps which dictate the way in which we learn. The gestaltists were not neurophysiologists, but they held that the gestalt was inherited and built into the neural wiring of the brain. Objects are perceived and remembered according to their similarities to a gestalt. Recognition is also governed by the common fate or movement towards each other of the outlines of objects, most notably by the degree of closure or stability (as in a square or triangle). Gestalt psychology was subjective and lacked experimental support, but it prefigured the revolt against Behaviourism which has been made possible by the advances in neurophysiology.

One consequence of behaviourist concentration on conditioning procedures was the emergence of learning theory as a psychological field separate from motivation, perception or sensation. But within learning theory, questions arose which the behaviourists found hard to answer with their experimental procedures. The questions centred around consciousness and motivation which the behaviourists disregard because they are irrelevant within the S-R framework. The attack came from three directions: ethologists like the Austrian, Konrad Lorenz, developmental psychologists led by the Swiss, PIAGET, and linguistics, especially Noam Chomsky of the Massachusetts Institute of Technology. Lorenz helped to restore instinct to a place in learning. Piaget established that there are stages in learning which exist before the presentation of stimuli. Chomsky went further: he returned to the eighteenth century notion that we inherit language structures which are part of the nervous wiring of the brain and enable us to learn to speak, read and write. All three attacks gained support from the growing understanding of the actual brain machinery which underlies behaviour.

Learning theory itself has been much influenced since the Second World War by cybernetics, the science of information and control. When computers were programmed to play chess, hopes ran high that artificial intelligence might provide independent insights into brain function. So far, computer scientists have not lived up to their own expectations in this respect, but the advent of new technology which permits the miniaturization of computer memory units to the point where the size of the machine as well as its complexity are analogous to the size and complexity of the human brain, may give new life to the use of logic machines to understand how we work.

As Wundt and James recognized, however, emotion, memory, perception and especially, sensation, are also elements of behaviour which open avenues for the observation of brain machinery. With the microelectrode – again, an example of better technology – it is possible to correlate the activity of individual neurons with the behaviour of the experimental animal as it sees, feels or learns. In this way, behaviourist techniques are being applied to neurophysiology. The new study is called both psychobiology and neuropsychology.

Thus, a bar of light flashed for a measured instant on the left eye of a rabbit will cause certain neurons in the rabbit's right hemisphere to fire. At the same time, its ears will twitch. Another example of the new experimental techniques: a measured voltage is sent through a microelectrode implanted in a carefully-defined region of the cat's hypothalamus, and the animal displays the arched back, the spitting and the erected fur characteristic of rage. Many laboratories are trying to analyze memory in terms of chemical events in neurons when conditioning occurs. It was work of this kind which led to the discovery of the biochemical disorder in the brains of patients with Parkinson's disease (see PSYCHOMOTOR DISEASE) and to effective drug therapy for that illness.

Although psychology is the study of the healthy mind, its funding often depends on the contribution it can make to the treatment of mental disorders. Clinical psychology has grown up beside the academic discipline. Psychotherapy has been directly responsive to theoretical developments, nowhere more so than in child development and education. At the periphery of the field, furthermore, social psychology continues to thrive. Whether group behaviour can be understood by extrapolating from individual behaviour remains a subject of controversy, but the influence of the group on the individual is profoundly significant.

## PSYCHOMOTOR DISEASE

Disorders and malfunctions of movement arising from disease in the CENTRAL NERVOUS SYSTEM. Thus, movement disorders due to disease in the peripheral nervous system, such as muscular dystrophy, are excluded. Movement disorders arising from damage are described under BRAIN DAMAGE. Psychomotor disease includes a huge catalogue of illnesses, and this entry describes:

1. Epilepsy and myoclonus
2. Multiple sclerosis and similar diseases
3. Parkinsonism and other extra-pyramidal diseases
4. Poliomyelitis and other infections (for syphilis and tuberculosis, see BRAIN DAMAGE)

**1. Epilepsy and myoclonus** Once called the divine madness, epilepsy is one of the oldest diseases known. In the United Kingdom, there are some 300,000 epileptics, and about 35,000 new cases are reported each year. The first attack occurs most often before the patient is 25, and in a large number of cases, before the age of four.

In a minority, epilepsy is caused by brain growths or brain injury, disease, malnutrition or congenital malformation. In the great majority of patients, however, there are no symptoms other than the seizures. They are always associated with abnormal electrical activity in the brain. There is evidence that a tendency towards epilepsy is inherited. Indeed, we are all thought to be potentially epileptic, and given an adequate challenge, would suffer a seizure. As with ANXIETY and DEPRESSION, there seems to be no clear demarcation between epileptics and non-epileptics. Non-epileptics – the majority of us – have very high seizure thresholds. In epileptics, the threshold is much lower for some reason. There is a continuum through the population from those at one extreme who are highly resistant, to those at the other who experience repeated seizures.

Epileptic fits are associated with CONVULSIONS, but convulsions are usually a symptom of only one form of the disease, grand mal epilepsy. Grand mal patients may signal the advent of a fit hours or even days before it occurs. They become irritable (see IRRITABILITY) or depressed and may feel giddy. In about three-fifths of these patients, the attack is preceded by an aura which lasts for no more than a few seconds and is followed by loss of consciousness. The content of the aura is associated with the focal origin of the abnormal electrical discharge. Thus, an aura consisting of visual hallucination accompanies a focus in the visual cortex at the back of the brain. An olfactory aura indicates that the focus is in the olfactory bulb at the front of the mid-brain. DÉJÀ VU or feelings of unreality may indicate a temporal lobe focus. A few grand mal patients run a short distance before they fall unconscious. They are said to have cursive epilepsy. In the rare patient, the aura contains sensations of pain. It is always followed by unconsciousness.

Convulsions may begin with a cry produced by contraction of the chest muscles forcing air through the partly-closed vocal chords. Convulsive muscular contractions are often asymmetrical and last for about thirty seconds. Contraction is followed by alternating relaxation and contraction with the intervals slowly lengthening until the fit ends. Unconsciousness may persist up to half an hour. When the patient comes to, he may suffer a severe headache. He often sleeps for several hours. In exceptional cases, abnormal mental states follow the seizure.

Grand mal epilepsy is relatively rare. It is not itself life-threatening, but continuous convulsions, called status epilepticus, occur occasionally and can be fatal. Status epilepticus almost always has a clearcut cause such as a brain tumour.

Minor forms of epilepsy are immensely variable. All forms that occur without convulsions were once called petit mal, but that diagnosis is now reserved for the little absences or blanks that begin in childhood and often continue for many years. The eyes roll up or the child freezes for a few seconds but without falling or losing consciousness. Such attacks can occur several times a day. They are almost always without known cause, usually associated with ELECTROENCEPHALOGRAM (EEG) abnormalities (see below), and in a few cases, may develop into more severe forms of epilepsy.

Temporal lobe epilepsy is a less severe form in which not only the focus but also the limits of electrical disturbance appear to be confined to one temporal lobe. In true temporal lobe seizures, the patient freezes but does not fall or experience convulsions. He may display AUTOMATISM such as laughing or running, and visual hallucination, presumably as a result of temporal rather than visual cortical activity. In rare cases, he may become angry or violent. When the brief loss of consciousness passes, he may be anxious or depressed. Middle-aged women patients often appear first with a fear of open spaces (agoraphobia; see ANXIETY) after seizures. The EEG may be a useful diagnostic tool to identify this form of epilepsy.

In many kinds of focal epilepsy, convulsions are restricted to the muscles in one part of the body. Jacksonian epilepsy, for example, usually occurs in either the thumb and index finger, the angle of the mouth or the great toe. The name was given to these curious attacks by the British neurologist, Hughlings Jackson (see PSYCHOLOGY), who first described them. They are usually a symptom of some underlying brain disease. In focal epilepsy, the electrical disturbance appears to affect only the relevant segment of the motor cortex although it may originate elsewhere in the brain. In some instances, such seizures may be stopped by firmly holding and massaging the limb where the convulsion begins.

Evoked epilepsy is a seizure brought about by an unusual sensory stimulus. In some patients, the seizure can take a grand mal form. Strobe lighting is perhaps the most common cause, but 'television epilepsy' is being reported with growing frequency.

Epilepsy is not necessarily associated with any other physical or mental abnormality, nor does it produce mental changes unless the fits are so severe and prolonged that they cause brain damage. Except in petit mal and temporal lobe epilepsy, even the patient's EEG may be normal. Indeed, epileptiform EEGs are found in otherwise normal individuals, especially in the normal members of the families of epileptics. If there is an identifiable cause of epilepsy, the attacks will stop when it is removed. Seizures caused by tumours usually cease after surgery, but the surgically-created scar can precipitate further attacks in a susceptible patient. In severe epilepsy, however, surgery may be the only method of control (see PSYCHOSURGERY).

For the majority of epileptics, either nothing can be done to correct the cause or the cause cannot be identified. It is important, therefore, to overcome the stigma still attached to epilepsy. Children often benefit from being allowed to live normal lives, attending school and engaging in sports. Their teachers and supervisors should be told about the possibility of an attack, but they should not be singled out otherwise. Even adult epileptics benefit from a regular job because it reduces the incidence of their attacks. Except under rigid controls, however, epileptics must not drive. In the United Kingdom, the law permits an epileptic to drive if he has been free of convulsions for three years, and providing he is willing to continue to take an anticonvulsant drug. He is permitted to choose to stop the drug, but the risk of relapse even after three years is 40 per cent. If he should have another seizure, he is required to pass another year free from attacks before he can obtain a driving licence. Similar laws exist in the United States, but they vary from state to state.

Anticonvulsant drug therapy usually controls symptoms, but as the relapse rate indicates, it is not a cure. Grand mal, focal and temporal lobe epilepsy are controlled with one of a diverse group of drugs including BARBITURATES, the hydantoins, especially phenytoin (Epanutin, Dilantin), and the acetylureas such as phenylethylacetylurea (Pheneturide). A newer agent, carbamazine (Tegretol), is now often preferred. All of these drugs cause sleepiness, and they may have other side effects. Grand mal drugs do not usually help petit mal epilepsy. It is controlled with ethosuximide (Zarontin) or older drugs such as trimethadione (Tridione) or paramethadione (Paradione). These drugs can exacerbate grand mal seizures. Children with petit mal, however, are often given phenytoin as prophylaxis against more severe seizures as well as one of the drugs suitable for petit mal. They may also respond well to sodium valproate.

A brief, shock-like muscular contraction called myoclonus is often a symptom of epilepsy, and it may also occur in DEMENTIA, infections causing brain inflammation (encephalitis) and brain damage. Indeed, perfectly normal people can experience myoclonus as they are drifting off to SLEEP; the cause is thought to be the erratic firing of neurons in the reticular activating system. When myoclonus is a symptom of disease, it may be controlled with anticonvulsant drugs, but in dementia, a TRANQUILLIZER is preferred.

Tetanus is a form of convulsive muscular activity caused by an imbalance in essential body minerals, especially calcium. It is not a psychomotor disease.

**2. Multiple sclerosis** (disseminated sclerosis) is a disease involving destruction of the myelin sheaths surrounding the axons of many neurons, especially in the central nervous system. Inflammation and demyelination are often seen in the optic tract and the neural pathways transmitting signals to muscles. Sclerosis means hardening, especially of nervous tissue, and refers to the appearance of characteristic plaques at the site of damage. The cause is unknown, but it is now thought to be a combination of two circumstances: an allergy-like reaction of the immune system, possibly conditioned by an inherited predisposition, to infections by one of several viruses, including measles. A variant brain protein has also been associated with the disease, and this is consistent with the inheritance of a variant gene (see GENETICS).

Multiple sclerosis occurs most often in northern Europe and Switzerland, less often in North America, and rarely in Japan, South Africa and tropical countries. It is thus associated with area, but not with race; amongst immigrants, the incidence is that of the mother country. It is primarily a disease of young adults, appearing between the ages of twenty and forty in two-thirds of all cases. More men suffer than women, but when a woman has the disease, she is often quite young and it runs its course more quickly than in men.

The disease is subject to great variations. A few patients undergo one attack which is the result of one episode of demyelination. The symptoms appear suddenly. The damage is never repaired but the remission lasts twenty or thirty years until the patient dies of some other cause. Even in these patients, the symptom-free period is called remission because it is not possible to say that the disease has been cured, nor that it will not recur.

At the other extreme are patients whose symptoms multiply continuously, without remissions. There have been patients who died a few months after the first symptoms appeared. The great majority fall between these extremes, of course. They experience some remissions before the appearance of new symptoms. The onset of the disease is insidious rather than acute. Although many patients can work normally for twenty years or more, others are confined to a wheelchair or to bed for months or even years before death. Prediction is impossible, but both the uncertainty and the remissions are consistent with the double-causation theory.

The first symptoms, in about a third of all patients, are weakness or loss of control of a limb. Another third experience visual deficiencies ranging from almost total blindness in one eye to nystagmus, an involuntary rolling movement of the eye, or a similar impairment. In the remaining third, the first symptoms are vertigo, tremor, loss of taste, epilepsy or impotence. It is often hard to diagnose multiple sclerosis because it may resemble other conditions such as diffuse sclerosis (usually a rapidly-fatal demyelinating disease of younger people), ATAXIA, syphilis, or indeed, HYSTERIA. Only as symptoms multiply does diagnosis become more certain. Nystagmus, for example, is seen in about 70 per cent of all cases. Mental efficiency may decline, and emotional changes often take place. The patient may feel euphoric (see EUPHORIA), but depression and irritability are more common. Loss of emotional control and DELUSIONS also occur. As the disease progresses, larger areas of behaviour become impaired and disability grows.

No specific treatment is accepted, but some evidence now supports doses of linoleic acid in the form of sunflower seed oil. If it is helping patients, the explanation could be that the fat molecules contribute to maintenance of myelin, a fatty substance. Movement disorders, tremor or spasticity may be controlled with a tranquillizer or an anti-epileptic drug such as carbamazepine. The patient should be kept mobile and at work for as long as possible.

Demyelination may cause other psychomotor diseases, but

with the exception of encephalomyelitis, they are fortunately rare. Several different forms of encephalomyelitis have been identified, but the disease process is understood in none of them. Acute disseminated encephalomyelitis can occur during measles, German measles, mumps and chicken pox and can follow vaccination against smallpox or rabies. The acute high fever and mental symptoms are usually rapidly fatal, but in some cases, the patient survives the acute phase only to suffer from Parkinson-like symptoms for the rest of his life. In other forms of the disease, the inflammation and demyelination seem to occur spontaneously. They are fatal and cannot be controlled with drugs.

**3. Parkinson's disease,** paralysis agitans, was first described by the English physician, James Parkinson, in 1817. Typically, the patient develops a curious flattening of the emotions and slowing of voluntary movement accompanied by rigidity and tremor.

Thanks to basic neurophysiological and biochemical research, there is fairly good understanding of the damage underlying the symptoms, but, as yet, the causes remain unknown. Changes in neurons appear in the basal ganglia, the mid-brain relay centres for movement orders from the cortex to the periphery and for sensory information coming in from the periphery. Neurons in one region of the basal ganglia, the substantia nigra (black substance), are especially implicated. They enlarge, develop abnormal inclusions and die. The change is associated with a decline in the normal quantities of the TRANSMITTER, dopamine, synthesized by these cells. Despite the fact that the ultimate cause of dopamine depletion is unknown, its discovery has led to an effective treatment for the first time. The drug is called L-dopa.

Before L-dopa, the average Parkinsonian patient had a life-expectancy of nine years after the first appearance of symptoms. The range is wide, however: from one to thirty-three years. The disease usually manifests itself between the ages of forty and sixty, but a rare form begins in adolescence. It is slightly more common in men than in women, and there is evidence that Parkinsonism runs in families. All colours, national groups and geographical areas are affected in about the same degree. Authorities differ on the incidence of the disease. Reports range between one in two hundred people and one in a thousand, but even the latter figure represents a high risk.

Intellectual activity is not damaged by Parkinsonism. The unblinking eyes and mask-like expression are deceiving. On the other hand, nine out of ten patients become depressed, and progressive DEMENTIA, once thought to be a rare complication, does occur. The slowing and disordering of movement increase as tremor and rigidity grow worse. Patients may find it hard both to initiate and to stop movement; this difficulty explains the peculiar forward-leaning gait so often seen. In late stages of the disease, pain may become severe. Weight loss accompanies autonomic symptoms such as hypothermia. It is important to keep the patient mobile as long as possible and to improve not only the quality of his life but also his mental outlook. Re-educational walking exercises are often helpful, and a walking stick may be essential. In some cases, special appliances such as chairs with seats that move up and down electrically can make the patient more comfortable. Surgery to destroy a tiny area in the thalamus relieves tremor, but it cannot stop the progress of the disease and is now seldom used.

Many drugs have been used in an attempt to control the symptoms, but they have all been of limited value. Among the most important are anti-spasmodics such as benzhexol (Artane) which often helps tremor, AMPHETAMINE for the control of excessive eye movement and to relieve depression (though tricyclics are now usually used for this purpose) and amantadine hydrochloride which helps movement and reduces rigidity in some patients.

L-dopa was introduced in 1967. Dopamine itself cannot be used to relieve the dopamine shortage because it will not pass the BLOOD-BRAIN BARRIER. The natural precursor of dopamine in the chain of synthesis is dopa, a mixture of two forms of the molecule. In crystalline form, D-dopa bends polarized light to the right (dextro), and L-dopa, to the left (laevo). Given as a drug, the natural mixture caused serious blood disorder, but L-dopa alone is almost entirely free of this side effect. It is usually given with another substance such as carbidopa which reduces the destruction of L-dopa by ENZYMES before it reaches the brain. Less L-dopa is required, and the patient suffers from fewer side effects. L-dopa has brought significant improvement to a large number of patients for a long period of time, several years in many cases. More recently, a synthetic drug, bromocriptine, has also proved to be an effective control for Parkinsonian symptoms. It seems to act in place of dopamine as a brain transmitter. The two drugs, L-dopa and bromocriptine, are now often given together in an attempt to prolong the usefulness of both. Neither is a cure, however, and eventually, both cease to be effective. The reason could be that more and more neurons are damaged, exacerbating the disease.

Parkinsonism, or symptoms indistinguishable from it, may follow sleeping sickness (encephalitis lethargica; see below) and severe hardening of the arteries. Such cases are extremely rare.

Abnormal changes in the basal ganglia cause several other movement disorders. Chorea is a slow, uncontrolled writhing which can extend to the whole body (compare Huntington's chorea, under DEMENTIA). It is accompanied by a biochemical disorder in the basal ganglia which involves the loss of an inhibitory transmitter, GABA. This disorder has an effect opposite to the biochemical error which accompanies Parkinsonism. Its cause is unknown.

In tardive dyskinesia (see -KINESIS), the patient also displays choreic movement. In this case, however, the cause is all too clear. The disease is entirely restricted to people who have received doses of the major TRANQUILLIZERS, usually for the control of chronic SCHIZOPHRENIA, over a period of years. Unfortunately, the symptoms may be not only irreversible, even when the drug is withdrawn, but they may become progressively worse. Tardive dyskinesia is probably a reflection of the action of the tranquillizers which alter the behaviour of neurons, particularly those in the basal ganglia, although the drugs are thought to work also in the limbic system.

Athetosis resembles chorea, but the movements tend to be slower and coarser. Both of these diseases can be inherited. Athetosis also sometimes follows treatment with L-dopa or the phenothiazine tranquillizers.

4. **Poliomyelitis** (infantile paralysis) is usually seen in children between the ages of one and five. It ceased to be a major threat about 1960 when vaccination against it, with either the Salk killed vaccine or the Sabin live, attenuated vaccine, be-

came a commonplace. Like smallpox, the disease may now disappear almost completely.

The transmissable organism which causes polio was discovered in 1909, but the enterovirus was actually identified recently. It spreads along neurons and in the blood. Some recovery from the paralysis usually occurs, but in a minority of cases, there is no improvement. The early symptoms include fever, headache, vomiting and diarrhoea. The paralysis may be localized or general. In the ascending form, paralysis begins in the legs and rises through the body. Without suitable breathing equipment, the patient dies when paralysis affects the chest muscles. A few cases also involve the brain stem so that the heart muscles as well as breathing are affected. Mortality varies from less than 5 per cent to more than 25 per cent during epidemics. No treatment is effective against the virus.

Several other viruses also cause inflammation and damage in the central nervous system. They include a number of different forms of encephalitis. The word itself means inflammation of the brain. The causative organism of encephalitis lethargica is thought to be a virus, but it has not been identified.

Rabies (hydrophobia) is a viral infection leading to inflammation and is usually fatal. The virus enters the body with the bite of a rabid animal and travels along nerves both outwards and towards the brain. The incubation period depends on the distance of the bite from the central nervous system. Thus, if the bite is on the leg, incubation takes about sixty-four days, but if it is on the head, about twenty-seven. Pain in the infected part is followed by depression, fear and disturbed sleep. Throat spasms are brought on by drinking, and the spasms extend to the muscles regulating breathing. Eventually, even the sound or thought of water can bring on the spasms. Salivation is heavy and vomiting frequent. Hallucinations may occur, but only rarely does the human patient bite. The excitement and spasms give way to paralysis which is rapidly fatal.

Vaccination is the only protection, and it is effective even if it is given after the bite. If symptoms develop, the best treatment is to control the spasms. Indeed, complete paralysis using the drug curare may be the only way to prevent spasms. The breathing is then maintained mechanically, and the patient has a chance of eventual recovery.

**PSYCHOPATHY** See HEALTH, MENTAL; PERSONALITY; RETARDATION

## PSYCHOSIS

(Greek: *psyche*=mind+*osis*=disorder) any severe mental disorder during which the patient loses touch with reality more or less continuously. Psychoses include all mental illnesses which are not neuroses (see NEUROSIS). Note that it covers ORGANIC diseases such as DEMENTIA, as well as FUNCTIONAL disorders, such as DEPRESSION of the cyclothymic and endogenous types, and SCHIZOPHRENIA.

The demarcation between neurosis and psychosis is uncertain. At some point, presumably, the patient ceases to realize how ill he is, or indeed, that he is ill at all. PSYCHOTHERAPY becomes difficult, if not impossible, because the patient cannot or will not cooperate in the treatment. Yet LAING, for example, holds that the schizophrenic inhabits a real world – real for the patient – which he has created in part as a protection against the 'other' world, and that it is the psychotherapist's job to gain entry into the patient's world. In any case, the distinction between neurosis and psychosis is of little value in the care and treatment of mental illness.

## PSYCHOSOMATIC DISEASE

(Greek: *psyche*=mind+*soma*=body) a disorder in which physical symptoms are in some degree caused by mental attributes such as ANXIETY or EMOTION.

Having thus defined the phrase, it is necessary to qualify the definition. Many authorities hold that the emotions can only be said to contribute to but not to cause. Asthma or migraine, for example, may be brought on or exacerbated by emotions, but the tendency towards the illness must pre-exist physically. Otherwise, it is argued, the emotions would manifest themselves in some other disturbance, such as ANXIETY or DEPRESSION. In the opinion of these authorities, psychosomatic diseases may be limited to asthma, migraine, the gustatory disorders – ANOREXIA, OBESITY, duodenal ulcer, colitis, chronic diarrhoea – and possibly high blood pressure.

At the other extreme are those doctors who argue that all diseases are affected by MIND, a function of the BRAIN, which is part of the body like the heart, skin and kidneys. There is evidence, for example, that cancer and tuberculosis occur more often in industrialized societies than in pre-industrial cultures (statistically balanced, of course, for population size and age), and many authorities believe there is no other explanation than STRESS. Some of these doctors admit that they do not understand the inter-connecting roles of mental and physical causes, and say that words like psychosomatic do no more than hide their ignorance.

Asthma, a spasmodic contraction of air passages in the lungs, is a classic psychosomatic disease. Like hay fever and many kinds of skin rash, asthma is caused in some part by an allergic reaction; that is, cells of the immune system respond to foreign matter, the allergen (or antigen), by synthesizing chemicals which precipitate a cascade of chemical events, ending with the contraction of the air passages in the lungs. Many asthmatics respond well to physical treatments which desensitize their immune systems for the allergen causing the cascade. Yet there is no doubt that PSYCHOTHERAPY, including hypnosis (see HYPNOTISM) and behaviour therapy, can cure the disease in other patients. Somehow, despite the continued presence of the allergen, the immune system is desensitized not by physical but by mental treatment. Acute asthma, called status asthmaticus, can be fatal, but it can usually be controlled with anti-asthmatic drugs if they are used quickly.

It has been suggested that psychosomatic illnesses have permitted the creation of works of genius by protecting their authors against interference from the normal entanglements of life. Thus, Charles Darwin suffered for almost fifty years from a self-diagnosed heart complaint. He seldom entered society and lived very quietly in the country while he got on with his research and writing. Similarly, Florence Nightingale came back from her exertions in the Crimea understandably exhausted. She took to her bed and, for thirty years, rarely left it. Yet during these years, she organized and instituted her major reforms, and she died at the age of ninety in 1910. The case that these illnesses were of a psychosomatic nature is interestingly argued by Sir George Pickering in *Creative Malady* (see *Further Reading*).

The definitions in this book stress the physical connection

between brain and body (see BRAIN; HEALTH, MENTAL; HORMONE; NEURON; PSYCHOLOGY). It has been pointed out that the autonomic nervous system is affected by hypothalamic emotional centres directly and by the hormonal output of the pituitary indirectly. The autonomic nervous system regulates the calibre of air passages in the lungs, the output of stomach acid and the strength and rate of heart beat, among many other functions. In other words, the connections between brain and body are clear, and it would be absurd to ignore them. But even if it is true that all disease is in some degree the result of psychic activity, the purpose of medical science is to find priorities that make treatment possible. Tuberculosis, for example, cannot occur in the absence of *mycobacterium tuberculosis*, regardless of the psychosocial conditions of the patient. Nor can it be cured unless the bacteria are neutralized within the body.

## PSYCHOSURGERY

Surgery on the BRAIN performed for the relief of symptoms of mental disorders.

Amongst doctors no less than amongst the lay public, few words are more emotive than psychosurgery. The comments by some British psychiatrists about their colleague, Dr William Sargent, the leading advocate of surgery as a legitimate and effective weapon, are often unprintable, if not libellous. Most of this heat is generated by surgical treatment of FUNCTIONAL disorders, ANXIETY, SCHIZOPHRENIA and especially DEPRESSION and obsessional neuroses (see OBSESSION).

A much larger number of operations on the brain for other reasons arouse little if any controversy. Few people would dispute the possible value of brain surgery for removal of tumours, repair of enlarged or weakened blood vessels and occasionally, for the opening of abscesses. Indeed, the relatively rare practice of thalotomy (removal of part or all of the thalamus) for the control of intractable pain of uncertain origin was usually considered to be justified before the recent discovery of less extreme techniques (see SENSATION). Surgery for the removal of epileptic foci or to divide the hemispheres of patients with severe epilepsy (see PSYCHOMOTOR DISEASE) is also uncommon, and seldom controversial, although the outcome is most uncertain, and drugs often provide more effective relief from even the most extreme symptoms.

Psychosurgery as a therapeutic tool in psychiatric disorders was first used in 1936 after it had been found that removal of the frontal lobe in a chimpanzee made the animal tractable in the face of challenges that had previously enraged it. A Portuguese neurosurgeon, Egan Moniz, performed frontal lobotomies on twenty violent schizophrenics who subsequently improved, according to Moniz. The operation was popular until about 1950 when side effects such as epileptic attacks began to be recognized, and questions were raised about the value of the operation.

Frontal lobotomy and prefrontal leucotomy describe the same operation, severance of major nerve tracts linking the frontal lobe to the mid-brain and the rest of the cortex. The frontal lobe is not removed. It seems probable, incidentally, that the accident described under BRAIN DAMAGE (pp. 52–3) was a frontal lobotomy.

Such gross interference has now been abandoned in favour of stereotactic operations, where the site is precisely specified and exactly restricted. The tracts most often selected link the frontal lobe to the limbic system through a mid-brain region called the cingulate gyrus. The limbic system contains nuclei, such as the amygdala and the hypothalamus, which regulate emotions. The modern operation is restricted to a tiny region in or near the cingulate gyrus. It may still be performed by cutting, but the lesion is commonly produced by freezing with liquid oxygen or by using radioactive yttrium.

Reports on the results of these operations claim rates of improvement ranging from 50 per cent to 89 per cent. There are two problems with these reports, however: most of the assessments are based in part on comparative TEST scores from tests given before and after operation. Apart from the intrinsic uncertainty of psychological tests given to mentally-disturbed patients, there is no way of controlling effects of extraneous factors, such as the greater care and attention given patients during and after an operation. The second problem arises because the assessments are made in part by the psychiatrist who has recommended the patient for psychosurgery. It is at least possible that with no intention to misrepresent, the psychiatrist will discover improvement to justify his recommendation. There is no certain statistical evidence that psychosurgery works. Even in the case of depression, where the claim has been made that the operation is justified by the risk that without it the patient might commit suicide, the facts are disturbing. There is growing evidence that suicide often follows psychosurgery; seven out of 154 patients in one series of operations subsequently killed themselves.

In the face of such uncertainty, let alone the absence of positive evidence supporting the procedure, would it not be better to avoid psychosurgery for functional disorders? On the one hand, some psychiatrists reply that they are compelled to use whatever techniques offer a chance to the patient which is greater than the risk. On the other hand, the balance of chance against risk is itself controversial.

Underlying this argument, moreover, is a serious problem in medical ethics. In most cases recommended for psychosurgery, the patient is so ill that his consent to the operation is meaningless if it can be obtained at all. Psychosurgeons reply that you don't wait to ask an unconscious man in cardiac arrest if you can give him open heart surgery. But is the analogy satisfactory? Psychosurgery for functional disorders is intended to change the patient's PERSONALITY. At the best, it is intended to make him happy and tractable. The danger that the operation will be misused is great because of the initial uncertainty of diagnosis. Thus, it is often recommended for severe endogenous depression, but seldom for reactive depression. Yet the symptoms of the two disorders are the same, and they can be confused. Even if the patient seems to be happier, there is a risk that the gain has been achieved at the price of the patient's original, unique self.

## PSYCHOTHERAPY

(Greek: *psyche*=mind+*therapeia*=treatment) treatment of mental disorders and diseases by mental, usually verbal, techniques rather than physical means. Psychotherapeutic techniques include art, music and occupational therapy, confession, persuasion, reassurance, re-education, sleep, suggestion, touch and sex therapy, HYPNOTISM and PSYCHOANALYSIS. This entry will also describe four of the more widely-accepted schools of psychotherapy (see also PSYCHIATRY, PSYCHOLOGY).

**1. Techniques**

A. Art, music and occupational therapy
B. Confession
C. Persuasion
D. Reassurance
E. Re-education
F. Sleep
G. Suggestion
H. Touch and sex therapy

**2. Schools**

A. Behaviour therapy
B. Brief-insight therapy
C. Existential therapy
D. Group therapy

**1. Techniques**

**1A. Art, music and occupational therapy** are non-verbal means of helping patients by encouraging them to draw on their own resources. Art includes painting, sculpture, crafts, acting and, with music therapy, the dance. Occupational therapy usually implies retraining. These techniques may be useful for patients of any age and in the treatment of conditions ranging from the most severe psychoses to the mildest neuroses. Paintings done by schizophrenics, moreover, may help the therapist to understand the internal logic of the patient's world. Excepting in the mildest cases, it is doubtful that these techniques are ever curative, but they can often give the patient a useful and satisfying niche in a world which is otherwise closed and hostile. The techniques are not used by psychoanalysts, and they are applicable in behaviour therapy only if retraining is required to overcome a phobia.

**1B. Confession** is best characterized by the ritual sacrament of the Roman Catholic Church. Psychotherapeutic regimens ranging from psychoanalysis to anti-psychiatry fulfil this priestly function for patients who do not believe in God or religious institutions.

**1C. Persuasion** implies that the therapist is trying to bring the patient to act in a defined way. The degree of persuasion obviously depends on the therapist, the patient and his disorder. For example, the therapist may want the patient to agree to some form of treatment such as hypnotism, and he may also wish to push the patient over some emotional threshold. Thus, an hysteric who accepts that logically his handwashing is unnecessary and a symptom of disordered behaviour may refuse to accept the fact operationally until he is bullied into it. There is always a risk that persuasion can push the patient away from the therapist and make the treatment more difficult. Only psychoanalysis eschews all use of persuasion, however. It is an essential part of any brief-insight therapeutic regimen.

**1D. Reassurance** in an attempt to increase the patient's feeling of security is a technique common to all physicians. Anxious and depressed mental patients as well as those suffering from ORGANIC disorders such as stroke (see BRAIN DAMAGE) and the early stages of DEMENTIA may be much in need of reassurance. Thus, it can help the patient to be told that his complaint is not unique. If his disorder can be treated, the patient wants to know that. When cure is impossible, as in dementia, the therapist may be able to comfort the patient by adopting a matter-of-fact approach to the condition (and probably by withholding ultimate diagnosis). In any case, this technique is exploited by all schools of psychotherapy.

**1E. Re-education** is also common to all psychotherapeutic regimens, though the rationale and the methods employed vary enormously. For example, FREUD maintained that by re-experiencing, with the analyst's guidance, an event which may have been repressed, and therefore harmful, the patient could perceive the event without its coat of guilt. On the other hand, the behaviourists seek to isolate and exclude the harmful response to a stimulus by repeating and intensifying the stimulus under controlled conditions. In both cases, if the treatment works, the patient will be able to see the event for what it was and to recognize the element in it which had disturbed him.

**1F. Sleep and rest** are techniques which were developed by Soviet psychiatrists following the teachings of PAVLOV. Pavlov believed that mental disorders were a result of conditioning. Shell-shock is a particularly vivid and dramatic example of this. Sleep allows the brain to recover naturally from such a TRAUMA. There is now growing evidence that the technique is effective against DEPRESSION and ANXIETY, and it has become part of the practice of behaviour therapy.

**1G. Suggestion** is re-education under the guidance of the therapist. The patient may be aware that the therapist is directing him, but the suggestion may also be made in a manner which does not require the patient's cooperation, as in hypnotism. The psychotherapeutic schools vary widely in the kinds of suggestion they practise and in the role assigned to this technique. Psychoanalysis, for example, generally eschews suggestion of any kind. Because of Freud's early use of the technique, hypnotism may be accepted, but its purpose is to release otherwise repressed memories rather than to permit post-hypnotic suggestion. Behaviour therapy accepts any form of suggestion that helps the patient to relearn inappropriate responses. The anti-psychiatric school would logically avoid any but the most overt suggestion. To do otherwise would be to threaten the trust inherent in the essential relationship between doctor and patient. Suggestion can, of course, be dangerously counterproductive if the therapist has not fully appreciated the underlying problems. Thus, a therapist hypnotizes a cigarette smoker whose habit is OBSESSIONAL as well as a sign of ADDICTION. He suggests that cigarettes in particular and tobacco smoke in general will henceforward be repulsive because they are dirty contaminants. The treatment appears to work, but within weeks, the reformed smoker is showing all the signs of alcoholism because the therapist has overlooked the obsessional element in the patient's behaviour.

**1H. Touch and sex therapy** are amorphous techniques emerging from the work of Wilhelm Reich, Geza Roheim and Herbert Marcuse. All three were originally trained as Freudians, but they broke with Freud both on psychoanalytic and on political grounds. Marcuse has become more important as a political thinker. Roheim's influence has been limited, but Reich exploited sexuality to a degree that brought him into frequent conflict with legal as well as psychoanalytic authority. On to Freud's theory of early sexuality, Reich grafted the hypothesis that mental disorders are caused by puritanical refusal to touch others, especially those who attract us, or to engage in sex freely in the same manner that we take food. Although Reich tried to reverse Freud's sexual conservatism, his doctrine was strangely restricted to heterosexual sex. Deviant sexuality was of no use to the neurotic. Reich said that sexual energy existed in quanta called orgones and claimed to have invented an orgone box which would concentrate and conserve the sexual energy of anyone who entered it. He was convicted of fraud in the United States and died in prison in 1957.

Orgone therapy included sexual intercourse with the therapist. Less adventuresome therapists have restricted themselves and their patients to talk and touch. The technique may be used in group therapy. It is no longer restricted to heterosexual relationships.

Sexual disorders and a fear of being touched are common symptoms of disorders ranging in severity from anxiety to schizophrenia. Both symptoms are aspects of behaviour which are regulated by prevailing cultural fashions. If psychotherapy redresses the balance by acting as a makeweight to excessive puritanism, it can be helpful, but there is no evidence that this alone removes neuroses. People who say that they have benefited from sex or touch therapy may in fact still be disturbed or, conversely, their disturbance may in any case have been within the range of normal, healthy self-doubt about their sexual behaviour.

**2. Schools of psychotherapy**

**2A. Behaviour therapy** is based on the theories of behaviourism (see PSYCHOLOGY). The originator of the school may be said to have been Pavlov, although his techniques were far more restricted than those used by later behaviourists. The principal new element in contemporary behaviour therapy is the operant conditioning introduced by SKINNER.

For example, a patient has a fear of open spaces, a common form of phobic anxiety. Treatment may begin with a discussion of the patient's fears. The therapist may then show him photographs, often of roads, parks and playgrounds in his own neighbourhood. In severely anxious people, even pictures can produce fear. The therapist talks to the patient, using persuasion and suggestion to ease the fear until the patient can look at and hold the photographs. The therapist may then suggest a walk or possibly a drive near the patient's home. The therapist accompanies the patient during the outing. In difficult cases, hypnotic suggestion may be used. The ultimate object is to retrain the patient so that he no longer experiences anxiety when he goes out alone.

Behaviour therapy also uses a negative technique. Called aversive or aversion therapy, it is designed to make a patient stop behaving in a certain way; for example, to stop smoking. The therapist utilizes every possible technique, including hypnotism to make the behaviour ugly and repulsive rather than desirable. There is a fair success rate with behaviour therapy of smoking, providing the smoker wants to stop, and that the smoking does not mask an obsessional disorder. Attempts to use aversive therapy, often under the orders of a court of law, to change criminal or deviant sexual behaviour, have been largely unsuccessful.

In principle, the behaviour therapist is not concerned with the reason why the patient suffers the disorder. This direct, operational technique saves time, but it will fail if the behaviour being retrained is a symptom of some more profound disturbance. Behaviour therapy is a rational approach to treatment which may help if the problem is sufficiently clearcut and not too serious. Psychotic disturbances almost certainly will not respond.

**2B. Brief-insight therapy** compresses the psychotherapeutic process into as few as twelve weekly interviews lasting thirty to forty-five minutes, each. It is designed to cut costs and make better use of trained personnel, and employs any technique that can achieve the goal of making the patient feel better, including group treatment, persuasion and suggestion. About 70 per cent of the time is devoted to winkling out the patient's symptoms and emotional problems, if possible with the assistance of abreaction (see PSYCHOANALYSIS). The therapist questions the patient and interprets his problems for about 20 per cent of the time, and the remaining 10 per cent is devoted to counselling. Brief-insight therapy may help less seriously disturbed patients, and may therefore, be the treatment of choice for the majority of patients who come to their general practitioners with mental problems.

**2C. The Existential school** holds that mental disorders arise from a false self-image which has caused the patient to form inappropriate relationships. It aims to teach the patient to know himself, his emotional needs and his abilities. Since the Second World War, existentialism in psychiatry has been principally the work of Viktor Frankl, a Viennese psychiatrist, but it owes much to ADLER and BINSWANGER (as well as to Jean-Paul Sartre, who introduced the concept of existentialism into philosophy). The existentialists attempt to find the right place in the world for the patient. They seek to deal with both outward, real problems, such as those which cause reactive depression, and with the inner, hallucinatory experiences of psychosis, a rare if not a unique claim for the efficacy of a psychotherapeutic technique. Existentialism is also the only school which consciously utilizes humour as a technique by evoking the absurdities in our self-misunderstandings as part of the therapy.

**2D. Group therapy** evolved in the United States in part to make psychotherapy cheaper by spreading available professional resources, especially in state-supported institutions. One psychotherapist meets and works with as many as a dozen patients at the same time. Group therapy has received support from those who decry the isolation of traditional psychiatry, believing that mental problems arise out of social conditions and ought to be treated socially.

The technique today incorporates a mélange of theoretical approaches ranging from traditional psychoanalysis to psychodrama. Immediately after the Second World War, the American psychiatrist, Kurt Lewin, developed the idea of 'group dynamics' and established T-(for training)-groups to adjust people to their roles in large organizations, governmental and industrial. T-groups were taken up by the Tavistock Institute of Human Relations in London where analysis 'of the group' and 'through the group' emerged in contrast with analysis 'in the group', which is more characteristic of the American method. The distinction is by no means absolute: in-group analysis implies the continued focus of emphasis on the relationship between therapist and individual patient. Analysis 'of the group' suggests emphasis on group dynamics, the treatment of everyone at the same time, and 'through the group' implies the treatment of the individual principally with the help of his fellow patients. In practice, the intention of all three forms is to involve the patient more actively in the therapeutic process by causing him to become therapist as well as patient.

The influence of psychoanalysis has been exerted mainly through the work of ALEXANDER, HORNEY, SULLIVAN and ROGERS, who created the Encounter group, his version of group therapy. In his book, *Games People Play*, Eric Berne, an

American psychiatrist, enunciated 'transactional analysis', based on a straightforward rewriting of the Freudian model (Id=Child; Ego=Adult; Superego=Parent). It has been used in group and family therapy, as well as in individual treatment. Family therapy attempts to discover and resolve marital and family problems by bringing together parents and children with the therapist. Despite its psychoanalytic origins, the technique now employs dynamic and even behaviourist practices in treatment.

Less orthodox approaches to group therapy may be exotic indeed. Psychodrama was invented by Jacob Moreno, an American, who found that a patient might respond to re-enaction of the traumatic situation with the help of other members of a group. Reich's pupil, A. Lowen, has perpetuated the less outrageous techniques of his teacher in bio-energetic therapy. Primal therapy, based on the theory that all neuroses begin with the birth TRAUMA, is the creation of Arthur Janov. Gestalt (German: form) therapy (not to be confused with gestalt PSYCHOLOGY) was developed by Frederick Perls, an American psychiatrist, who held that neurosis arises out of the splitting of the 'wholes' which normally unify mind-body, and individual-environment. In the group, gestalt therapy uses games in which patients play roles according to agreed rules. Body language, a phrase introduced by M. Argyle, a British doctor, to describe non-verbal means of communication, is an important element in gestalt therapeutic games, as it is in psychodrama and other group techniques.

The Esalen Institute in Big Sur, California, has used all of these techniques in combination with Yoga and the teachings of Zen Buddhism. Esalen is, perhaps, the most typical example of the 'human potential movement', the conscious attempt by psychotherapists to use whatever tools are needed to enable participants to recognize and achieve their potentials.

Both the objective and the eclecticism are laudable. In Britain, largely through the influence of the Tavistock Institute, as in the United States, the theoretical and practical elements of group therapy have tended to relax and open up mental medicine. The solemn, sometimes lugubrious image of psychoanalysis has begun to disperse.

Unfortunately, it is impossible to evaluate the effectiveness of group therapy because controls required to assure scientific objectivity cannot be introduced. The experience of Alcoholics Anonymous and similar organizations operating in the field of heroin addiction suggests that group therapy may have use for the addict. In some instances, the technique has been trivialized. In others, the group has become an ominous extension of authority, a development forecast by Lewin's T-groups. Large corporations have lent financial backing to the movement because they have found in group therapy an apparent answer to the stressful competitiveness which they encourage in their executives. Thus, what began as a way of cutting the cost of treatment has become an expensive form of recreation. In the United Kingdom, however, group therapy within the National Health Service still serves its original purpose.

**PSYCHOTOMIMETIC** See HALLUCINOGEN

**PUERPERAL MANIA** See MANIA

**PYRAMID** See BRAIN

# R

**RECEPTOR**

A molecule or group of molecules, part of an organic cell, which attracts and binds chemically other molecules, thereby leading to some change in the cell's function. Receptors are most often found in the cell membrane, but they may also exist inside the cell, for example, in the nucleus. No receptor has yet been exactly described; that is, the distribution of atoms in the molecule is not precisely known. To this extent, receptors are hypothetical.

Nevertheless, the indirect evidence that such molecules exist is overwhelming. The number of foreign molecules they bind, the probable number of receptors in a selected cell and the nature and time course of the chemical event originating from binding by the receptor can be measured. The probable atomic arrangements of several receptors have been described, and no evidence has been found to contradict the existence of receptor molecules, in cell membranes, for example. On the contrary, the atomic constituents can be identified at the putative receptor sites. Perhaps of even greater significance, no other hypothesis explains the response of cells to HORMONES, TRANSMITTERS and drugs of all kinds, so efficiently.

Although no cell contains a receptor for every possible chemical, the diversity that does occur is astonishing. Some receptors will bind whole classes of chemicals. This may be the case, for example, with the amine-based transmitters such as noradrenaline, dopamine and serotonin. Others, such as the antigens and antibodies that mediate immunological reactions, may be much more selective. Both the number and location of receptors in a cell membrane may be influenced by the foreign chemical they bind. Thus, when muscle cells are innervated by neurons which cause them to contract, as happens during normal growth or repair, the receptors for the transmitter, acetylcholine, move to the site where the axon bulb approaches closest to the muscle cell membrane. What is more, there is evidence that the muscle cell synthesizes new receptors under these circumstances.

The notion of receptors was formulated by the German bacteriologist and pharmacologist, Paul Ehrlich, about 1900. Ehrlich supposed that cells bear tiny arms or claws – chemical molecules, of course – which grab and hold drug molecules floating in the blood and other body fluids. The concept remains very little changed, except that it is necessary to see the receptor as a participant in the change initiated by the foreign molecule, rather than as a passive lock into which a key has been inserted. The actual chemical bonds formed between foreign molecule and receptor cause a change in the shape and function of both, such that a new sequence of events follows.

Once the bond is broken, furthermore, the receptor returns to its original shape and function. The bond may be broken by one of several different chemical events. For example, an ENZYME may intervene. Thus, cholinesterase is an enzyme which breaks the acetylcholine molecule causing it to be released by its receptor. The entire combination may be broken down enzymatically and the receptor replaced by a new one. Such a sequence is seen in the immune system, but less often in nervous tissue. The change inside the cell following the linkage may be self-limiting; that is, the last chemical step in the sequence may be release of the receptor. The study of receptors and their ligands – the molecules with which they are linked – is one of the most active research fields in biology, with immense relevance to the understanding of mental disorders.

**REICH, W.** See PSYCHOTHERAPY

## RETARDATION

(Latin: *retardare*=to slow down, impede) 1. absence of normal mental development. 2. failure of the BRAIN to grow normally due to ORGANIC factors.

**1. Absence of normal mental development.** The definition encompasses all aspects of mental development, intellectual and emotional. It includes conditions as diverse as AUTISM, sensory and emotional deprivation in infancy, nutritional deficiencies and genetic errors. In fact, it is too broad to be useful.

**2. Failure of the brain to grow normally due to organic factors.** Organic factors affecting brain development will be either congenital or environmental. For the specific GENETIC disorders related to mental retardation, such as Down's syndrome, see SYNDROME. For environmental factors, see BRAIN DAMAGE. This entry describes two types of congenital factors associated with retardation: A. biochemical disorders, and B. hormonal disorders (see also HORMONE). To these should be added 'non-specific retardation', the commonest form. The cause may be inherited, but it is still not identified.

**A. Biochemical disorders** affecting brain development are metabolic errors. Any departure from the norm which affects tissue development is almost certain to have an impact on the brain. Thus, foetal anoxia (see BRAIN DAMAGE) disturbs growth, especially brain growth. However, three classes of biochemical disorder have pronounced retardational effects: disturbances in the metabolism of amino acids, lipids and carbohydrates.

The amino acids are constituents of all proteins and of some TRANSMITTERS. The commonest amino acid disorder, phenylketonuria, affects about forty infants a year in the United Kingdom. It is inherited as a recessive trait (see GENETICS).

Because of a defect in the ENZYME needed to convert one amino acid, phenylalanine, to another, tyrosine, too much of another chemical, phenylpyruvic acid, appears in the blood and urine. At birth, the infant appears to be normal, but retardation affects his movement as well as his intellect. CONVULSIONS may occur. Fortunately, the disease can be identified by routine testing before symptoms appear, and careful dietary restriction of phenylalanine intake will prevent their appearance. At present, phenylketonuria cannot be cured.

Lipids are fat-like molecules which make up many organic substances including the steroid hormones, cell membranes and the myelin sheaths of NEURONS. Disorders of lipid metabolism are inherited in almost all cases. For example, infantile amaurotic idiocy is caused by deficiency of an enzyme, hexosaminidase, which leads to excess lipid deposits in the brain and retina (see SENSATION) causing mental failure, blindness and paralysis. In fact, the symptoms are produced by two different diseases: Tay-Sachs (identified in the 1880s) is confined to infants born to Ashkenazic Jews, and Sandhoff's (identified in 1968) is also infantile amaurotic idiocy, but in non-Jewish children. The symptoms are the same, but the enzyme disturbance is not. There are two forms of the enzyme, hexosaminidase A and B; only the A form is deficient in Tay-Sachs disease, but both are deficient in Sandhoff's disease. Both diseases are clearly inherited due to a recessive, non-sex-linked gene.

Carbohydrate metabolic disorders are also inherited. They affect the patient's ability to digest or eliminate sugar. These diseases are very rare. They cannot be cured, but the symptoms can be controlled by dietary regulation.

**B. Hormonal disorders** that cause mental retardation include several rare diseases often associated with the pituitary. Thus, diabetes insipidus, a disease characterized by excessive water output and thirst, may be caused by insufficient antidiuretic hormone (ADH; it acts to reduce water excretion). The disease may be inherited, and it can be treated with vasopressin, the hormone that antagonizes the effect of ADH. In another form of diabetes insipidus, ADH is normal and the disease is due to a kidney abnormality. Both conditions lead to mental retardation, but the chain of events is not understood.

Hypopituitarism (inadequate pituitary secretion) is usually associated with adrenal and thyroid gland malfunctions because those glands are regulated by pituitary hormones. Defects may include abnormal growth, anxiety, tremor and hyperactivity as well as retardation. Dosage with pituitary hormones may control the symptoms, but the retardation is often not reversible.

Hypoparathyroidism is a disorder in which the parathyroid gland secretes too little hormone, causing an imbalance of the minerals in the body. Calcium is especially affected. It is a more common disorder than the diseases associated with hypopituitarism, and its origin is unknown. Injections of parathyroid hormone prevent the symptoms from becoming worse, but retardation is irreversible.

**ROGERS, CARL RANSOM**

Psychologist, emphasized client-therapist relationship; originated Encounter groups (see PSYCHOTHERAPY). b. Oak Park, Illinois, 1902. Student, Union Theological Seminary, New York, but decided to take up psychology. Columbia University Teachers' College, MA, 1928; PhD, 1931. Director, Society for Prevention of Cruelty to Children, Rochester, New York, 1930. Lectured, University of Rochester, 1935–40. First director, Rochester Guidance Centre, 1939. Professor of clinical psychology, Ohio State University, 1940. Professor of psychology, University of Chicago, 1945–57. Helped to establish University counselling centre. Professor of psychology and psychiatry, University of Wisconsin, 1957. *The Clinical Treatment of the Problem Child*, 1939. *Counselling and Psychotherapy*, 1942. *Psychotherapy and Personality Change*, 1954. *Client-centred Therapy*, 1957. *On Becoming a Person*, 1961. *Carl Rogers on Encounter Groups*, 1970.

# S

**SADO-MASOCHISM** See DEVIATION, SEXUAL

**SANITY**

(Latin: *sanitas*=soundness) soundness or normality, especially of the MIND.

The word has a social and legal meaning, but is no longer used in medicine. In the negative form, insanity, it still appears in the names of some hospitals and prison hospitals.

Like mental HEALTH, sanity is defined socially, but retains additional weight because the social judgment has been embodied in laws that try to define criminal insanity. In general, a criminal is said to be sane when he knows the meaning and moral content of his act. The notion of temporary insanity is also embodied in law and means that the criminal was insane only for the duration of the criminal act. Thus, murder committed in a fit of fury caused by sexual jealousy might be adjudged an act of temporary insanity, but in the United States and the United Kingdom, it is usually left up to juries to determine how the facts fit the law. Psychiatrists called as witnesses often differ. Therefore, the courts are sensitive to the public attitude to the act itself, and to the conventional distinction between sanity and insanity.

The second important legal aspect of sanity concerns the hospitalization of mental patients who are, in law, too ill to decide for themselves. In the United Kingdom, certification for admission to hospital because of a mental disorder without the consent of the patient requires the agreement of two doctors, and it must be reviewed within three weeks. The procedure is controversial. Some psychiatrists, such as the American, Thomas Szasz, argue that any committal without the patient's informed consent is contrary to the Hippocratic oath (see PSYCHIATRY). Inasmuch as unconscious patients with a serious physical disorder are commonly hospitalized by one attending physician, however, it is hard to see what moral objection there can be to the principle of hospitalization without consent for mental patients. Protection of the patient's rights depends ultimately on the social definition of sanity, as well as on medical knowledge and experience.

## SCHIZOPHRENIA

(Greek: *schizein*=to divide+*phren*=mind) a group of diseases identified by symptoms of emotional abnormality (see EMOTION), thought disorder (see COGNITION), disturbances of MOTIVATION, stupor or catatonia, and DELUSIONS often associated with hallucinations (see DREAM). Its causes are unknown, and it is not curable. Schizophrenia is not fatal, but about 20 per cent of all schizophrenics attempt SUICIDE, and life expectancy amongst schizophrenics is probably less than half that of the general population. Roughly one-quarter of all schizophrenics suffer only one acute attack and are thereafter normal. In about one half, there are remissions or symptom-free periods, but the illness recurs. After the third or fourth recurrence, the patient is usually chronically ill for the rest of his life. The remaining 25 per cent of schizophrenics are chronically ill from the outset and must be continuously hospitalized.

Although it is much more serious, schizophrenia is like ANXIETY, DEPRESSION, MELANCHOLIA and other FUNCTIONAL disorders: it can be diagnosed only because of its symptoms. Despite its relative severity, moreover, there are borderline cases of people with schizoid characteristics who are able to carry on relatively normal lives given a measure of support from those close to them.

Schizophrenia was identified by KRAEPELIN in 1896. He called it dementia praecox ('early madness') because the symptoms appear more often in adolescents and young adults than in other age groups. In 1911, BLEULER established the name 'schizophrenia'. He compared studies of many patients by various doctors in different countries, and found that one symptom, the splitting off of intellectual activity from emotional response, seemed to be almost, if not absolutely, universal. Typically, the patient's intellect is relatively unclouded. He is aware of the nature of pain, fear, anger or love, and when he senses these emotions himself, moreover, he is alive to their content and object. But he cannot feel the emotions of others. Inflicting pain on others is meaningless. Only a minority of schizophrenics are aggressive or dangerous, and those few act only occasionally, but when they strike, they do so with utter ruthlessness. Schizophrenia means a division of facets of a normal mind, rather than the presence of two or more personalities, though multiple-personality may also betoken the disease.

Psychiatrists admit that the conditions they call schizophrenia because the symptoms are similar may, in fact, be different diseases. It is now customary to distinguish four broad types of schizophrenia. A patient may display more than one type, but seldom more than two at a time. As his illness progresses, however, he may move from one type to another.

**1. Hebephrenic.** The majority of those in whom symptoms appear before the age of thirty are called hebephrenic schizophrenics. (Hebe was the Greek goddess of youth.) The principal manifestation is thought disorder. Symptoms first appear as an inability to concentrate, a dreaminess which is characteristic of normal adolescence. Abstraction is often accompanied by HYPOCHONDRIA which is focused on masturbation (see DEVIATION, SEXUAL) or menstruation, and other physical aspects of puberty. The patient becomes boastful, grandiose or pseudo-profound. He may talk for hours or write voluminously about the meaning of life or the paradox of good and evil, saying nothing. His thoughts may reveal delusions, but hallucinations occur only in later stages. Both DEPERSONALIZATION and DEREALIZATION often occur, especially early in the illness when the patient comes to realize that he is not behaving normally. Separation of thought from AFFECT may be accompanied by a sense of the bizarre which assures the patient success as a comedian or a clown. Indeed, some great entertainers, such as the late Lenny Bruce, may have been mild hebephrenics. On the other hand, depression can also mask early schizoid symptoms, and depression is often accompanied by a sense of serenity. Slowly, the symptoms become exacerbated. As with all types of schizophrenia, there may be periods of remission when the patient is not only free of symptoms but capable of insight into his condition. Artists, for example, have painted their delusions, and poets have described them. Given the opportunity, creative patients may continue to work productively throughout their illness, often with moving and beautiful results.

**2. Simple schizophrenia** is characterized by shallow emotional responses. It may be very hard to diagnose because simple schizophrenia often lacks the more florid symptoms such as catatonia, delusions and hallucinations. Though paranoia is sometimes among the symptoms, especially in later years, it may not be easy to identify. The patient gives what appears to be a rational explanation for his paranoid hatred or fear. In fact, because behaviour is often merely odd, simple schizophrenia may escape diagnosis until the person commits some stupid, brutal crime, often against someone close to him. He may never again act violently, but then after the first, acute episode, he is closely watched, if not legally restrained. The patient expresses no malice towards his victim, and may scarcely recognize that he has inflicted pain. In a sense, the simple schizophrenic is intellectually poles apart from the hebephrenic, and indeed, it is possible that the social background, if not the intelligence, of the two types often differs. Simple schizophrenics tend to come from poorer, less well-educated groups. On the other hand, simple schizophrenia may either precede or follow a hebephrenic or a catatonic attack.

**3. Catatonia.** Both the dreaminess of the hebephrenic and the shallowness of the simple schizophrenic merge into the absent-mindedness and the eventual stupor of catatonia. In its most extreme form, catatonia is total withdrawal, a kind of conscious unconsciousness, but the symptoms take many forms including excitement, posturing, repetitive but meaningless movement (called stereotypy) and partial or total immobility. Sleep disturbance can occur in all types of schizophrenia, but it is notably a symptom of catatonic types. Hebephrenic schizophrenics display irrational speech patterns, but the speech disorders in catatonic schizophrenia extend to sound distortions or to gibberish which the patient treats as a secret language. Catatonic behaviour may persist, though in other respects the patient seems to be temporarily improved. In this matter, however, his institutional environment is an important determinant. If he can be given activities which he recognizes as being normal and useful, he often responds. Physically, the catatonic schizophrenic is sallow and greasy with mottled, cool arms and legs. His body weight may remain low, even if the patient's appetite is good. His blood pressure is low, and the pulse rate and respiration slow. Thus, mental symptoms are almost always accompanied by physical symptoms that are characteristic of catatonic schizophrenia.

**4. Paranoid schizophrenia** differs from the other three types in two major respects: it is more often a disease of middle or old age, and it is the least variable in its symptoms. Paranoid patients seldom display catatonia or disturbances of thought and feeling. They suffer primary delusions which are commonly well integrated into their environments. Thus, a husband feels that his wife is controlling his mind, whereas an unmarried patient never invents a spouse. The primary delusion, for example, a voice, is followed by a secondary delusion, consisting of an interpretation of the primary experience. The patient who thinks he is Napoleon sees his real wife or the nurse as Josephine. Once established, the form and content of the delusion tends to be invariable until the patient dies. Hallucinations often accompany the delusions. There may be periods in which the patient is free of the delusions, but they are seldom completely abandoned. On the other hand, they tend to become less well-integrated into the environment as time passes. Paranoid patients are usually distressed by their delusions, but some accept them cheerfully. A patient who believes that another patient is trying to poison him, says so openly, but lives in perfect amity with his supposed enemy. He may even live at home, tend his garden and visit his relatives while retaining the delusion that a neighbour intends to destroy him. Yet another group of paranoid patients successfully separate the real world from their delusional world. Such a patient lives a normal life until some accidental event releases the delusional flow. A different personality appears, full of anger and resentment against the persecutor, but in time – or after a night's sleep – the old self reasserts its dominance. As the years pass, the delusional self may become weaker and less coherent, but the correct trigger still calls it forth. A psychiatrist may try to split off a delusional complex from the normal personality by encouraging useful pursuits and family life. Such a course sometimes succeeds, but it leaves the patient aloof and lacking in empathy. Naturally, he avoids the old trigger events. The disease appears to be contained in these patients, but it cannot be said to have been cured.

Symptoms of schizophrenia vary with the social experience of the patients but, broadly speaking, they are remarkably consistent in outline regardless of geography, climate or culture. Indeed, the same is true of the other functional disorders. The content of a delusion or the object of a phobic anxiety depend upon environment, but in both cases the unreality reflects a profound, but so far unidentified, psychobiological disturbance.

In the United Kingdom, the risk of schizophrenia is about 1.3 per cent of men up to age 55, and about 1.23 per cent up to 75. In women, the risk is 1.08 per cent and 1.3 per cent, respectively. Thus, there is a slight preponderance of male patients under 55, and a reversal of the male:female incidence in later life. The figures are almost the same in all out-bred communities (that is, the ordinary community where marriage is not restricted by geographical or cultural circumstances), but rise in in-bred communities, such as those found in Arctic Sweden, Iceland and the population of Geneva, Switzerland. No community has been found which is free of schizophrenia.

Theories about environmental and psychic causation abound, but there is very little hard evidence to support any of them. FREUD, for example, held that in schizophrenia, the Id has overcome and totally defeated the Ego, so that reason is lost. He recognized that psychoanalysis has no role to play in treatment of the disease. Because of the distortions in written and spoken thought displayed by schizophrenics, furthermore, it has been suggested that their PERCEPTION is disordered, resulting in anomalous and bizarre misconstructions of the real world. Indeed, the hypothesis seems to be undeniable, but does it really advance our understanding of schizophrenia? The perceptual argument is a little like saying that water running up hill does so because it 'misinterprets' gravity. To make water rise, there must be a pump in the system somewhere and, similarly, errors in perception must also have a cause.

Perhaps the most useful psychological hypothesis concerning the origin of schizophrenia was introduced by the British psychiatrist, Gregory Bateson, in 1956. Bateson and his associates suggested that the families, especially the parents of schizophrenics, devise for the future patient a 'double bind'; that is, the child who becomes a schizophrenic is told one thing is true when his senses say the opposite. His mother, for example, stresses her love for the child, but she cannot hide successfully the resentment she feels because the child has destroyed both her freedom of action and her figure. The frequent repetition of such situations, it is argued, cause the child to divide his cognitive (see COGNITION) from his emotional life, thus producing the most common symptom of schizophrenia. Note that a 'double bind' family could explain the apparent inheritability of the disease. LAING has pointed out, moreover, that society often deals the potential schizophrenic a similar series of divisive blows. For example, he hears the principle of justice for all elevated by parents, teachers and politicians, but he observes that the courts are less sympathetic to minorities and to the poor than to the majority and the rich. Though the 'double bind' hypothesis is well grounded, its major shortcoming is incompleteness. Thus, only about 1 per cent of a population becomes schizophrenic, yet 'double bind' conditions probably apply to a far higher proportion. The question is, what keeps most of us sane? One way to look for the answer is to discover physical characteristics which are aberrant in the schizophrenic. Obviously, physical characteristics may be inherited.

That inbreeding increases the incidence of the disease lends credence to the view that it is affected by inheritance. Studies of twins, one of which has been diagnosed for schizophrenia, are less clear than was once thought to be the case, but on the whole, the incidence of the disease is higher in fraternal twins than in the general population, and much higher in identical twins. Fraternal twins develop from two ova and are as likely to develop the same traits as any other siblings. Identical twins develop from a single ovum and can be genetically-identical individuals. Thus, if a characteristic is inherited, both identical twins are likely to have acquired it, and fraternal twins are about as likely to inherit as any other brother or sister. Yet if schizophrenia is inherited, the question remains: what is inherited? (See also GENETICS)

Because schizophrenia occurs most often at the two periods of sexual change – puberty and menopause – it was once thought that the disease might be related to the underlying hormonal alterations. No such error has been found. Nor has it been possible to isolate any other gross physical abnormality which might be related to schizophrenia. For example, brain degeneration which characterizes DEMENTIA does not occur in schizophrenia. Many schizophrenics suffer from poor general health, but this is hardly surprising with people who are often chronically ill. One more curious extraneous fact has never been explained: a majority of schizophrenics are born in the first half of the year.

In the absence of obvious physiological changes, attention has turned to brain biochemistry. The AMPHETAMINES and HALLUCINOGENS, especially LSD, produce schizophrenia-like reactions, and the amphetamines, mescaline and LSD are chemically-related to TRANSMITTERS, the first two to noradrenaline and LSD, to serotonin. It made sense, therefore, to investigate synthesis and breakdown of the natural transmitters to determine whether some error in brain chemistry was producing a hallucinogenic substance in schizophrenics. There have been some challenging discoveries: thus, the urine of schizophrenics contains unusual chemical breakdown products of both noradrenaline and serotonin. The technique used to isolate these chemicals, chromatography, has revealed them as distinctively-coloured spots. The most striking is mauve, but unfortunately for the understanding of schizophrenia, similar mauve spots have been found in the analysis of urine from mentally-retarded children. It may indeed reflect a significant biochemical disorder, but we are no closer to understanding its nature.

Some authorities, led by the American biochemist, Linus Pauling, believe that schizophrenia occurs because schizophrenics utilize vitamins differently from normal people (see PSYCHIATRY). They have tried megavitamin therapy with various combinations of B and C vitamins, so far without positive results.

Perhaps the most useful hypothesis under investigation suggests that the disease arises because of an imbalance in the transmitters. As in Parkinsonism (see PSYCHOMOTOR DISEASE) and dementia, it is possible that some nervous pathway, the behaviour of which is normally regulated by both excitatory and inhibitory transmitters (for example, serotonin and GABA, respectively), has lost cells or the ENZYMES from cells so that one of the transmitters is either incorrectly made or inadequately supplied. There is evidence that RECEPTORS for the transmitter, dopamine, malfunction causing a blockage in these neural pathways. The British psychiatrist, T. J. Crown, divides schizophrenics into two categories depending on two different receptor responses in patients. On this biochemical basis, he distinguishes acute from chronic schizophrenia. The former may be reversible, but the chronic disease is probably not.

A different line of enquiry into the causes of this baffling and terrible disorder was first suggested in 1973 by two American doctors, who have received support from Russian scientists. They proposed that a slow virus (see DEMENTIA) might be involved in the development of schizophrenia. In 1979, further evidence for this theory was found in the blood of some schizophrenic patients, but it is not clear whether the viral particles accompany the disease or are a cause. If they are causative, then schizophrenia could be a transmissable, infectious disorder, and the evidence of heritability would have to be re-examined. Either a virus or a gene could cause a biochemical disorder affecting transmitters.

At present, treatment of schizophrenia is symptomatic. The doctor tries to control excitement or depression, delusions or paranoia, and to keep the patient's life as normal as possible. PSYCHOTHERAPY is directed at minimizing the effects of aberrant behaviour, rather than at finding a cause for it. LAING's work in particular seeks to understand the psychological content of the illness in order to help the patient around the distortions in his mind. But psychotherapy must be used with care because it can make the symptoms worse in some schizophrenics.

Institutionalization of chronic schizophrenics is now avoided where possible by the use of halfway houses, if the patient's family cannot cope. Thus, TRANQUILLIZERS are helpful in part at least because they make it possible for the patient to live in a home atmosphere. Even in hospital, every attempt is made to create a community in which the patient plays an active role. Occupational therapy is often of value, especially for younger patients in whom remissions are to be expected.

The first, and still the leading tranquillizer for schizophrenics is chlorpromazine (Largactil, Thorazine). Introduced in 1950, chlorpromazine has revolutionized the treatment of mental illness, especially of schizophrenia, by making it possible to control patients over long periods without constraints. Those who complain that mental wards are often filled with drugged zombies forget the degrading strait jackets and the terrible screams and moans that typified pre-chlorpromazine mental hospitals. It is possible that tranquillizers are sometimes used for the convenience of the staff rather than the well-being of the patients, but no doctor condones such a practice. Tranquillizers are not cures, but they are relatively free of undesirable side effects.

For acute schizophrenic attacks, newer tranquillizers such as haloperidol (Serenace, Haldol) may be used. Fluphenazine enanthate (Moditen enanthate) or fluphenazine decoanate are long-acting tranquillizers sometimes used for chronic patients, but they may have depressive effects.

Propranolol (Inderal) was introduced in 1964 for the prevention of acute and painful heart attack called angina pectoris. In 1972, it was found that the drug controls acute schizophrenic episodes, and there is evidence that it may even produce periods of remission in chronic schizophrenia. Propranolol is particularly effective for the suppression of auditory hallucinations. The manner in which the drug helps the heart is understood, but there is no explanation of its value as an anti-schizophrenic drug.

A new drug chemically related to the natural OPIATE, enkephalin, but without pain-killing activity, may also alleviate schizophrenic symptoms. In 1979, one carefully designed experiment brought dramatic improvement in patients given the substance. Again, there is no molecular explanation for its action.

SHOCK THERAPY has been used to control schizophrenia, but except with the catatonic type, its value has never been demonstrated. PSYCHOSURGERY is seldom used. Although it is thought by some to have helped a minority of severely-ill older patients, the procedure may destroy what remains of the patient's personality.

**SELYE, H.** See STRESS

**SENILE DEMENTIA** See DEMENTIA

**SENILITY** See AGE

**SENSATION**

(Latin: *sensatio; sensus; sentire*=to think) information about the environment, including the body. Sensation depends upon the various senses. From the physiological standpoint, each sense has three parts: a receptor consisting of specialized NEURONS either in isolation or collected together, afferent neurons from the receptor to the third part, the CENTRAL NERVOUS SYSTEM (CNS) where a group of neurons receive and process the signals. (Afferent neurons convey signals from the CNS to the muscles and glands.) Note that all sensations are encoded as identical nerve impulses. To distinguish amongst them, we must have an intact receptor, intact afferents linking that receptor to the BRAIN, and an intact brain region competent to receive that sensation.

The five traditional senses – sight, sound, touch, taste and smell – provide data about external environment, as do pain, temperature and pressure. Balance, hunger and thirst and proprioception – that is, the body sensations – convey information about location of the body in space and its internal chemical conditions. The diverse senses are described in alphabetical order, as follows:

1. Balance
2. Feeling (pressure, temperature, touch)
3. Hearing
4. Hunger and thirst
5. Pain
6. Proprioception
7. Smell and taste
8. Vision
9. Extra-sensory perception (ESP)

**1. Balance.** The principal receptor organs for the sense of balance are the vestibulary systems located in the ears. Some additional information about balance is conveyed by proprioception and vision. Each vestibular system consists of three tiny semicircular canals and the utricle and the saccule. The semicircular canals lie at approximately right angles to each other in the bone of the skull. The utricle connects the two ends of each canal to the saccule which opens into the cochlea, that portion of the inner ear specialized for hearing. Both the middle and the inner ear, including the vestibulary system, are enclosed within the bone of the skull.

Balance consists of two different sensory elements: gravity and acceleration. Gravity sense is the function of the utricle and

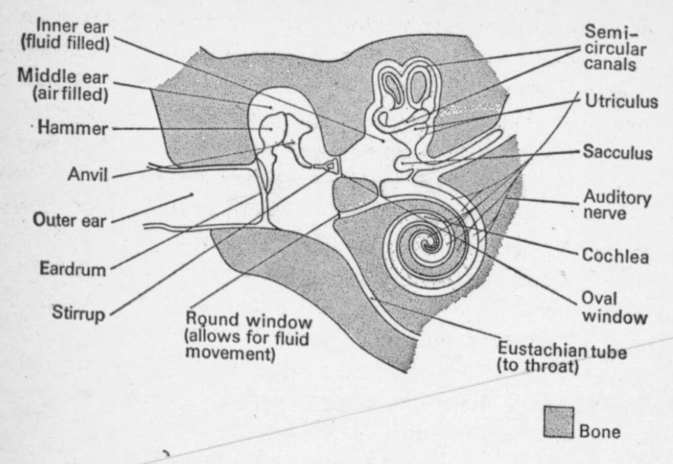


Diagram of the inner ear and vestibular system in section.

saccule in each ear. In addition to a viscous fluid which fills all parts of the inner ear, the tiny chambers contain a weight called an otolith, a gelatinous membrane in which lime has been deposited. The otolith is attached to hair-like processes of neurons. When the head moves out of vertical, gravity pulls the otolith. Thus, a tilt to the left causes the otolith in the left vestibulary system to pull more strongly than the one on the right. Both otoliths exert maximal pull when their owner is upside down.

Acceleration sense depends on the semi-circular canals. Each canal contains an enlargement of its wall projecting into a ridge or crista which partly blocks the canal. The inner surface of the crista is lined with neurons from which hair-like processes extend into a gelatinous mass, the cupola, which rests on the crista nearly completing the blockage. When the head turns, the fluid in the semicircular canal moves in the opposite direction, causing the cupola to swing like a flap hinged to the crista, and carrying the neuronal processes with it. Thus, the mechanism registers acceleration and deceleration. It also registers angle of movement, because one of the canals is more affected by the movement than the other two. If movement continues at the same speed and angle, however, the fluid no longer moves and the cupola returns to a neutral position. It is then that proprioception and vision are required for information about balance. Sudden deceleration causes the cupola to reverse direction and produces a sensation called reverse vertigo.

The most important brain centre receiving and processing data on balance is probably the cerebellum, but signals from the vestibulary systems also go to the cortical regions responsible for sensations of feeling. Indeed, there is not a single balance centre analogous to the primary visual cortex (see **Vision,** below).

2. **Feeling** consists of pressure, temperature and touch data. Although pressure, temperature and touch are separate sensations, depending on distinctive, specialized nerve endings, they tend to be intermixed both physiologically and subjectively.

Unless it is the skin, there is no grand organ of feeling like the eye or the ear, and the skin serves many additional functions such as protection and temperature regulation. The specialized neuron endings which sense pressure, temperature and touch are mixed in all parts of the skin surface, but their density varies. Thus, they are more dense in the face, lips and finger tips than on the back. The endings are also mixed in their responses to stimuli. There are three types of endings: single neurons sense heat, cold and pain. Single neurons encapsulated in specialized skin layers or corpuscles respond to fine touch, such as a pin prick, and to pressure. Complexes or groups of unencapsulated neurons are thought to respond to rough touch, such as stretching. These modalities of sensation are continuous both physically and subjectively, rather than discrete and distinct from one another. A pin prick begins as pressure, for example, and either heat or cold can cause pain. It is possible to obscure the response of each type of specialized ending to different kinds of stimulation, but the subjective response varies from person to person.

The specialized feeling neurons from a single area of skin form nerve trunks, often large enough to be visible to the naked eye, which run to the spinal cord at the appropriate level; that is, legs at the bottom and arms at about the upper third. In the spinal cord, sensory neurons make contact with an interneuron within the cord itself. This interneuron may form a synapse with a motor neuron which returns directly to the sensory area, for example a finger tip, and these two neurons provide the physiological basis for the simplest reflex action. The interneuron may also link the specialized sensory cell to the brain stem. There, the signal is routed to the primary and secondary sensory regions of the cortex, and in the case of temperature, to the hypothalamus. Feeling inputs are also received by the colliculi on top of the brain stem where they are projected as a map of the body surface and brought into neural contact with similar auditory and visual maps. This is the first example here of the physiological reflection of the external world by neurons inside the CNS, which is fundamental to the translation of nervous signals into subjective images.

**3. Hearing.** The ear has three chambers: the outer ear ends at the ear drum. The middle ear is a short, hollow chamber containing three tiny, articulated bones linking the ear drum to the outer membrane of the inner ear, a sort of second ear drum. The chamber is filled with air which enters via the Eustachian tube. The bones convert sound waves to mechanical energy which agitates the membrane of the inner ear and the perilymph, the viscous fluid that fills the bony inner chamber, or cochlea, a curled, shell-like chamber carved out of the bone. (The perilymph also fills the vestibulary system which is part of the inner ear.) The array of specialized nerve endings in the cochlea which are analogous to the retina in the eye is called the organ of Corti, after the Italian anatomist who first described it. It consists of a membrane, the basilar membrane, a long, thin sheet of tissue roughly one cell thick, along which are arranged some 16,000 acoustical units. Each unit is made up of two types of cells named for their shapes: pillar cells and finely-ciliated hair cells. The terminals of the cochlear neurons turn around the hair cells. Axons of the cochlear neurons form the auditory nerve which is analogous to the optic nerve.

The mechanisms which convert the mechanical agitation of the perilymph to electrochemical neuronal signals are still not fully understood. The ear can distinguish roughly 16,000 different pitches, and there are about the same number of acoustic units in each organ of Corti (that is, in each ear). The hair cells are thought to respond to the longer wavelengths or lower pitches. Higher pitches may cause movements in the basilar membrane which would also have the effect of stimulating auditory neurons. With an oscilloscope, an instrument designed to project electrical impulses on to a television tube, it is possible to show that the organ of Corti generates two kinds of signals. One looks continuous, rather like a wave, and its amplitude is directly proportional to the displacement of the innermost of the three bones of the middle ear. This signal is not a neuronal impulse, and its origin and function are unclear. The second signal is nervous, however. It originates in the cochlear neurons, and its rhythm or frequency is the same as the frequency of the tone being received by that ear. Thus, both amplitude and frequency are signalled by the organ of Corti, but only the frequency signal seems to reflect known neural mechanisms.

The auditory nerves, one from each ear, enter the brain stem where they connect with two groups of neurons. The largest group enters the cortex, and some of these neurons cross to the opposite hemisphere, in a manner analogous to visual neurons in the optic nerve. The smaller group of neurons run to the inferior colliculi where they form a map of the auditory field which is in contact with similar maps of the feeling and visual sensations. The primary auditory centres are in the temporal cortex. A few auditory neurons also run through the brain stem and the brain itself directly from one ear to the other. This arrangement does not occur with optic neurons. It is possible that the input at one ear modifies the behaviour of the other ear in some way.

4. **Hunger and thirst** are sensations distinct from a socially-determined sense of hunger at meal times or ADDICTION to a certain drink, like alcohol. Both hunger and thirst have a physiological foundation in groups of neurons in the hypothalamus.

The hypothalamus contains two types of neuron related to hunger. Glucoreceptors are neurons sensitive to the blood concentration of glucose, the sugar most often used by body cells as a source of energy. The glucoreceptors form satiety centres. When blood sugar reaches an appropriate level, which is not fixed, and changes with conditions, the satiety centre signals, and hunger ceases. A local injection of glucose at the satiety centre causes a starved animal to stop eating. Conversely, blockade of the centre by a local anaesthetic encourages the experimental animal to continue to eat indefinitely.

The second type of hypothalamic neurons affecting hunger form a feeding centre which is independent of the glucoreceptors. It may actually control the psychological perception of hunger.

Thirst is regulated by hypothalamic neurons which form a drinking centre. The neurons respond to salt concentrations in body fluids. When the salt concentration rises, the drinking centre signals, and the animal seeks water to restore the appropriate water balance. Again, the drinking centre response is not a fixed, preset event, but one which alters according to the conditions and experience of the organism. Thus, learned responses to food and drink help to determine sensations of hunger and thirst, as we all know.

**5. Pain.** Despite its survival value and its psychological significance, pain is one of the least well understood sensations. Except for the multitude of isolated, specialized neurons in the skin which also sense temperature, there are no pain sensors as such. Nor is there a unique nervous pathway taking data about pain to the CNS, as distinct from temperature or pressure. Indeed, contrary to popular wisdom, the brain contains no single pain centre.

The sensation of pain is further complicated by the influence of environmental conditions, such as sex, age, social status and cultural factors. For example, boys do not cry, but girls may. Indian fakirs are capable of withstanding burnings and stabbings which would reduce westerners to a jelly. Before the discovery of ANAESTHESIA, patients went through amputations with astonishing stoicism. There is, moreover, an element of awareness in the sensation of pain. If your attention is held elsewhere, you may be unaware that you have hurt yourself. Thus, soldiers in battle have continued to fight despite severe wounds which they do not notice until the immediate danger has passed. These commonly-observed experiences demonstrate the importance of learning and current activity on the sensing of pain. Cortical association areas govern the sensation as markedly as the thalamus which relays all sensations of feeling.

The most useful theory about how pain is sensed was developed by the neurophysiologists, Patrick Wall and Ronald Melzack, English and Canadian respectively, in the late 1960s. They proposed the gate theory founded on the existence in the spinal cord of a physiological mechanism which swings like a gate, allowing pain signals to reach the brain or not, depending on the degree of stimulation and the state of the organism.

The details of the theory are controversial. It is known that different neurons transmit signals at different speeds. In general, the larger the neuron, the faster it transmits. Larger neurons transmitting pain signals from the skin can be shown to respond with relatively less stimulation than the smallest neurons. In other words, the large fibres have a lower threshold of pain, and the small fibres, a high threshold. The hypothetical gate is made by these two types of neurons. The larger neurons deliver pain signals first to the spinal cord, where they are said to stimulate inhibitory interneurons, which prevent the signal from reaching the brain. That is, the large, fast neurons close the gate. The small, slow neurons which require more stimulation before they will signal are said to excite other spinal cord interneurons, cancelling the inhibition and opening the gate so that pain messages reach the brain. The state of learning and attention are also said to affect the responsiveness of the spinal cord neurons to inhibition or excitation because the cortex sends out signals itself.

According to the gate theory, if the large neurons could be selectively stimulated without causing the small fibres to signal, pain would be reduced. Indeed, electrical stimulation through the skin may reduce severe pain without anaesthesia. Implants in the spinal cord are another source of electrical stimulation aimed at closing the gate. They can be energized either by the patient or by the doctor using a radio signal originating at a distance from the patient. Spinal cord implants have shown promising results, but they are inconsistent. During the late 1970s, implants have been tried in the brains of patients who are disabled by chronic pain. Tiny stimulators appropriately placed with relation to the thalamus are thought to cause neurons to release enkephalin, the natural OPIATE which may normally inhibit pain sensation in the brain (see also TRANSMITTER).

Acupuncture is the ancient Chinese therapy for both diseases and pain. It employs needles placed in the body at appropriate points. Acupuncture, too, may control pain by causing the release of enkephalin, but suggestion (see HYPNOTISM) is thought to play a role. Chinese doctors do not use acupuncture to control pain unless the patient agrees, and it is seldom used for this purpose on children.

**6. Proprioception** means the sensing of the self. It consists of sensations from muscles, joints, gut and organs concerning their position and chemical status. (Data about chemical status is sometimes called interoception, in which case proprioception refers only to data about position.) Proprioception is the only sensation that is usually sensed unconsciously, as it were, and affects equally unconscious muscular and glandular responses. On the other hand, it is normally possible for a person to tell the position of an arm or leg with his eyes closed. The impairment of this kinaesthetic sense may be symptomatic of nervous disease.

Proprioceptive responses are not reflex, however; the nervous signal does not pass through the spinal cord without arousing the brain. Movement responses in reply to signals about posture, for example, usually require the intervention of the cerebellum if not the secondary sensory-movement centres in the cortex. Similarly, an excess of carbon dioxide in the blood triggers deeper and more rapid breathing by stimulating neurons in the brain stem.

The specialized nerve endings in muscles and joints which signal information about posture and position are similar to those which underlie feeling. The chemical receptors in blood vessels, the gut, kidneys and brain stem are more mysterious. It can be demonstrated that these tissues respond to changes in their chemical environment, but the neuron endings responsible have not been positively identified. Inasmuch as different chemicals are involved – for example, blood-borne carbon dioxide affects the brain stem and blood salt (carbonic acid) content affects the kidneys – there may be different chemoreceptors in each tissue.

**7. Smell and taste.** The nose is of course the organ of smell, and the mouth, of taste. Each has its own specialized receptors, nervous pathways to the brain and responsive brain centres, but they influence each other, largely by association in the cortex. An unpleasant odour, for example, can reduce the appetite for a sweet. Both are chemical senses; that is, they depend on the binding of molecules to neurons especially adapted to receive them. Incidentally, smell and taste are thought to be the oldest senses, from the evolutionary standpoint (although Colin Blakemore, the British neurophysiologist, has suggested that hearing, based on mechanical wave motion, may be older).

The nose contains olfactory neurons in an area about the size of a fingernail in the roof of each nostril. They specialize in different types of odours, such as acrid or smoky, but they are not sensitive to odours such as those related to baking or brewing. Presumably, the man-made smells are learned. The receptor axons synapse with olfactory neurons which lead to the olfactory centre in the mid-brain. In humans, the centre is smaller than in other animals because the human cortex, which evolved out of the olfactory bulb, is so much larger, and performs so many other functions. As a result, human vision and hearing respond to a greater variety and complexity of stimuli than do these senses in most other animals. Vision and hearing make discrimination and evaluation more subtle and diverse. We are not more clever than other animals, but simply better informed.

Taste depends on four classes of sensation: sour, salt, bitter and sweet. The receptors are neurons on the tongue and at the back of the mouth. They may be specialized in one class of taste, but twenty or thirty of them form the taste buds which respond to a minimum of two and perhaps to all four, classes. The tip of the tongue, where relatively more taste buds are concentrated, is most sensitive to sweetness, the edges to sour and salt and the root to bitterness. Possibly because rubbing wears away cells at the tip of the tongue, there is a tendency for taste sensitivity to change with age.

Some taste receptor neurons run to the salivary glands, but most link with neurons in the face, teeth and jaws which also carry signals originating in receptors for feeling and motion. Thus, taste has no distinctive neural trunk leading to the brain like the olfactory or the optic nerve. Taste neurons end in the mid-brain, especially in the hippocampus, reticular formation and hypothalamus, but some taste signals are also carried into the sensory-motor cortex.

Disorders of taste and smell are common (see AGEUSIA, ANOSMIA). Both senses become less acute with age, but many people seem to live most of their lives without a sense of smell. Conversely, taste or smell hallucinations may be symptomatic of mental disorder.

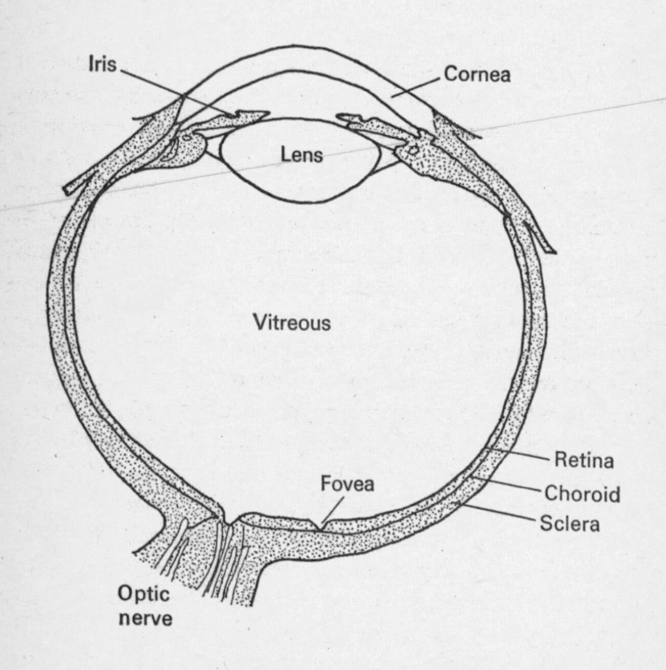


Horizontal section of the eye.

**8. Vision** is better understood than other sensations, perhaps because the eye is both easily removed and self-contained. The eyeball is a tough wall of tissue, the outer portion of which is transparent, forming the cornea. It is filled with a viscous fluid, the vitreous humour. The lens and the lens-regulating muscles, and the iris and muscles controlling its size, focus light on the sense organ on the back of the eyeball, the retina. The retina lines just over half of the inner rear surface. The blackness of the pupil is the reflection of the darkness within the hollow eyeball.

Unlike other sense organs, the two retinas are forward growths of the brain itself. In the human eye, they contain two kinds of receptors, rods and cones, on top of two layers of cells which receive, mix and begin to process the data collected by receptors. Rods and cones, so-called because their specialized dendrites take roughly these shapes, lie at the back of the retina with their light sensitive regions – rod or cone – oriented away from the light towards the back of the eye. The light penetrates the other cell layers to be reflected from the inner coating of the eyeball, the choroid, on to the receptors. Each rod and cone contains thousands of molecules of a light-sensitive pigment, rhodopsin in the rods and iodopsin in the cones. The vitamin A molecule is an essential constituent of both types of visual pigment. There are three kinds of cone cells, depending on the form of the iodopsin in each. Because of slight differences in molecular structure, one is most sensitive to red light, one to blue, and one to green. Rhodopsin responds best to white light. Rods and cones are mixed across the surface of the retina, but there are relatively more rods towards the periphery, and the cones are especially frequent around the fovea, a pit-like region near the front-back axis of the eyeball. Nearby the optic nerve leaves the eye. The fovea itself is a blind spot, lacking both rods and cones. The cone cells concentrated around the fovea make this the point of most acute vision because these colour-sensitive cells signal only when they are stimulated by bright light. Rod cells respond to lower levels of illumination, and the concentration of rods at the periphery of the retina make this region useful for peripheral and night vision. A quick glimpse is registered out of the corner of the eye, but if you want a good look, you have to gaze directly at the thing.

Above the rods and cones in the retina are interneurons, the bilateral, amacrine and interplexiform cells, which collect and transmit signals from the receptors to the innermost cell layer, the ganglion cells. The axons of ganglion cells form the optic nerve when they leave the eyeball. There are between 100 and 130 million rod cells and 5 to 7 million cone cells in each retina, but only about half a million ganglion cells. Thus, an immense amount of mixing and organization is accomplished by the retina before the signals reach the brain. For example, each ganglion cell responds to signals from a group of rod and cone cells in the same area of the retina. Some ganglion cells signal when the centre of the area is stimulated and stop signalling when the periphery is stimulated. Other ganglion cells respond to the opposite situation, firing when light has stimulated receptors at the periphery of the group and ceasing to fire when those at the centre are stimulated. These events are evidence that the processing and interpretation of visual information begins in the eye itself.

Just inside the cortex towards the middle of the head, the optic nerves meet at the optic chiasm where they both divide and cross. Axons from the left side of both eyes (the right visual field, because the lens reverses the image as it enters the eye) continue to the right side of the brain. Those from the right side of both eyes go to the left hemisphere. Thus, both halves of the visual field are available to both sides of the brain. Because our eyes are about two inches apart, the two overlapping fields are slightly out of register. The resultant stereoscopic effect is normally perceived as depth.

At the optic chiasm, some of the ganglion cell axons from each eye leave the optic nerve and run to the colliculi where they are organized into a map of the whole visual field which is juxtaposed to analogous maps of the feeling and hearing fields. However, the bulk of the optic nerves pass to the lateral geniculate bodies in each hemisphere, whence they are distributed to the visual cortex at the back of the brain. Until the signals reach the visual cortex, they retain a similar organization to that which they were given by the ganglion cells; for example, they continue to have their characteristic on-off fields.

The visual cortex is organized in layers, like the rest of the cortex, and there is evidence that columns of cells exist throughout the visual cortex which contain groups of neurons with the same function. Thus, there are cells which fire when a dark field is divided from a light field by a straight line vertically. Others fire when the line is horizontal, and others, when it is diagonal. Another type of visual neuron responds to a moving light at certain orientations; yet another, to coloured light of specific wave length; still others prefer light from one eye or the other – or both. At least some of these cells, moreover, learn to signal. If they are not stimulated by light at a certain time after birth, they lose entirely the ability to signal – at least in kittens. Columns of cells with different orientation sensitivity and dominated by one eye or the other exist in groups, and the mixed cortical columns of cells with distinctive signalling functions are organized into a map of the visual field, one map in each cortical hemisphere. The analysis of light carried out in the primary visual cortex is a function of both inherited wiring and experience. Visual PERCEPTION itself appears to take place in the secondary visual cortex, forward of the primary region, where it is made possible by association with MEMORY and with other kinds of sensation.

**9. Extra-sensory perception.** There are, therefore, eight senses, or indeed, twelve if one counts the feelings and hunger and thirst and smell and taste separately. Many people believe that together with some other animals, we possess yet another sense: extra-sensory perception. ESP can include precognition, contact with the spirit world and various kinds of unassisted movement. Perhaps the most positive scientific statement that can be made about ESP is that there is no proof it does not exist. There is equally no proof that ESP does exist. By definition, it involves no known sensory equipment. It is not possible to point to an eye for precognition, for example. Nor has it been possible to demonstrate ESP by psychological experiments, despite at least fifty years of trying. For example, the numerous attempts to test precognition under controlled conditions have been inconclusive. In 1978, it was suggested in Great Britain that school-aged children display precognitive powers which they later lose, but the evidence is, at best, controversial. By contrast, it is possible to point to BIOFEEDBACK and HYPNOTISM as forms of behaviour which do occur, even though they are as yet without adequate explanation. One must be sceptical about the existence of ESP, but scepticism is not disbelief.

## SEXUAL DEVIATION See DEVIATION, SEXUAL

## SEXUALITY

The quality of being sexual or of possessing sex. Sex is a physiological attribute determined by the genes. Sexuality, a broader term, includes in addition to sex, sexual roles, sexual power and sexual preference, all strongly if not wholly determined by experience. Thus, women are the only female animals perpetually ready, physiologically, to engage in sexual acts, but no human, female or male, is in fact always ready for sex (see DEVIATION, SEXUAL; GENETICS).

Surprisingly little is known about the psychological aspects of ordinary sexuality, perhaps in part because the range of normal practices is well-nigh infinite. In the same way, relatively little is known about the psychology as distinct from the sociology of normal eating and drinking. They are not 'problems'. The lack of data makes it hard to answer the questions that otherwise unexceptional people put to their doctors, priests or radio DJs. For example:

'My husband wants sex more often than I do. Which of us is right?' The answer must be neither – or both. You have to work it out between you.

'My boyfriend says, "Why won't you? Everyone else does." What should I do?' Work it out between you, but never do anything because 'everyone else does'.

'Is what I feel love, or lust?' Only you can know, but given that it isn't love, what's the matter with lust, anyway?

'My wife is no longer interested. Am I to play the field? take a mistress? go to prostitutes?' You will have to decide, preferably with your wife's agreement. Perhaps you both really want another partner.

'Isn't sex connected with having children? So isn't contraception wrong?' Sex is connected with having children, yes, but for better or worse, in western society, sexuality is not. Your church may advise you, but you must decide.

'I'm not satisfied when he/she finishes.' (Yes, women do sometimes achieve satisfaction before men.) 'What shall I do?' There are many possible answers: more, and more varied, sex play, variations in position, even variations in role. Ultimately, they all boil down to two: either work it out between you, or change partners.

According to the present western view, sexuality is for pleasure and, incidentally, also for procreation. Inasmuch as most of us believe that without pleasure, the sex act is meaningless, it is best to behave in such a way as to maximize pleasure.

But pleasure is just as hard to define as any other EMOTION. In sex, for example, pleasure need not include orgasm. It almost certainly always does mean that your sexual partner enjoys the act too. Perhaps above all, pleasure grows with the kind of practised skill that allows you to forget about what you are doing and to get on with doing it.

## SHOCK THERAPY

An epilepsy-like seizure artificially induced to treat mental disorders. The most commonly-used form, electroconvulsive therapy (ECT), employs an electric current to produce the seizure.

The therapeutic effect of ECT depends on the CENTRAL NERVOUS SYSTEM seizure and not on muscular CONVULSION. ECT is given, therefore, after the patient has taken a BARBITURATE to relax him and to reduce the risk that he will bite his tongue or hurt himself in some other way during the shock. Everything possible is done to reassure the patient, and he is always accompanied by a medical attendant. Electrodes are attached to the head, on top of the hair, so that 70 to 120 volts pass through the head for a period lasting between 0.4 and 0.6 seconds. (The current used in British lamps and appliances is 240 volts, and in American, 120 volts.) Pure oxygen may be given through a mask for a short time during and after the shock. The patient loses consciousness briefly and may have a headache and experience confusion when he regains consciousness. ECT is often administered in a series of six to ten doses, each separated by a few days.

When shock therapy was first introduced during the 1930s, the seizure was induced by drugs such as camphor or metrazol. Insulin became popular because it is a natural substance. It causes shock by suddenly reducing the amount of sugar in the blood, a deprivation to which the brain is exquisitely sensitive, but the dose must be carefully controlled. ECT was developed by Ugo Corletti, a Milan doctor, and rapidly replaced the drugs because it is more easily regulated. Chemicals remain in the body until they are broken down or excreted, but the electric shock ends when the current is switched off. On the other hand, the idea of an electric shock can be frightening.

New inhalant drugs, such as flurothyl (Indoklon), are now sometimes preferred.

There is little doubt that shock therapy is an effective treatment for endogenous DEPRESSION. Tests show that shock produces longer remissions in severe depressive illness in more patients than either drug therapy or PSYCHOTHERAPY used alone or together. Since 1939, furthermore, shock therapy has significantly reduced SUICIDE amongst depressed patients. The treatment is not a cure, however. Some of the remissions might have occurred without shock therapy. Many patients are frightened by the procedure, especially by ECT, and some improvements can be explained by the patient's attempt to avoid later sessions in a series. Doubtless, other patients respond as much to the extra care and attention that accompanies shock therapy as to the treatment itself. There is even a salutary story about ECT in a major English mental institution: a newly appointed head psychiatrist decided that after five years without a complete service, the ECT equipment needed a thorough overhaul. When the workmen pulled the heavy transformer away from the wall, they found that its plug was lying on the floor beneath the machine. Hundreds of patients had received no shock at all. Yet despite such evidence, real or apocryphal, shock therapy does help many seriously depressed people.

ANXIETY may be exacerbated by the treatment, and SCHIZOPHRENIA is seldom helped. In addition to headache and confusion, the procedure can cause temporary amnesia. Occasionally, more lasting amnesia has been reported, and in older patients, there may be some intellectual deficit following a series of treatments. Oxygen is used to reduce the risk of damage to the brain, either from the shock or from the seizure. The claim by some opponents of shock therapy that it can cause lasting brain injury has been supported by cases in the United States where Courts have awarded damages to patients. It is important to remember, however, that a jury decision does not create a law of nature, and is not the same as a controlled scientific experiment. The occurrence of lasting brain damage from ECT is without experimental proof.

It is certainly a cause for concern, however, that after forty years, there is still no answer to the question, how does it work?

Somehow, the shock probably alters the balance between the chemical transmitters. Thus, the fact that shock may help depressives but makes anxiety worse, may reflect the different transmitter imbalances thought to underlie these respective conditions. There is evidence that post-synaptic NEURON response to serotonin, dopamine and noradrenaline – all excitatory transmitters in the brain – is enhanced following shock, and that the function of the inhibitory transmitter, GABA, may be reduced. It is also possible that brain chemicals related to the natural OPIATE, enkephalin, mediate the effects of shock. If the sequence of biochemical events in the brain following shock could be clarified, our understanding of the physical causes of mental disorders would also be greatly clarified.

Any procedure which depends on a brain seizure is extreme, on the face of it. If it was possible to find out how the seizure produced by a shock helps the patient, a less dramatic technique might be found to serve the same purpose. It might also be possible to use a physical test, like a blood test, to replace the present hit-or-miss choice of patients whom shock may help by a more rational selection technique.

**SIGHT** See SENSATION

## SKINNER, BURRHUS FREDERIC

Behavioural psychologist who introduced the concept of instrumental or operant conditioning (see PSYCHOLOGY). b. Susquehanna, Pa., USA, 1904. Hamilton College, New York, BA, 1926. Harvard, MA, 1930; PhD, 1931. Research fellow, National Research Council, Harvard, 1931–33. Junior fellow, Harvard Society of Fellows, 1933–36. Instructor, assistant and associate professor in psychology, University of Minnesota, 1936–45. War research sponsored by General Mills, 1942–43. Professor of psychology, Indiana University, 1945–48. Professor of psychology, Harvard, 1948–74. Guggenheim Fellow, 1944–45. *Behavior of Organisms*, 1938. *Walden Two*, 1948. *Science and Human Behavior*, 1953. *Verbal Behavior*, 1957. *Technology of Teaching*, 1968. *Contingencies and Reinforcements; A Theoretical Analysis*, 1969. *Beyond Freedom and Dignity*, 1971. *About Behaviorism*, 1974. *Particulars of My Life*, 1976.

## SLEEP

A temporary state of rest for body and MIND during which CONSCIOUSNESS, MOTIVATION and body functions are partially suspended.

Like many of the definitions in this dictionary (for example, consciousness, DEPRESSION, motivation), the foregoing description of sleep is symptomatic. No one knows exactly what happens in the brain when we fall asleep and wake up, and even less is known about the function sleep performs. We eat to obtain energy. We procreate to perpetuate the species. No one knows why we sleep.

The most obvious explanations, rest and repair, cannot be the whole story. It is true that growth HORMONE is found in the blood during sleep. This implies that children grow during sleep and adults make body repairs. On the other hand, both rest and repair in muscles and other tissues that are not being used or stressed take place during restfulness. Any kind of rest will restore the mechanical efficiency of muscles after exercise. Nor is sleep the only way of resting the brain. There is evidence that students taking examinations do better if sleep intervenes between revision and exam, but it is not clear whether the results of the experiment can be generalized. Certain kinds of relaxation may produce exam results that are not significantly worse.

There is a change in brain rhythms during sleep (see ELECTROENCEPHALOGRAM), but no reduction in the percentage of body heat put out by the brain. In other words, there appears to be no reduction in total brain activity during sleep. Indeed, dreaming (see DREAM) implies a shift in ATTENTION rather than unconsciousness. Nor are the SENSATIONS cut off. A parent's quick response to the sound of the child's cry and the way that a light, touch or sound are worked into a dream indicate that the signals are getting through. The vegetative functions, breathing, heart beat and digestion, are altered during sleep, but they are monitored by the brain. In many essential respects, the brain does not sleep, but sleep deprivation leads to the collapse of both mental and physical abilities, which can even be fatal.

Control over wakefulness is exercised by that part of the brain called the reticular activating system. Damage to this nerve tract can produce a state of permanent somnolence. Thus, the reticular activating system is needed to keep awake. It links the limbic system of the mid-brain to the brain stem, and is, therefore, involved in the coordination of attention and motivation with vegetative functions. Sleep is also associated with a shift in the TRANSMITTER balance found in the reticular activating system. Noradrenaline is associated with wakefulness and the lightest sleep (REM sleep, see below), and serotonin, with deep sleep. Drugs chemically related to serotonin may help insomniac depressive patients to sleep. Changes have also been observed in the excitability of neurons linking the reticular activating system to the cortex. These neurons are in the pyramidal tracts which relay signals about sensations to the cortex and motor commands to the periphery. They signal slightly less readily during sleep than during wakefulness, but no reason for the difference has been found. Because biochemical shifts such as those in the reticular activating system are rhythmic, they are thought to be brought about by hormonal fluctuations in response to dark-light cycles, but there is little hard evidence to support the theory.

The best approach to a poorly-understood phenomenon is, of course, more detailed observation. Accordingly, the scientists interested in sleep have built up an impressive body of data from the observation of sleeping human subjects. A volunteer is first allowed to become accustomed to the light electrodes that are taped to the scalp, the skin beneath the eyes and the eyelids. Except when tests are being made with drugs, the volunteer must learn to sleep naturally with these impedimenta in place. Psychological attributes such as dreaming are observed by awakening the subject at an appropriate time. The electrodes have made it possible to identify four major sleep phases, although they naturally blend into one another.

When we go to sleep, we slip more or less quickly through the first three phases into deep sleep. In this phase, alpha and beta EEG rhythms characteristic of wakefulness continue, but about 50 per cent of the EEG trace shows the delta rhythm. Breathing is noticeably slowed and relatively shallow, and heart beat is slowed. Muscular relaxation is greatest during phase four sleep, and yet, curiously, sleep-walking usually occurs during this phase.

In phase three, the relaxation is less general and the EEG rhythm shows only between 20 per cent and 50 per cent delta activity. The sleeper is proportionately closer to wakefulness. Similarly, phase two sleep shows about 20 per cent delta waves.

Phase one sleep, which normally intervenes between sleeping and waking, is also called rapid-eye movement – REM and paradoxical sleep. REM refers to the eye movements that can be seen quite clearly beneath the closed lids of the sleeper. These movements have often been associated with dream events, and this is the sleep phase during which most if not all dreaming occurs. It is also called paradoxical sleep because the EEG consists primarily of waking rhythms with a small admixture of delta waves. Muscular activity approximates wakefulness, and we toss and turn more than in the deep sleep phases. Breathing is faster and less even. Erections may occur. The body looks as though it is preparing to awaken.

The whole sleep cycle takes place three or four times during the night before phase one leads to awakening. REM sleep occupies about 20 per cent of the night's sleep, and the other three phases, about equal amounts of the remaining 80 per cent.

These proportions of the night spent in each sleep phase seem to be essential for health. A subject who is awakened regularly during one sleep phase will compensate for this disturbance by extending the interrupted phase when he is again allowed to sleep without interruption. BARBITURATES and the minor TRANQUILLIZERS selectively reduce REM sleep, replacing phase one with the other three phases. When the drugs are stopped, the subject experiences a disproportionate amount of REM sleep and of dreaming. It seems probable that the different phases perform different functions, but what they are is not known.

Most of us suffer occasional bouts of insomnia. As we grow older, these annoying periods of wakefulness tend to occur more often in the second half of the night. They are usually associated with some obvious daytime events, especially worries that are taken to bed. Sufferers from insomnia find their own ways of coping with wakefulness. Some count sheep. Others contemplate an imagined object, a mandala, or even some part of their own bodies. Still others read or listen to the radio until they feel drowsy again. It may help if you realize that there is no general standard for the correct amount of sleep.

Children are said to need more sleep than adults. Eight hours a night is the span approved in Britain and the United States, but individual variations are enormous. Some of us make up for lost sleep with catnaps. Some can do with less. Our need for sleep varies, furthermore, with our physical and psychological condition. Later in life, people appear to require less sleep, but extreme old age is often characterized by long periods of sleep during the day as well as at night, almost like infancy.

In some cases, insomnia is, of course, a symptom of illness. Anxious and depressed patients suffer from wakefulness, especially in the second half of the night. Anorectics (see ANOREXIA NERVOSA) are often insomniac, but they welcome wakefulness because they think it contributes to weight loss. Sleeplessness can also occur during physical illness. Restoration of normal sleep is always desirable, and a tranquillizer may be helpful. Barbiturates are less often used as HYPNOTICS today because they can be addictive and poisonous.

To avoid sleep, an AMPHETAMINE such as benzedrine may be helpful for a short period. The user must remember that the sleep lost will have to be made up. Use of a sleeping pill to overcome the effect of an excitant drug, a course sometimes followed by athletes, or other entertainers or politicians, is a shocking abuse of the body, the effect of which is unpredictable. Like barbiturates, amphetamines are potentially addictive and poisonous.

Caffeine in tea and coffee is also a CNS excitant drug (see ANALEPTIC). In quantity, it can help people to wake up and to stay awake, and the action of caffeine is likely to be more gentle than that of the amphetamines. Black coffee is almost always an antidote for barbiturate overdose. The most common side effect from excessive use of caffeine is increased jumpiness. As with stronger drugs, caffeine wakefulness must be made up for with sleep at a later day. Normal consumption of tea or coffee (three or four cups a day for adults) should be without ill effects. Whether tea or coffee in the evening will keep you awake depends more on you than on the beverage. Tea contains more excitant drugs than coffee, and real cocoa also contains an excitant. Some people are certainly more sensitive to caffeine than others, but the objective evidence is inconclusive. If you think the evening drink will keep you awake, of course, the thought often becomes a self-fulfilling prophecy.

**SLEEPING MEDICINE** See HYPNOTIC

**STAMMER**

A speech impairment characterized by abrupt interruptions or repetitions of sounds or syllables. In the United States, more often called stutter.

About 1 per cent of British school children suffer the disability. It is more common in boys than girls and tends to run in families. Stammer rarely develops after the age of seven or eight. It is often associated with left-handedness or ambidexterity. The stammerer may break his speech with pauses filled with hisses or grunts. Often, he develops a simultaneous TIC. Reiteration of syllables may be triggered by difficulties with consonants, especially t, d, p, b, k and hard g. Stammerers can usually sing without impairment, and they will often speak normally when angry or alone.

The disorder is probably not physiological in origin. It is thought to begin when the child is learning to speak. He may be unusually impatient or self-conscious. If the child's normal hesitancy and repetitiveness provokes anxiety in his parents, his tension is increased, and the provocative speech defect may be perpetuated.

Mild stammer often disappears spontaneously. More severe cases may be controlled or corrected with patient and informed treatment. If stammer is associated with left-handedness in a child who has been taught to use his right hand, a return to the left hand can help. The child is taught to relax, and given exercises to relax his breathing and improve control over lips, jaws, tongue and palate. Then, under guidance, he begins to practise words, often by singing, or in time with a metronome. It is important that doctors try to explain the probable origin of stammer to parents and teachers in order to reduce the tensions which the adults easily communicate to the child.

**STIMULANT** See ANALEPTIC

**STIMULUS-RESPONSE** See PSYCHOLOGY

**STRESS**

Pressure, especially that executed by diffuse environmental circumstances on the body. Stresses may include injury, exposure, disease, mental distress and deprivation.

Behind the idea of stress is the theory of physiological balance introduced by the French physiologist, Claude Bernard, over a century ago and given the name 'homeostasis' by the American physiologist, W. B. Cannon (see CONSCIOUSNESS). Any influence which pushes the body out of balance exerts stress.

The Canadian physician, Hans Selye, holds that stress affects the whole body, but especially the adrenal glands because they produce HORMONES which help the body to prepare itself against threats. Injury probably lowers resistance to disease, and worry increases the seriousness of physical illness. As with PSYCHOSOMATIC disease, stress is a catch-all word to cover a multitude of related causes when it is not possible to isolate a clear sequence of causative events.

**STROKE** See BRAIN DAMAGE

**STUTTER** See STAMMER

**SUICIDE**

(Latin: *sui*=of himself+*caedere*=to kill) killing oneself.

Almost as many people commit suicide each year in Great Britain and the United States as are killed by road accidents in these two countries. In the 1960s, the official figures were over 5,200 and 19,000, respectively, but because of reluctance to report suicides, they are thought to occur as much as 25 per cent more frequently. Work in the United States suggests that there may also be a new category of 'murder suicide'. The suicide kills himself along with the other passengers in a plane crash. Some road accidents may also be disguised suicides. It is possible that these bizarre tragedies are correlated with publicity given murder and suicide by the media.

Like other extreme behaviour, suicide has been intensively studied, and a mass of descriptive details have emerged:

More men than women kill themselves.

In Great Britain and the United States, whites kill themselves more often than blacks.

The largest increase in the number of suicides has been in the age group under thirty, but the greatest risk is in the age group over sixty.

Suicide is more common in northern Europe than in the south.

The suicide rate reaches a peak during periods of economic depression, and falls to the lowest point during war.

Urban-rural differences in the suicide rate have declined in recent years. The suicide rate continues to rise in rough proportion to the size of the conurbation in England, but the trend is not so clear in the United States.

The theory that DEPRESSION and suicide occur more often in developed than in underdeveloped countries is not proven.

It is still customary to distinguish suicide from attempted suicide. The incidence of attempted suicide is hard to establish, but probably six to eight times as many people try to kill themselves as succeed. Many authorities hold that a deliberate act of self-injury differs from suicide, however, only in the degree of success achieved, and that the underlying causes are the same. It is a serious mistake, certainly, to accept the common wisdom that attempted suicide is merely an attention-getting device, that the attempt will not be repeated because it produces a kind of catharsis which clears the subject's system, or that people who talk about it never do it. Talking about suicide is a real danger signal (see 9, below). No one knows how many people actually make a later suicide attempt which is successful because statistics are obscured by continued unwillingness to report deliberate self-injury as distinct from accident.

One major British psychiatric textbook states that patients who display two of the following twelve symptoms are at risk of committing suicide, and those with more than two are at serious risk:

1. Depression, especially with guilt feelings
2. Regular insomnia with serious worry about it
3. Severe HYPOCHONDRIA, especially about venereal disease, cancer or heart disease
4. Attempted suicide

5. Male over 55
6. Alcoholism or other drug addiction, past or present
7. Physical illness, especially if it is disabling to a previously active man
8. Loneliness
9. Talk about suicide
10. Family history of suicide
11. Unemployment or financial difficulties
12. 'Towards the end of a period of depressive illness when the mood persists but initiative and power of decision are recovering.' (Slater and Roth, p. 797; see *Further Reading*)

No reason has been given for the ordering of the list of symptoms.

Suicide is indicative of a serious but poorly-understood disorder. At its simplest, the disorder reflects a reversal of the normal, biological tendency of living tissue to protect and perpetuate itself. A suicide attempt which fails may indeed be a form of moral blackmail, a scream of outrage against individuals or 'society', but it could have succeeded. The social-psychological intention is less important than the biologically-deviant attempt at self-destruction.

The question of suicide in the presence of a diagnosed, incurable disease – for example, terminal cancer – must be looked at in this light. If the patient knows that he is almost certainly going to die anyway, probably in pain, his decision to kill himself is less deviant, at the least. Under such circumstances, suicide is akin to the behaviour of other dying animals which leave their usual society to die alone, perhaps more quickly.

Since 1961, suicide has ceased to be a crime in Britain. It is rarely treated as such in the United States. Although decriminalization is both morally and medically sensible, the attention of the law guaranteed that in the event of an attempted suicide, responsible authorities tried to isolate and protect the patient. They might even have sought for causes. The right to kill yourself, like any other freedom, adds to the burden carried by the individual – and suicides are people who are least able to carry the weight.

**SULCUS** See BRAIN

## SULLIVAN, HENRY STACK

Psychiatrist, concerned with the role of environment in individual's conflicts, and attempted psychotherapy of schizophrenia. b. Norwich, NY, 1892. d. Paris, 1949. Chicago College of Medicine and Surgery, 1917. Worked at psychiatric centre of St Elizabeth's Hospital, Washington, DC. Clinical Research, Sheppard and Enoch Pratt Hospital, Towson, Md., 1923–30. Research director from 1925. Helped establish Washington, DC, School of Psychiatry, 1936. With UNESCO from 1945. Helped establish World Federation for Mental Health. *The Interpersonal Theory of Psychiatry*, 1953. *The Fusion of Psychiatry and Social Science*, 1964.

## SUPERIORITY COMPLEX See ADLER, PSYCHOANALYSIS

## SYNAESTHESIA

(Greek: *syn*=with+*aesthesia*=to feel, perceive) a crossing of senses; SENSATION of one kind causes PERCEPTION of another sensation.

In exceptional cases, synaesthesia occurs to normal people. The experience is unusual even in abnormal states, but it may be a part of schizophrenic DELUSIONS (see SCHIZOPHRENIA), and of mescaline-induced hallucinations (see HALLUCINOGEN). For example, the sound of a workman hammering causes the subject to see dots of colour spaced in relation to the rhythm of the hammer. It has also been reported that the thought of lemon flavour produces the sensation of a blue colour. The application of the word 'blues' to a kind of music expresses exactly the meaning of synaesthesia.

The physiological basis for the experience is unclear. NEURONS carry signals from the taste buds to a brain region not primarily devoted to taste: the sensory region of the cortex which deals with feeling. These neurons may be carrying signals of touch, temperature or pressure, rather than taste as such. In other sensory pathways and in the colliculi, where visual, auditory and feeling maps of the body are juxtaposed, sensations are not normally confused. It is probable that synaesthesia is an accident of association, rather than an actual mis-recording of sensory data.

**SYNAPSE** See NEURON

## SYNCOPE

(Greek: faint) sudden loss of consciousness due to a fall in blood supply to the BRAIN.

Syncope is the result of a reflex action. For example, an emotional shock causes heart beat to slow and the blood vessels in the gut to relax. Too little blood reaches the brain momentarily, and the person faints. When he falls, gravity restores blood circulation in the head, and he recovers consciousness.

Syncope is rarely fatal itself. Although it can occur after a stroke, in rare brain diseases which suddenly cut off blood supply from one region of the brain, and in patients with circulatory disease, it seldom indicates organic disease. Syncope often accompanies hysterical attacks (see HYSTERIA), and can occur during bouts of phobic ANXIETY. Fainting after standing for a long period, for example, on parade, reflects the pooling of blood in the legs. It can be prevented by occasionally flexing the leg muscles.

Vertigo or pallor frequently presage syncope. You should quickly sit down and lower your head to waist level. If you are there when someone faints, the best treatment is to loosen the clothes and stand aside.

## SYNDROME

(Greek: concurrence) a set of symptoms which occur together. They are often named after the physician who observed the syndrome in a group of patients. With the demonstration of the germ theory of disease during the nineteenth century, it became possible to diagnose on the basis of cause rather than symptoms. Syndromes were, of course, diseases of unknown origin, but many of them still are. Although syndromes affect many organs and parts of the body, those described in this entry include mental retardation and brain malformations amongst their symptoms. With the exception of Down's syndrome, they are rare.

1. Down's syndrome
2. Gerstmann's syndrome
3. Klinefelter's syndrome

4. Korsakov's syndrome
5. Tourette, Gilles de la, syndrome
6. Miscellaneous

**1. Down's syndrome** (John Langdon Down, English, 1828–96) is also called mongolism because of the typical fold of skin over the inner corners of the patient's eyes and the coarse, straight hair. It occurs in about 1 in 650 births, but the incidence increases with the age of the mother. About half of all Down's patients are born to women over forty.

The degree of mental and physical retardation varies greatly. Physical abnormalities affect the skull, skeleton, hands, feet, heart and gut. The children may seem to grow normally at first, but their mental age usually remains between 5 and 8 years. Most of them are simple and affectionate. Those who live past forty often develop signs of presenile DEMENTIA.

In 1959, Down's patients were found to have 47 chromosomes instead of the normal 46 (see GENETICS). One of the small chromosome pairs, known as chromosome G, fails to divide when the ovum is formed. If that ovum is fertilized, the new cell contains three rather than two of chromosome G – a condition known as trisomy. It is this error which occurs more often with age, but it is very rare that later children are also affected. There is a much less common form of Down's syndrome, however, which occurs regardless of age; in this form, either the ovum or the sperm is abnormal. There is a high risk that later children of these parents will also display Down's syndrome.

As yet, there is no explanation for the symptoms which are produced as a result of chromosome G trisomy. By examining a small amount of the amniotic fluid surrounding the foetus, a technique called aminocentesis, it is possible to inspect foetal cells under a microscope early in pregnancy and to determine whether they contain any chromosomal abnormality. If they do, the parents can be advised so that they can make a decision about an abortion.

**2.** In **Gerstmann's syndrome** (Joseph Gerstmann, Austrian, 1887–), the patient is unable to name or select individual fingers on his own hand or on the hand of the doctor. The patient also has AGRAPHIA, ACALCULIA, right-left disorientation, and in some cases, ALEXIA. These disorders are caused by damage to a part of the cortex, the dominant angular gyrus (see BRAIN). The symptoms may grow worse with age.

**3. Klinefelter's syndrome** (Harry F. Klinefelter, Jr, American, 1912–) has been diagnosed in male patients confined to hospitals for the criminally insane (see SANITY). The symptoms are dwarfism, a eunuch-like appearance, underdeveloped testes, abnormalities of the sex HORMONES and severe mental retardation. These patients display an abnormality of the sex chromosomes, with two or three female chromosomes instead of one, plus the male chromosome: XXXY or XXY (normal: XY).

**4. Korsakov's syndrome,** also called Korsakov's psychosis (S. S. Korsakov, Russian, 1853–1900) is dominated by a kind of AMNESIA, and may be the same as Wernicke's encephalopathy (see BRAIN DAMAGE, part 4). The patient cannot retain or recall new memories, although his MEMORY for past events may be relatively undisturbed. The memory defect affects time perception so that the patient is almost unaware of duration. He may also experience periodic bouts of euphoria.

Korsakov's syndrome is often caused by a B-vitamin deficiency resulting from chronic alcoholism. However, the syndrome may follow anoxia, carbon monoxide poisoning, epilepsy, syphilis, brain tumour, certain other less common brain disorders, and electroconvulsive therapy (see SHOCK THERAPY). The symptoms reflect damage to certain mid-brain and cortical structures, especially in the left temporal cortex, but the amnesia can be corrected with vitamin therapy providing the damage is neither too extensive nor long term.

**5. Tourette, Gilles de la, syndrome** (French, 1857–1904) was the subject of a British television report in 1977, but it is extremely rare. The patient is normal mentally; his MEMORY and INTELLIGENCE are not affected. Beginning in childhood, however, he displays severe TICS including speech containing barks, grunts and obscenities, ECHOLALIA and repetitions of movements. Lefthandedness is more common amongst these patients than in the general population. It is thought that the syndrome may be due to FUNCTIONAL causes rather than ORGANIC. A major TRANQUILLIZER, haloperidol, may help.

**6. Miscellaneous:** bizarre and extremely rare syndromes, with their principal symptoms.

'Cri du chat' – a chromosomal disorder causing severe retardation, an underdeveloped brain and a cat-like cry.

de Lange's – retardation, dwarfism, cranial and facial distortions.

Donohue's – also called leprechaunism.

Menke's – a sex-linked genetic disorder possibly due to poor copper absorption, causing white 'kinky' hair, epilepsy, brain degeneration and, usually, death in early childhood.

Riley-Day – a genetic disorder mainly of Jewish children, possibly due to an error of metabolism affecting TRANSMITTERS and causing high blood pressure, high fever, vomiting, epilepsy, various sensory defects and early death.

Sotos – precocious puberty, abnormally large head, face, hands and feet, and excessive growth up to the age of five.

**SYPHILIS** See BRAIN DAMAGE

**SZASZ, T.** See HEALTH, MENTAL; PSYCHIATRY; PSYCHOTHERAPY

# T

**TASTE** See SENSATION

**TEMPORAL** See BRAIN

**TENSION** See STRESS

**TESTS**

Hundreds of tests are used by doctors to measure and diagnose. Taking the pulse and percussion require nothing but the hands, and some training. The familiar thermometer tests temperature, the stethoscope, heart and lung action, and the sphigmomanometer, blood pressure. All tests assume prior agreement on a standard of normality. Thus, 37°C is a standard norm for body temperature, but one's own temperature varies around this norm from hour to hour. Physical norms usually permit variation within a prescribed range.

Psychological testing is also based on norms which are drawn from observation and statistical analysis, like physical norms.

Thousands of people have been asked the same questions under conditions which are as near as possible the same; for example, writing with a pencil on a standard test sheet. Their replies, categorized by age, sex, educational level, parents' income, marital status of parents, number of brothers and sisters, and so on, provide a statistical picture or curve which shows a standard performance. Like the physical norms, the curve shows a range within which normal variation occurs.

The norms on which psychological tests are based can seldom be seriously questioned. However, controversy may surround the interpretation of the meaning or importance of the questions asked, the conditions of testing and the interpretation of results. Exactly the same doubt may be raised about the meaning or importance of a temperature of 37.5°, the only difference being that temperature testing requires only one observation whereas psychological testing for a trait such as INTELLIGENCE needs dozens.

Psychological tests measuring intelligence were introduced in 1908 by a French psychologist, Alfred Binet, working with a psychiatrist named Simon. The tests were designed to measure the mental age of the subject compared with a standard of 100 for his contemporaries. If the subject's score is 110, his quotient is 10 per cent above the norm for his age. If it is 90, his quotient is 10 per cent below the norm. The same kind of IQ tests are used today, modified by various authorities to overcome difficulties of interpretation in earlier tests. For example, the original version of the earliest American IQ tests, the Stanford-Binet tests as revised by L. M. Terman and M. A. Merrill in 1937, were not applicable in the United Kingdom because many of the words and phrases had to be 'translated' into British English. The simplest and one of the earliest revisions was prepared for the Scottish Council for Research in Education by D. Kennedy-Fraser in 1945. Perhaps the most commonly used general intelligence test in Britain is the Wechsler Adult Intelligence Scale (1955) which is suitable for ages from 15 to 75.

Special tests have been developed to score skills such as reading, spoken vocabulary, arithmetic, drawing and special skills such as reading speed and fluency, spelling, handwriting, spatio-mechanical judgment and clerical ability.

For the measurement of emotional stability and neurotic (see NEUROSIS) traits, the EYSENCK Maudsley Medical Questionnaire (1947) and the Minnesota Multiphasic Personality Inventory are widely used. Such tests consist of questions about preferences and attitudes rather than about subject matter or skills. They are designed to be taken by adults. An entirely different approach is illustrated in the ink blot tests, the best known of which were designed by the Swiss psychiatrist, Herman Rorschach (1884–1922). The subject is asked to interpret the blot; that is, to describe what he sees in it. These tests are much harder to standardize and more controversial than the question-and-answer tests. Interest and attitude tests also study values (Allport-Vernon-Lindzey, 'Study of Values'), socio-political position (Eysenck Inventory of Social Attitudes, Radicalism-conservatism and tough-tender mindedness), masculinity-femininity (Slater Selective Vocabulary Test of Masculine and Feminine Interests) and technical and academic interests (for example, Devon Interest Test of Technical and Academic Interests by Wiseman and Fitzpatrick).

**T-GROUP** See PSYCHOTHERAPY

**THALAMUS** See BRAIN

**THORNDIKE, EDWARD LEE**

Psychologist who postulated laws of LEARNING and directed United States education towards an emphasis on social utility. b. Williamsburg, Mass., USA, 1874. d. Montrose, NY, 1949. Harvard, PhD, 1901; dissertation: *Animal Intelligence*, described experimental animal psychology which he originated. Professor of educational psychology, Teachers College, Columbia University, 1904–40. Introduction to the Theory of Mental and Social Measurements, 1904. *The Principles of Teaching Based on Psychology*, 1906. *Education: A First Book*, 1912. *Educational Psychology* (3 volumes), 1913–14. *The Psychology of Wants, Interests and Attitudes*, 1935. *Human Nature and Social Order*, 1940.

**THOUGHT** See COGNITION

## TIC

(French: *tiquer*=person with a tic) 1. habit spasm. 2. a quick, spasmodic, repetitive movement, or twitch.

Tics are more often seen in children between the ages of two and thirteen than in later life. They include clearing the throat, blinking, turning the neck and opening the mouth, twitching hands, jerking the arms and grimacing. Tics are thought to be one extreme form of HYPERACTIVITY.

Children with tics may be lonely and mildly neurotic (see NEUROSIS). In most cases, it will disappear given time, but if it is severe, behaviour therapy (see PSYCHOTHERAPY) may help.

Tic douleureux is a facial spasm often accompanied by severe pain. It is a neuralgia; that is, a disorder affecting a nerve, in this case the trigeminal. No mental disorder is involved.

## TOLERANCE See ADDICTION

## TOMOGRAPHY, COMPUTERIZED TRANSAXIAL

A technique combining x-rays and computer analysis which permits the visualization of serial sections of a tissue such as the BRAIN. The usual x-ray picture is a single exposure which reveals hard tissue, such as bone, but does not show up soft tissue clearly. In tomography, the x-ray tube moves so that only tissue in a selected plane appears, and in computerized transaxial tomography, the computer sums the images in one plane so as to distinguish the soft tissues as well as hard tissue. The machinery was developed by EMI and is perhaps the most important new technique for the study and diagnosis of living brain tissue since Roentgen's discovery of x-rays. It is particularly useful for the identification and localization of brain tumours (see BRAIN DAMAGE) and may be helpful in the diagnosis of epilepsy (see PSYCHOMOTOR DISEASE) and DEMENTIA.

Computerized tomography may also be used to reveal the inside of other parts of the body; for example, to obtain cross-sectional images of the chest or gut. Its value for diagnosis outside the brain is less clear, however, because simpler and older techniques provide almost the same kind of information. A whole body scanner costs roughly £300,000 at 1979 prices, furthermore, and the question of value is directly related to the comparative cost of less sophisticated diagnostic mechanisms.

**TOUCH** See SENSATION

**TOUCH THERAPY** See PSYCHOTHERAPY

**TOURETTE, GILLES DE LA, SYNDROME** See SYNDROME

**TRANQUILLIZER**

A drug which quiets and calms but does not affect awareness. Until tranquillizers became available, only HYPNOTIC drugs could be used to control ANXIETY, DEPRESSION and SCHIZOPHRENIA, but sedatives such as BARBITURATES and bromides make the patient sleepy. Major tranquillizers were the first to be introduced and are used for the treatment of schizophrenia and endogenous depression. Minor tranquillizers reduce anxiety and control insomnia due to worry or minor pain.

The tranquillizer era began in 1950 with the synthesis of chlorpromazine (Thorazine, Largactil), the first of a series of compounds called phenothiazines. They include fluphenazine (Moditen), prochlorperazine (Stemetil) and thioridazine (Melleril). Chlorpromazine revolutionized the management of serious FUNCTIONAL disorders. For centuries, mental hospital wards had been like Bedlam. Almost overnight, they became relatively placid, with ambulatory patients able to tend to their own basic needs. Many people object to the drugged appearance of patients under tranquillization, but rarely do the patients themselves resist medication.

Like all of the tranquillizer drugs, chlorpromazine must never be taken by a person who is going to drive a car. It can cause a fall in blood pressure on standing up, especially in older people, and it may produce allergy-like reactions and motor disturbances. The phenothiazines are not addictive (see ADDICTION), nor are they effective poisons. The drugs act in mid-brain centres affecting emotion, and in the cortex.

Haloperidol (Serenace) is also a major tranquillizer with therapeutic uses similar to those of chlorpromazine, and with similar side effects. It has a different chemical make-up, however. Reserpine, a derivative of the Indian plant, *Rauwolfia*, controls schizophrenic symptoms, but its side effects are much more severe than those of the other major tranquillizers. Though reserpine is still prescribed for the control of high blood pressure, it is now seldom used for mental disorders. All major tranquillizers may also cause tardive dyskinesia (see PSYCHOMOTOR DISEASE) after chronic use.

The first minor tranquillizer, meprobamate (Equanil, Miltown) was developed in 1954. In 1960, chlordiazepoxide (Librium) was introduced and it has been followed by others in the chemical class, benzodiazepines. They include diazepam (Valium), oxazepam (Serenid, Serax) and nitrazepam (Mogadon). Chlordiazepoxide and diazepam are prescribed by British doctors more frequently than any other drugs. They have never been used successfully to commit suicide, but they may be addictive. Some patients also display allergy-like reactions to them. Even the minor tranquillizers tend to build up in the blood, and they impair the ability to drive. However, newer, short-acting benzodiazepines such as methyprylone may be effective tranquillizers which can be safely used before driving. The benzodiazepines are thought to facilitate the action of the inhibitory TRANSMITTER, GABA. There is now evidence, furthermore, that the BRAIN contains a natural tranquillizer analagous to the natural OPIATE, enkephalin, and that at least some tranquillizers act at RECEPTORS for the natural chemical.

A tranquillizer is often given to prepare a patient for surgery, for the control of MOTION SICKNESS and to help addicts through withdrawal.

**TRANSACTIONAL ANALYSIS** See PSYCHOTHERAPY

**TRANSMITTER**

(Latin: *trans*=across+*mittere*=send) a chemical released by a stimulated NEURON which diffuses across the synaptic gap and changes the electro-chemical properties of a post-synaptic neuron. The transmitter may decrease resistance to the flow of an electro-chemical current across the neuron membrane, thus increasing the probability that the post-synaptic neurons will be stimulated to signal. Such transmitters are excitatory.

Another transmitter may increase resistance, decreasing the probability that the post-synaptic neuron will signal. Such a transmitter is inhibitory. There is also evidence that transmitters may in some cases alter the behaviour of the presynaptic neuron, as well; that is, the behaviour of the neuron which has released the transmitter.

The theory that a chemical carries the electro-chemical nervous signal across the synaptic gap was enunciated early in this century. Its validity was demonstrated in 1921 by Otto Loewi, a German neurophysiologist. Loewi's experiments revealed the role of noradrenaline, closely related chemically to adrenaline (epinephrine), as a transmitter of signals regulating heart beat. Noradrenaline thus transmits signals between a peripheral nerve, the vagus, and heart muscle, and it plays a similar role at many other involuntary muscle sites.

Most voluntary muscles are regulated by neurons which use acetylcholine (ACh) as a transmitter. Noradrenaline and acetylcholine are also transmitters in the brain, but there they share the responsibility with a number of other chemicals. No one is yet sure how many others. Thus, dopamine and serotonin (5-hydroxytryptamine, 5-HT) are also excitatory transmitters in the brain. In the cortex, however, the most important excitatory transmitter is thought to be glutamic acid. Noradrenaline, dopamine and serotonin may also act as inhibitory transmitters depending on where in the brain they are released. Gamma-amino-butyric acid (GABA), glycine and taurine are thought to act only as inhibitors. Thus, in the hippocampus, glutamic acid excites and GABA depresses signal output. One of the most interesting recent transmitter discoveries has been enkephalin, an inhibitor which acts like a natural OPIATE, reducing SENSATIONS of pain.

All of these substances consist of small, nitrogen containing molecules. Glycine and glutamic acid are amino acids, nitrogen compounds which are used by cells for the synthesis of proteins (see ENZYME). GABA and taurine are also amino acids, but they do not become part of proteins in humans and other higher animals. The transmitters are synthesized by the neurons that release them. At the same time, neurons are among the most active protein-synthesizing cells in the body. How the neuron determines whether to use the amino acids as transmitters or as bricks for the construction of proteins is not known.

Both glutamic acid and dopamine, moreover, are the chemical precursors of other transmitters: GABA and noradrenaline, respectively. Note that glutamic acid and GABA have opposite effects, the former being excitatory and the latter, inhibitory. Inasmuch as one neuron synthesizes only one transmitter, as far as is known, which one is released must somehow be determined by the neuron.

Glial cells (see BRAIN) may also store amino acids and possibly some other transmitters for the neurons nearest to them, but, in general, transmitters are synthesized in the neuron body. The molecules are transported along the axon, probably in minute tubules. In the axon bulb, transmitter molecules are stored in sacks or vesicles. The effect of the electro-chemical signal is to cause these vesicles to merge with the neuron membrane releasing their contents into the synaptic gap. When the molecule reaches the post-synaptic membrane, it becomes attached to a RECEPTOR, causing a change in the shape of the receptor which alters the structure and function of the whole membrane.

The signal thus transmitted must stop once it has been registered. Otherwise, a new signal can have no effect. Once the receptor changes shape, it is thought to release the transmitter molecule. Either the transmitter too has been changed in the process, so that it no longer functions, or it is destroyed by enzymes in the synaptic gap. For example, the ACh molecule is split by an enzyme called cholinesterase. The releasing neuron probably reabsorbs some of the transmitter, possibly unchanged. Noradrenaline, for example, may be broken down both in the synaptic gap and in the cell where it has been synthesized by monoamine oxidase (see DEPRESSION). A third enzyme also attacks noradrenaline in the synaptic gap.

This classical picture of the operation of transmitters has been modified by the discovery of a chemical, Substance P, which alters the activity of some neurons, especially neurons in the basal ganglia affected by dopamine and GABA, but is not a transmitter as such. The cells that synthesize Substance P have not been identified.

Though one neuron synthesizes only one transmitter,

neurons in the brain may be affected by more than one. Thus, a neuron in the cortex may be excited by acetylcholine and inhibited by GABA. In the cerebellum, neurons appear to respond only to one transmitter, and it may be that in other parts of the brain, the same restriction applies. The potential physical relationships, however, are enormously complex. Not only does one neuron form thousands of synapses, but its activity is influenced by transmitters of opposite sign, so to speak, one saying 'fire', and the other 'remain silent'. The neuron itself must add and subtract the transmitter signals it receives by means of the functioning of its membrane molecules. Neurons releasing and responsive to different transmitters exist side by side, forming tracts which carry signals with different, possibly contradictory content. The transmitters themselves must compete for raw materials with other products made by the same cells; for example, proteins such as enzymes. The magnitude of the neuron's potentialities is surpassed only by the vast number of neurons in the brain.

It is scarcely to be wondered at that things go wrong from time to time. Indeed, we may think it even more astonishing that they go right most of the time for most of us. Nor is our practical ability to help a patient much advanced by the knowledge that depression is caused by an imbalance in transmitters. The nature of the putative imbalance is bound to take years to unravel. It is necessary not only to trace chemical cause-and-effect, but also to describe the manner in which environment acts as a trigger to internal chemistry.

**TRANSSEXUALISM** See DEVIATION, SEXUAL

**TRANSVESTISM** See DEVIATION, SEXUAL

**TRAUMA**

(Greek=wound) a wound; by extension, an emotional upset which causes mental damage. Trauma underlies most, if not all, NEUROSIS.

Birth trauma is an injury to the infant at birth. In PSYCHIATRY, the phrase has been extended to include hypothetical mental STRESS produced by the process of birth. FREUD referred to it as a prototypical example of neurosis caused by trauma.

The American psychiatrist, Arthur Janov, has given the birth trauma a central role in all mental illness, identifying it as 'the primal scream' and elaborating a system of 'primal therapy'. He does not explain how the vast majority of mankind, 'born of woman' though they are, escape without even a neurotic disorder (see also PSYCHOTHERAPY).

**TRAVEL SICKNESS** See MOTION SICKNESS

**TRICYCLIC DRUGS** See DEPRESSION

**TUMOUR** See BRAIN DAMAGE

# U

**UNCONSCIOUS** See CONSCIOUSNESS; PSYCHOANALYSIS; SLEEP

# W

**WATSON, JOHN BROADUS**
Psychologist who codified and publicized the stimulus-response approach to behaviour and named it Behaviorism (see PSYCHOLOGY). b. Greenville, S.C., USA, 1878. d. New York City, 1958. University of Chicago, PhD, 1903. Assistant and then instructor, University of Chicago, 1903–08. Professor of psychology, Johns Hopkins University, 1908–20. Resigned because of publicity aroused by divorce from first wife. Formed advertising agency, 1921; retired, 1946. Introduced the word 'behaviorism' in an article: *Psychology as a Behaviorist Views It*, 1913. *Behavior: An Introduction to Comparative Psychology*, 1914. *Psychology from the Standpoint of Behaviorism*, 1919. *Behaviorism*, 1925. *Psychological Care for Infant and Child*, 1928.

**WERNICKE'S ENCEPHALOPATHY** See BRAIN DAMAGE; SYNDROME

**WITHDRAWAL** See ADDICTION

**WUNDT, W.** See PSYCHOLOGY

# Further reading

Much of the data in *The Dictionary of Mental Health* was taken from research papers. No attempt is made to acknowledge these sources because this is a book for the lay person who will not, in most cases, possess the scientific background needed to appreciate the detailed contributions of workers in the various fields. The *Dictionary* is firmly rooted in the physio-chemical behaviour of the nervous system, and research in neurology, biochemistry, physiology and biology is of major importance in all the definitions. PSYCHOLOGY and PSYCHIATRY, subjects of greater interest to the lay public, are fields in which, by and large, new results of significant research appear more quickly in books, to say nothing of the popular media. In no field, however, is the following list a complete bibliography. Such a monumental collection of titles would take more space than the *Dictionary* itself, and it would meet only very imperfectly the needs of the interested reader for whom this selection of Further Reading is intended.

Four general textbooks have been regularly consulted:

GOODMAN, LOUIS S. and A. GILMAN, editors, *The Pharmacological Basis of Therapeutics*, 5th edition, New York, London and Toronto, Macmillan, 1977.

LINDSAY, PETER H. and D. A. NORMAN, *Human Information Processing: An Introduction to Psychology*, New York and London, Academic Press, 1972.

SLATER, ELIOT and M. ROTH, *Mayer-Gross, Slater and Roth, Clinical Psychiatry*, London, Baillière Tindall, 1977.

WALTON, JOHN N., *Brain's Diseases of the Nervous System*, 8th edition, Oxford, New York and Toronto, Oxford University Press, 1977.

Major works by the influential psychologists and psychoanalysts are listed under their names in the *Dictionary*. All of the books so listed are available in English in any reasonably good library; most of them are in print, a majority in paperback editions.

Specific reference is made to the following additional books in the entries noted:

BERNE, ERIC, *Games People Play, The Psychology of Human Relationships*, New York, Grove Press, 1964. (PSYCHOTHERAPY)

CLARE, ANTHONY, *Psychiatry in Dissent, Controversial Issues in Thought and Practice*, London, Tavistock, 1976. (NEUROSIS)

FLAVELL, J. H., *The Developmental Psychology of Jean Piaget*, New York, London and Toronto, Van Nostrand, 1964. (PIAGET)

LURIA, A. R., *The Man with a Shattered World*, Harmondsworth, Penguin, 1975. (BRAIN DAMAGE)

PICKERING, GEORGE (SIR), *Creative Malady*, London, Allen and Unwin, 1974. (PSYCHOSOMATIC DISEASE)

SZASZ, T. S., *The Myth of Mental Illness, Foundations of a Theory of Personal Conduct*, London, Paladin, 1972. (PSYCHIATRY)

Finally, books which may be of general interest. All of them are now available in paperback editions.

BLAKEMORE, COLIN, *Mechanics of the Mind*, Cambridge, London, New York and Melbourne, Cambridge University Press, 1977. Beautifully-illustrated general lectures by a brilliant research worker.

BROWN, D. and J. PEDDER, *Introduction to Psychotherapy: An Outline of Psychodynamic Principles and Practice*, London, Tavistock, 1979. Relates the newest techniques to traditional psychotherapy.

CHOMSKY, NOAM, *Language and Mind*, New York, Harcourt Brace and Jovanovich, 1972. The best general introduction to Chomskyian linguistics.

FISHER, RICHARD B. and G. A. CHRISTIE, *A Dictionary of Drugs*, Revised edition, London, Paladin and New York, Schocken, 1975. Introduction for the lay person to the way medicines work in the body.

GARDNER, HOWARD, *The Shattered Mind, the Person after Brain Damage*, New York, Random House, 1974. Lucid descriptions of how stroke and other brain damage helps the understanding of brain function.

GREGORY, RICHARD L., *The Intelligent Eye*, London, Weidenfeld and Nicolson, 1970. Brilliant and entertaining introduction to visual perception.

LORENZ, KONRAD, *On Aggression*, London, Methuen, 1963. The best and most readable statement of the ethological view of behaviour.

MELZACK, R., *The Puzzle of Pain*, Harmondsworth, Penguin, 1973. The gate theory clearly explained by one of its propounders.

MILLER, G. A., *Psychology: The Science of Mental Life*, Harmondsworth, Penguin, 1966. A good history with reviews of the main theories.

OATLEY, KEITH, *Brain Mechanisms and Mind*, London, Thames and Hudson, 1972. Well-illustrated review of brain physiology and biochemistry.

ROSE, STEPHEN, *The Conscious Brain*, London, Weidenfeld and Nicolson, 1973. An excellent general introduction to the same complex field.

SACKS, O., *Awakenings*, London, Duckworth, 1973. Case histories of patients with Parkinson-like symptoms who were helped by L-dopa, but only briefly. Deservedly, a classic of popular psychiatry.

## REFERENCE

A DICTIONARY OF BRITISH FOLK CUSTOMS
Christina Hole £2.50
Every folk custom, both past and present, is described with its history, development and present-day usage. The book includes a nationwide calendar showing what happens, where and when.

A DICTIONARY OF DRUGS
Richard B Fisher and George A Christie £1.25
From everyday aspirin and vitamins, to the powerful agents prescribed for heart disease and cancer, this is a revised reference guide to the gamut of drugs in today's pharmaceutical armoury.

A DICTIONARY OF SYMPTOMS Dr Joan Gomez £1.95
A thorough-going and authoritative guide to the interpretation/ of symptoms of human disease.

THE ENGLISHMAN'S FLORA Geoffrey Grigson £1.95
A latter-day herbal of the medicinal and culinary purposes of the flowers and plants of the English countryside: magic, myth, lore and truth. Illustrated.

LIFE ON MAN Theodor Rosebury 60p
Man is literally covered with animal life. 'This brave and original study from so many angles – clinical, literary, anthropological . . . gave me great delight.' *Anthony Burgess.*

THE LIFE SCIENCE P B and J S Medawar £1.25
As the frontiers of biological knowledge continue to be extended, this is a timely critical appraisal of the central thinking of biologists

MIND-REACH Russell Targ and Harold Puthoff £1.50
The most persuasive argument yet about Extra Sensory Perception. The authors conducted rigorous scientific tests and proved that Extra Sensory Perception exists. This is the evidence.

THE MYTH OF MENTAL ILLNESS Thomas S Szasz £1.50
'I submit that the traditional definition of psychiatry, which is still in vogue, places it alongside such things as alchemy and astrology and commits it to the category of pseudo-science.' *Thomas Szasz.* The book that rocked the psychiatric establishment.

THE SELFISH GENE Richard Dawkins £1.25
A provocative appraisal of social biology – the genetics of selfishness and altruism. 'This important book could hardly be more exciting.' *The Economist*